ANIMAL BEHAVIOUR AND DRUG ACTION

*A leaflet giving details of the Ciba Foundation Colloquia on
Endocrinology, Colloquia on Ageing and Study Group volumes is
available from the Publishers*

Ciba Foundation
Symposium
Jointly with the
Co-ordinating
Committee for
Symposia on
Drug Action

ANIMAL BEHAVIOUR
AND
DRUG ACTION

Editor for the
Co-ordinating
Committee

HANNAH STEINBERG, Ph.D.

Editors for the
Ciba Foundation

A. V. S. de REUCK, M.Sc., D.I.C.

and

JULIE KNIGHT, B.A.

With 103 illustrations

1964

LITTLE, BROWN AND

COMPANY

BOSTON

THE Ciba Foundation, a unique international institution, owes its inception to the generosity of CIBA Limited, Basle. However, being established under British trust law, it enjoys complete independence in practice and policy.

Under the guidance of its distinguished Trustees, the Foundation offers accommodation to scientists from all over the world at its home in Portland Place. Foremost in its activities is the organization of small conferences, the proceedings of which are published in book form in the manner of the present volume. The Foundation convenes many other informal discussions between research workers of different disciplines and different nationalities and each year invites an outstanding authority to deliver a special lecture. An exchange programme between French and British postgraduates is conducted and a library service is available. Furthermore, the Ciba Foundation attempts in every other way possible to aid scientists, whether they be Nobel Laureates or young graduates making their first original contribution to research.

The purpose of the Ciba Foundation, which is to promote international co-operation in medical and chemical research, is symbolized in the armorial bearings by five interlaced rings representing the continents, a black sacrificial cock (emblem of Aesculapius) holding a medical caduceus, and three regular hexagons for chemistry. Its domicile in London is indicated by the red sword of St. Paul and the British lion; the wyvern and the crozier, symbols associated with Basle, refer to the sponsoring firm located in this ancient Swiss town.

Preface

THIS symposium is the tenth in a series of annual meetings organized by the Co-ordinating Committee for Symposia on Drug Action of the Biological Council; it is also the first British meeting on Animal Behaviour and Drug Action of which the proceedings have been published in book form. The intended scope of the symposium was the rôle and limitations of animal behaviour studies in the investigation of drugs which affect the central nervous system, placing roughly equal emphasis on the evaluation of methodology and of the results obtained.

The symposium was divided into two parts. The first consisted of a meeting at the Middlesex Hospital Medical School at which papers were read and briefly discussed before an audience of about three hundred and fifty people. The papers were intended to survey the field in a broad way, with particular emphasis on the analysis of the way drugs act, both at the strictly behavioural level and in terms of neurophysiological and biochemical factors, and on the analysis of the interaction between drugs and the experimental circumstances which results in the behavioural effects observed. The part played by behavioural tests on animals in the screening of new drugs for clinical use in man was also examined.

The second part of the symposium, held at the Ciba Foundation, consisted largely of unscripted discussion by a panel of about thirty invited participants; several of the topics opened up at the earlier sessions were explored in greater depth, in particular the problem of legitimate extrapolation from effects in animals to effects in man.

A great deal of work is now being done in psychopharmacology and the material presented in this volume is necessarily only a sample; it is difficult to draw general conclusions, but the content does perhaps indicate how our understanding of the mode of action of centrally acting drugs is advancing, and that the study of behaviour has a crucial part to play in this understanding.

The main responsibility for the symposium rested with the British Pharmacological Society, with the co-operation of the Biochemical Society, the Physiological Society, the Royal Society of Medicine, the British Psychological Society and the Association for the Study of Animal Behaviour. The Organizing Committee of the symposium consisted of W. A. Bain, F. Bergel (Chairman of the Co-ordinating Committee for Symposia on Drug Action), P. B. Bradley, A. V. S. de Reuck (Ciba Foundation), A. Herxheimer, H. McIlwain (Chairman of the Organizing Committee), M. Shepherd, A. Summerfield and Hannah Steinberg (Secretary of the Organizing Committee).

The Organizing Committee is grateful to the Middlesex Hospital Medical School for the facilities provided for the first part of the symposium, to the Wellcome Trust for generous financial support, and to the Ciba Foundation for providing the setting for the second part of the meeting, for extending its hospitality to members of the symposium and for assistance with travelling expenses, and for providing editorial facilities for the production of this volume.

Contents

Middlesex Hospital Medical School Sessions

Session 1: Behavioural Analysis of Drug Action

Chairman: J. H. Gaddum

Session 2: Neurophysiological and Biochemical Correlates of Behavioural Effects of Drugs

Chairman: W. S. Feldberg

Session 3: Factors which Modify Effects of Drugs on Behaviour

Chairman: A. Summerfield

Session 4: Relevance of Behavioural Effects of Drugs in Animals to Effects in Man

Chairman: Sir Aubrey Lewis

Ciba Foundation Sessions on Intermediation between Administered Drugs and Behavioural Effects

Chairman: J. M. Barnes

Session 1: The Biochemical Approach

Session 2: The Electrophysiological Approach

Session 3: The Neurophysiological Approach

Session 4: The Pharmacological Approach

Ciba Foundation Sessions on the Relevance of Behavioural Effects of Drugs in Animals to their Effects in Man

Chairman: M. Shepherd

Session 5: Extrapolation from Animals to Man

Session 6: Clinical Implications

Membership

List of those presenting papers or contributing to the discussion on Animal Behaviour and Drug Action held at the Middlesex Hospital Medical School and the Ciba Foundation, 25–28th March, 1963

V. C. Abrahams	.	National Institute for Medical Research, London
J. M. Barnes .	.	M.R.C. Toxicology Research Unit, Carshalton, Surrey
S. A. Barnett .	.	Dept. of Zoology, University of Glasgow
H. J. Bein .	.	CIBA Ltd., Basle
F. Bergel .	.	Chester Beatty Research Institute, London
I. L. Bonta .	.	Pharmacological Research Dept., N.V. Organon, Oss, Netherlands
P. B. Bradley .	.	Dept. of Experimental Neuropharmacology, The Medical School, University of Birmingham
Annie M. Brown	.	M.R.C. Laboratory Animals Centre, Carshalton, Surrey
P. L. Broadhurst	.	Dept. of Anatomy, The Medical School, University of Birmingham
J. Bureš . .	.	Czechoslovak Academy of Sciences, Prague
M. R. A. Chance	.	Ethology Laboratory, Uffculme Clinic, Birmingham
J. Cole . .	.	Physiology Laboratory, University of Oxford
H. O. J. Collier	.	Parke Davis and Company, Hounslow, Middlesex
L. Cook . .	.	Dept. of Neurology, Smith, Kline and French Laboratories, Philadelphia
D. P. Dearnaley	.	Physiology Laboratory, University of Oxford
P. B. Dews .	.	Dept. of Psychiatry, Harvard Medical School, Boston
R. E. Edwards .	.	Psychopharmacology Service Center, National Institute of Mental Health, Bethesda
W. S. Feldberg	.	National Institute for Medical Research, London
J. H. Gaddum*	.	A.R.C. Institute of Animal Physiology, Babraham, Cambridge
M. Hamilton .	.	Dept. of Psychiatry, University of Leeds
D. P. Hendry .	.	Dept. of Psychology, University of Durham
A. Herxheimer	.	Dept. of Pharmacology, London Hospital Medical College, London

*Now Sir John Gaddum

S. M. Hilton . .	National Institute for Medical Research, London
W. M. Hollyhock .	Chemical Defence Experimental Establishment, Porton, Wiltshire
C. W. Hume . .	Universities Federation for Animal Welfare, London
H. M. B. Hurwitz .	Dept. of Psychology, Birkbeck College, London
S. Irwin . . .	Neuro-Psychopharmacology Research, Schering Corporation, New Jersey
P. A. J. Janssen .	Research Laboratory Dr. C. Janssen, Beerse, Belgium
M. E. Jarvik . .	Dept. of Pharmacology, Albert Einstein College of Medicine, Yeshiva University, New York
C. R. B. Joyce .	Dept. of Pharmacology, London Hospital Medical College, London
D. Knight . .	Dept. of Psychology, University of Exeter
H. W. Kosterlitz .	Dept. of Physiology, University of Aberdeen
Sir Aubrey Lewis .	Institute of Psychiatry, Maudsley Hospital, London
R. E. Lister . .	Pharmacology Laboratory, J. F. Macfarlan and Company Ltd., Edinburgh
H. McIlwain . .	Institute of Psychiatry, Maudsley Hospital, London
E. Marley . .	Institute of Psychiatry, Maudsley Hospital, London
N. E. Miller . .	Dept. of Psychology, Yale University, New Haven
W. H. Morse . .	Dept. of Pharmacology, Harvard Medical School, Boston
Ruth Payne . .	Beecham Research Laboratories, Betchworth, Surrey
R. W. Russell . .	Dept. of Psychology, Indiana University, Bloomington
M. Shepherd . .	Institute of Psychiatry, Maudsley Hospital, London
L. Stein . .	Dept. of Psychopharmacology, Wyeth Laboratories, Philadelphia
Hannah Steinberg .	Dept. of Pharmacology, University College, London
A. Summerfield .	Dept. of Psychology, Birkbeck College, London
R. H. J. Watson .	Dept. of Nutrition, Queen Elizabeth College, London
L. Weiskrantz .	The Psychological Laboratory, Cambridge
C. W. M. Wilson .	Dept. of Pharmacology, University of Liverpool

Session 1: Behavioural Analysis of Drug Action

CHAIRMAN: Dr. J. H. Gaddum

THE ANALYSIS OF MOTIVATIONAL EFFECTS ILLUSTRATED BY EXPERIMENTS ON AMYLOBARBITONE SODIUM*

N. E. MILLER

Department of Psychology, Yale University

WE need to develop a science of psychopharmacology which one day may provide a rational foundation for the use of drugs in mental illness in the same way that organic chemistry does for the synthesis of new compounds. In working toward this goal, I have already stressed the desirability of using a variety of behavioural measures in order to reduce the possibilities of being misled by side effects that may be specific for a given test, and I have described a number of behavioural tests for use in studying the effects of drugs on motivation.[†] In this paper, I shall describe a different, though somewhat related, approach.

The basic idea is to select a drug that is known to have interesting clinical effects on human patients, and that also seems to have generally similar effects on animal subjects. Then rigorous experimental methods are used with animals to try to determine more specifically what the behavioural effects are and how they

* Work on this paper and on studies cited in it was supported by Grant MY2949 from the National Institute of Mental Health, United States Public Health Service.

† Some of the earlier experiments in this paper have been summarized in Miller, N. E., and Barry, H., III (1960). *Psychopharmacologia*, **1**, 169; and in Miller, N. E. (1961). *Amer. Psychologist*, **16**, 12.

are achieved. A variety of behavioural techniques are used to test a number of alternative hypotheses. One needs to know precisely what the behavioural effects are before trying to relate them to the results of powerful new neurophysiological and biochemical techniques for studying pharmacological action in the brain.

SIGNIFICANT CLINICAL EFFECTS OF BARBITURATES ON FEAR

Studies of men in combat show that practically all the common symptoms of neuroses, and even psychoses, can be produced by intense fear and conflict, two related factors which also seem to play a significant rôle in clinical studies of civilian mental disorders (Freud, 1936; Dollard and Miller, 1950). A variety of clinical studies show that amylobarbitone sodium is useful in the therapy of combat neuroses and of at least certain civilian disorders in which fear and conflict play a prominent rôle (Grinker and Spiegel, 1945a, b). Experimental studies show that this drug seems to have a similar effect on animals by differentially reducing the fear-motivated avoidance component of a conflict (Bailey and Miller, 1952). The following studies were aimed at increasing our understanding of exactly what this effect is and how it is achieved.

On the basis of dose-response studies, a dose that seemed to be maximally effective in conflict situations was selected. This dose was then used in most of the other studies.

APPARENTLY SIMILAR EFFECTS ON RATS

Fig. 1 shows the effect of an intraperitoneal injection of 20 mg./kg. of amylobarbitone sodium on a variety of experimental tests of fear and conflict in the albino rat. In the *telescope alley* test on the first trial the rat runs one foot to the reward, where he never receives electric shock. Therefore, this trial is labelled "zero" on the ordinate which indicates threat of shock. On each successive trial, the rat is required to run an additional foot, and occasionally receives shocks at the goal which, when they occur, are stronger the longer the distance to the goal on that particular run. As in all the experiments to be described, shocks are given via a grid under the rat's feet through a series resistance of 200,000

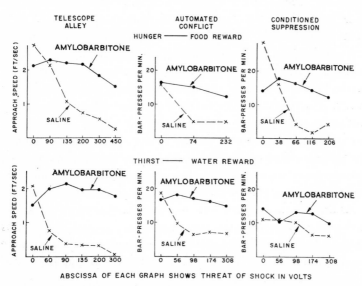

FIG. 1. Effects of intraperitoneal injection of 20 mg./kg. amylobarbitone sodium administered to Sprague-Dawley albino rats 20 minutes before testing in six experiments on fear and conflict, by different techniques described in the text.

ohms which accounts for the high voltages required. Current is 60 cycle a.c. On the test trial shown in Fig. 1 no shocks were delivered; rats are motivated only by fear and the abscissa is therefore labelled "threat of shock".

In the *automated conflict* test, rats press a bar for a reward on a variable-interval schedule; an increasingly loud tone signals unpredictable shocks on the bar, which, when they occur, are increasingly strong the louder the tone.

The *conditioned suppression* test is similar except that the shock is delivered via the grid floor and is inescapable, so that we are measuring conflicts with "freezing" rather than active withdrawal from the bar. This test is like the one for conditioned emotional response (CER), except that the intensity of tone and threat of shock are varied. All the tests mentioned here have been described in more detail by Barry and co-workers (1962a, b and c).

In order to control for any effects specific to the approach drive, animals in the experiments represented in the top row of Fig. 1 were motivated by hunger and rewarded by food and those in the bottom row were motivated by thirst and rewarded by water. The results under all of these various conditions are highly similar. Looking at the beginning of each curve, representing performance with little or no fear, it can be seen that in general the amylobarbitone reduced performance below the placebo level. These results show that the drug did not simply produce an increase in the approach drive or act as a general stimulant.

As the rats encountered cues to which increasingly strong fear had been conditioned, the performance following placebo was markedly reduced. The performance under amylobarbitone sodium was not affected nearly as much; thus this drug improved performance under fear.

These experiments demonstrate a striking effect on rats consonant with clinical observations on people; the amylobarbitone improved performance by reducing the relative strength of the fear-motivated habits. How was this effect achieved: directly, by selective action on the brain mechanisms involved in fear or indirectly by other means?

PRIMACY OF HABIT VERSUS DIRECT ACTION ON FEAR

In experiments on the effects of drugs on conflict the habit of approach is established first, after which the animals are taught to avoid. Perhaps the drug reduces the fear-motivated avoidance not because it has a selective effect on certain fear centres, but rather because it has a selective effect on the more recently established habit. Masserman (1943) has assumed that recent habits may be more susceptible to drugs and experimental work by Szwejkowska (1959) and Konorski and Szwejkowska (1952) indicates that the first established habits may be especially dominant.

In one experiment on this problem, we established the fear of the tone in the Skinner box before we trained the animal to press a bar to secure food there. Then we tested the effects of amylobarbitone sodium. If this drug primarily affects fear, the results should be similar to our previous ones, but if it primarily affects the most recent habit, our results should be completely reversed. The results were in fact essentially the same as those of our previous experiment.

In another test we used a technique analogous to our telescope alley. We used a *shuttle alley* eight feet long with a light bulb at either end. Five seconds after the light at one end started flashing an electric shock was delivered to the sections of the grid floor. It was strongest at the lighted end and progressively weaker in farther sections, with the furthest one having no shock. In this way we trained the rats to shuttle from one end of the alley to the other, always staying away from the flashing light. After they had learned this, we gave the hungry rats trials in which they started at alternate ends of the darkened alley and found pellets of food in tiny cups in the centre of each one-foot section as they progressed toward the opposite end. Finally they were given trials with the light flickering at the far end from the start and with unpredictable shocks at the grid becoming stronger, as before, nearer to the flashing light.

Following this training the animal was given, in a balanced order, drug and placebo tests without any shock on the grid. Fig. 2 shows that under amylobarbitone sodium the animals approached farther toward the flashing light into sections with a higher threat of shock than they did after a placebo. Since the habit of approaching was established after the fear of sections nearer the flashing light, we would expect exactly the opposite results if the main effect of the drug had been to weaken most the habit most recently established. Thus, the results of this experiment in the alley confirm those of the preceding one in the

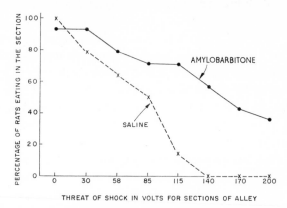

THREAT OF SHOCK IN VOLTS FOR SECTIONS OF ALLEY

FIG. 2. In the shuttle alley, amylobarbitone reduces the strength of the originally learned habit of avoiding electric shock associated with a flashing light more than it does that of the subsequently learned habit of advancing to eat pellets of food found in cups spaced at 1-foot intervals.

Skinner box, showing that the effect of the drug is not primarily on the most recently established habit.

STIMULUS CHANGE VERSUS DIRECT ACTION ON FEAR MECHANISM

A number of experiments have shown that at least when the fear is attached to external cues, changes in the stimulus situation reduce stimulus-generalization in the fear-motivated habit of avoidance more than in the hunger-motivated habit of approach. Thus, Fig. 3 shows that changing animals into a different alley produces a greater decrement in their avoidance than in their approach.

But this is exactly the same kind of effect that is produced by the amylobarbitone sodium. Perhaps this drug does not have a direct effect specific to the fear mechanism, but only affects fear indirectly by changing the stimulus situation. To test for this possibility, we performed an experiment in which we gave half of the animals their avoidance training in the normal state, as is

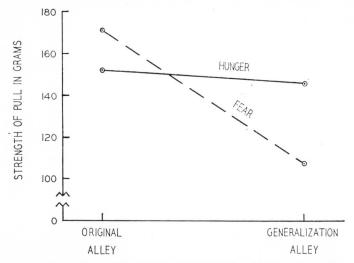

FIG. 3. The gradient of stimulus generalization of avoidance motivated by fear contrasted with that of approach motivated by hunger. (The strength of pull of each rat was measured twice in the same alley in which it was originally trained and twice in a different alley, with the sequence of testing balanced.) (From Murray and Miller, 1952.)

customarily done, but gave the other half their avoidance training under the influence of the drug. Then half of each of these two groups was tested following a placebo injection and the other half following the drug injection. The experiment was performed in the telescope alley.

The 2×2 design and the results are summarized in Table I. Adding up the rows shows the effect of having had the amylobarbitone sodium during training. The effect is in the direction of fear reduction, but is not reliable. Adding up the columns shows the effect of having had the amylobarbitone during testing. The difference is larger and is statistically reliable. Since amylobarbitone during testing produced faster running irrespective of whether or not the animals had received their fear training with this drug, we must conclude that this superior performance is not due to any way in which the drug produced a change in the stimulus situation.

Table I

AVERAGE SPEED OF APPROACH IN THE LAST 6 INCHES OF THE TELESCOPE ALLEY DURING A SERIES OF TESTS FOR FEAR WITHOUT SHOCKS

Training	Testing		Sum
	Amylobarbitone	Saline	
Amylobarbitone	1·00	0·82	1·82
Saline	1·14	0·54	1·68
Sum	2·14	1·36	3·50

Trials in which the rat failed to reach the goal are scored as zero speed. Speed of approach is in feet per second.

POSSIBLE EFFECTS OF DRUG ON DISCRIMINATION

Although amylobarbitone sodium does not achieve its fear-reducing effect primarily by producing general changes in the stimulus situation, it is conceivable that it interferes in some way with the ability of the rat to discriminate the cues of danger. For example, it might make him less perceptive of the presence or absence of the tone which signals the presence or absence of the possibility of electric shock in the Skinner box. In this case, the behaviour would be changed toward the average of that in the safe and dangerous conditions. Compared with the sober state, performance would be depressed in the safe, and improved in the dangerous conditions, which is exactly what we observed.

To test for this possibility we trained a new group of rats in a different discrimination in the same apparatus. Instead of signalling shock, the same tone signalled that the bar would no longer deliver food. After the rats had learned a discrimination which reduced their rate to approximately the same level as the shock did, we gave them tests with amylobarbitone sodium.

The results are presented in Fig. 4, which shows that this drug does not seem to reduce the decrement produced by the gradually increasing tone which was associated with non-reward in the Skinner box.

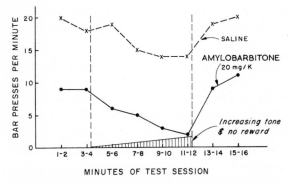

FIG. 4. Amylobarbitone sodium does not seem to reduce the decrement produced by a gradually increasing tone which has always been associated with non-reward in a Skinner box.

It is interesting to note, however, that in this case the drug produced a much greater reduction in the performance before the tone was sounded than we have seen in our other tests in which the tone elicited fear. Is this because the animals in the previous experiment had some fear of the apparatus even when the tone was not sounding, so that their performance during this period was depressed under the placebo injection and relieved somewhat by the drug? The high initial rate of the placebo animals in this last test would tend to support such a conclusion. In any event, in this last experiment the results seem to suggest that the drug did not markedly disrupt the discrimination, although the fact that the drug and placebo curves are on such different parts of the scale represented on the ordinate makes any comparison of them dependent on the somewhat questionable assumption that the units of measurement along the ordinate are functionally equal.

We also ran a similar type of test in the alley. Instead of giving stronger shocks for trials with longer runs, we reduced the quantity of reward, which was four pellets for the first trial of running the one-foot length, two for the second trial of running the two-foot length, one for the third trial at the three-foot length, and none for the fourth, fifth and sixth trials of running progressively further distances. We call this the *frustration alley* test.

The results showed that amylobarbitone sodium speeded up running on the non-rewarded trials, much as it did in the fear trials shown in Fig. 1. Apparently, the amylobarbitone either reduced the discriminability of the cues indicating that the trial was going to be non-rewarded, or counteracted the effect of frustration from non-reward. How can we decide between these two alternatives?

The assumption that the drug reduces the effects of frustration, rather than interferes with the discrimination, can conceivably explain the puzzling discrepancy between the results of this experiment and those of the preceding one. In the bar-pressing test, the animals were rewarded on a one-minute variable-interval schedule, so that even with the tone off, their bar-presses frequently were not rewarded. A considerable amount of evidence indicates that under such conditions of partial reinforcement, the animal learns not to be disturbed by the frustrational aspects of non-reward. Thus, the lower rate of bar-pressing with the tone on may have been a pure function of the lack of the reward as an incentive without involving any appreciable disturbance from the emotional effects of frustration. If the drug primarily removes these emotional effects, it should have less effect on the rate of bar-pressing which was already on a variable-interval schedule.

EFFECT OF AMYLOBARBITONE SODIUM ON EXPERIMENTAL EXTINCTION

The puzzling results of the preceding two experiments have suggested that amylobarbitone sodium may reduce the emotional effects of frustration by non-reward in the same way that it does fear established by painful electric shock. In order to test for this possibility, Barry, Wagner and I designed an experiment on the effects of this drug on experimental extinction. In order to control for possible effects of stimulus change between the sober and the drugged state we used a 2 × 2 × 2 design.

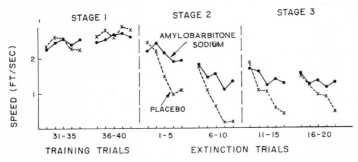

FIG. 5. Comparison between groups which differ in their current drug or placebo condition.

In the first stage of the experiment, hungry Sprague-Dawley rats were thoroughly trained to run down a six-foot alley for food. Half of them were trained with amylobarbitone sodium, and the other half following placebo. The effects during this training are shown in the left-hand corner of Fig. 5. It can be seen that the drug has little effect on the running speed of the rats on the five trials of each of the last two days of rewarded training.

In stage 2, each of the foregoing two groups was divided into two subgroups, one of which was given non-rewarded trials following an injection of amylobarbitone sodium, and the other group following an injection of isotonic saline. Five non-rewarded trials were given on each of two days. Since there was no appreciable difference between the groups originally trained with or without drugs, these two subgroups have been combined to show only results of animals tested with or without drugs. It can be seen that while the placebo animals extinguished rapidly, those with the drug extinguished much more slowly.

In stage 3, each of the four subgroups from the preceding stage was divided into two subgroups, one of which continued experimental extinction with drug and the other without. Since there were no marked effects of preceding conditions of extinction or training, the various subgroups are combined to show the comparison between animals currently under drug and those currently not. Again, the results are quite similar to those in stage 2.

The foregoing results are congruent with the hypothesis that this drug has the differential effect of weakening the emotional or, in other words, frustrational effects of experimental extinction more than it does the habit of continuing to run. In other words, the drug seems to weaken these frustrational effects in the same way that it does fear. This would account for the anomalous results in the experiments on discrimination.

On the other hand, it is conceivable that experimental extinction may involve a discrimination between a sequence of rewarded trials and a subsequent sequence of non-rewarded ones. For this reason, it seems desirable to try to measure approach and avoidance separately in a situation in which any effects on discrimination would be expected to affect both equally.

SEPARATE TESTS OF APPROACH, ESCAPE AND AVOIDANCE

Three different groups of rats were trained to run down a short two-foot alley with a grid in the start box and runway, and a wooden floor in the goal box. All groups were hungry. Rats in one group ran for food as a reward; those in another to escape a mild electric shock; and those in the third to avoid a stronger electric shock. Levels of shock and reward were adjusted so that by the end of training all three groups were running at approximately the same speed. Then each of the groups was tested in a balanced order following a placebo injection and injections of different amounts of amylobarbitone. The results are shown in Fig. 6. It can be seen that the drug produced a greater decrease in the escape motivated by pain plus fear and the

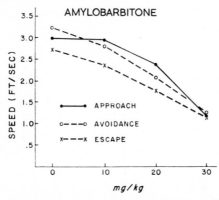

FIG. 6. The separate dose-response effects of amylobarbitone sodium on the speed to approach food, and to avoid or escape shock.

avoidance motivated only by fear, than in the approach to food motivated by hunger. These measures of the effects of the drug separately on approach, avoidance, and escape responses fit in with the results of the previous experiments on conflict behaviour and lend strong support to the idea that this drug does indeed have a differential effect on the mechanism of fear.

WILL THE FRIGHTENED ANIMAL WORK TO INJECT HIMSELF?

From other experimental work, we already know that a sudden reduction in the drive of fear acts as a reward to produce learning.

If amylobarbitone does indeed produce a marked reduction in fear, we would expect that a reasonably rapid and painless infusion of this drug through a chronic catheter via the jugular vein into the heart would be rewarding to a frightened animal. This prediction involves an additional and quite different way of testing for the fear-reducing effects of this drug.

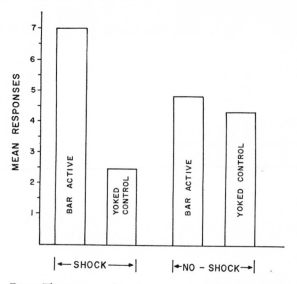

FIG. 7. The mean number of responses made by the animals when shock and no-shock conditions were alternated daily.

The prediction was tested by using pairs of animals in adjoining Skinner boxes, connected up so that the bar in one box was active, with each press injecting 0·05 ml. per bar-press of a solution of 40 mg./ml. amylobarbitone sodium into both rats. The bar available to the other rat which was used as a yoked control was connected only to a counter but *not* to any injection apparatus. Since the paired rats were treated exactly alike in all other respects, any differences between them must be due to a rewarding effect of the association between pressing the *active* bar and receiving injections.

In the initial stages of training, both animals received brief, unavoidable shocks of 0·1 second duration and 1 mA intensity via the grid floor once every 60 seconds. On certain trials these shocks were omitted.

The results are shown in Fig. 7. Rats with the active bar delivering the injection did far more bar-pressing than the yoked controls with an inactive bar. Bar-pressing of this kind occurred primarily on days in which the animals received the brief strong shocks and hence presumably were motivated by a high level of fear. The results of this quite different kind of test add additional confirmation to the hypothesis that amylobarbitone affects the fear mechanism (see also Davis and Miller, 1963).

A DIFFERENT TYPE OF AVERSIVE STIMULUS

Finally, it should be noted that practically all the tests of fear and conflict in the literature use painful electric shock as the means of eliciting fear and conflict. Thus it is conceivable that the results are specific to something about the pain mechanism of eliciting fear and should not be generalized to other aversive situations. In order to test for the generality of the kinds of results we have been describing, a student developed a technique of administering 1 per cent hydrochloric acid into the rat's mouth by a mouth fistula. He trained rats to press a bar for food on a variable–interval schedule in a Skinner box. Then he paired a tone with the presentation of such very sour, but presumably not painful, injections of mild acid into the mouth. After a number of such trials, the tone would depress the rate of bar-pressing just as much as though it had been associated with electric shock. In other words, it was possible to use the sour taste as the reinforcement for a conditioned emotional response (CER). I had hoped to be able to tell you whether or not amylobarbitone sodium would have the same effect on an emotional disturbance reinforced in this way as it does on one reinforced by painful electric shock. Various delays prevented me from completing this experiment, but its rationale and method are clear.

GENERALIZATION FROM THE DRUGGED TO SOBER STATES

The chronic administration of a fear-reducing drug can reduce chronic anxiety, but drugs cannot discriminate between realistic

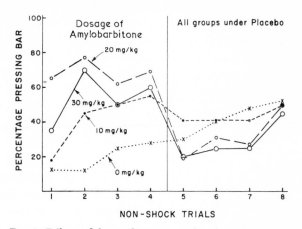

FIG. 8. Failure of drug effect to generalize from drugged to sober state. Amylobarbitone caused animals to resume pressing the bar which delivers food and had delivered shock, but on subsequent placebo trials they regressed to a level below that of controls which were without drug throughout.

and unrealistic dangers. In order to get a more discriminative result it is often desirable to make use of a temporary drug-induced reduction of an unrealistic fear to retrain a patient by psychotherapeutic techniques. For such use it is important that the relearning should transfer from the initial drugged to the subsequent sober state. As a test of such transfer we trained hungry rats to press a bar for food. Then we punished each bar-press with an electric shock. Next, the shocks were permanently turned off and the task was to retrain the rats to press the bar. Different groups were given different doses of amylobarbitone during retraining. As Fig. 8 shows, this drug improved the performance on bar-pressing. But when it was withdrawn, the rats regressed to the level of those that had been retrained on placebo.

The foregoing result clearly shows that one cannot rely on automatic transfer of training from the drugged to the sober state. It agrees with those of the earlier experiments in this paper indicating that the effect of this drug is primarily on performance, rather than on learning.

It will be important to find out whether various techniques, such as gradual withdrawal from the drug during retraining, can improve the transfer. Perhaps some other drug can be discovered that will produce more transfer and hence be more useful in emotional re-education, or in other words, psychotherapy.

SUMMARY

One way of discovering basic principles of psychopharmacology is to study drugs that have definite clinical effects on people and apparently similar ones in animals. In such cases, rigorously controlled experiments on animals can help to pinpoint the behavioural effects of the drugs. A series of such experiments on amylobarbitone sodium illustrates the types of alternative hypotheses that must be checked; it shows that in an approach-avoidance conflict this drug reduces the avoidance motivated by fear more than the approach motivated by hunger or thirst. This result seems to be produced by a differential effect on the fear mechanism rather than only by a differential effect on the oldest habit, by changes in the stimulus situation, or by interfering with the discriminability of the danger signal. As predicted from a fear-reducing effect, frightened rats learn to press a bar to inject themselves with amylobarbitone via a chronic jugular catheter into the heart, and extinguish this habit after the fear-arousing momentary electric shocks are turned off. An additional experiment shows that this drug reduces the rate of experimental extinction of a habit previously rewarded by food. Thus it seems to counteract frustrational inhibition in addition to fear. In one experiment on learning to extinguish fear, the beneficial effects of the drug on performance did not transfer to a subsequent test without drug.

REFERENCES

BAILEY, C. J., and MILLER, N. E. (1952). *J. comp. physiol. Psychol.*, **45**, 205.
BARRY, H., III, and MILLER, N. E. (1962a). *J. comp. physiol. Psychol.*, **55**, 201.
BARRY, H., III, WAGNER, A. R., and MILLER, N. E. (1962b). *J. comp. physiol. Psychol.*, **55**, 464.
BARRY, H., III, MILLER, N. E., and TIDD, G. E. (1962c). *J. comp. physiol. Psychol.*, **55**, 1071.
DAVIS, J. D., and MILLER, N. E. (1963). *Science*, **141**, 1286.
DOLLARD, J., and MILLER, N. E. (1950). Personality and Psychotherapy. New York: McGraw-Hill.
FREUD, S. (1936). The Problem of Anxiety. New York: Norton.
GRINKER, R. R., and SPIEGEL, J. P. (1945a). Men Under Stress. New York: Blakiston.
GRINKER, R. R., and SPIEGEL, J. P. (1945b). War Neurosis. New York: Blakiston.
KONORSKI, J., and SZWEJKOWSKA, G. (1952). *Acta Biol. exp. (Warszawa)*, **16**, no. 7.
MASSERMAN, J. H. (1943). Behavior and Neurosis. Chicago: University of Chicago Press.
MURRAY, E. J., and MILLER, N. E. (1952). *J. exp. Psychol.*, **43**, 222.
SZWEJKOWSKA, G. (1959). *Acta Biol. exp. (Warszawa)*, **19**.

DISCUSSION

Abrahams: I should like to make a suggestion concerning one way in which barbiturates could bring about the effect that Professor Miller has described. Over the past few years Hilton and I have performed a number of experiments which lead us to believe that the defence reaction is reflexly organized at the level of the brain stem (Abrahams, V. C., Hilton, S. M., and Zbrozyna, A. [1960]. *J. Physiol. [Lond.]*, **152**,

54P; [1960]. *Ibid.*, **154**, 491). By the defence reaction we mean the graded behavioural response whose initial sign is alerting, and which may culminate in the familiar signs of "fight or flight". When we used electrophysiological techniques to examine afferent connexions which might be concerned with the mediation of this behavioural reflex (Abrahams, V. C., Hilton, S. M., and Malcolm, J. L. [1962]. *J. Physiol. [Lond.]*, **164**, 1), we found that we were dealing with an afferent system whose properties paralleled those of the "collateral afferent system" described by Starzl and his co-workers (Starzl, T. E., Taylor, C. W., and Magoun, H. W. [1951]. *J. Neurophysiol.*, **14**, 479). One characteristic of this system is its sensitivity to barbiturates. Is it not possible that in the experiments you have described you are dealing with activity in a similar system, and is it then not possible that your results have been due to an action of barbiturates on such afferent pathways?

Miller: I have been primarily concerned with discovering exactly what the behavioural effect is. It would be an advantage to follow this with an attempt to correlate the behavioural with the neurological effects. This correlation is an extremely important problem to investigate, but I am not expert enough in neurophysiology to judge your hypothesis, although it sounds plausible.

Chance: I should like to question whether you have in fact been describing the behavioural responses of your animals, Professor Miller, because you used the word "fear". This is a human term, and I do not think that you can deduce what reaction in an animal corresponds to our fear reaction. All you can do is to describe what the animal does.

I was very impressed with your early work because that is exactly what you did there. For example, you said then that the animal went along the runway to a certain point, and its conflict was measured by the distance it had run. However, most of the experiments reported here have been discussed in "second order" terms, which refer to a completely different aspect of the behaviour of the animal, and I do not quite understand how you bring in this idea of fear.

Miller: Certainly, one can limit oneself to the observed behavioural results of these experiments in exactly the same way as I did in the earlier studies of conflict. In the present experiments, the animal ran a certain distance toward the goal where he had been shocked and the drug caused the animal to run further, or to be more likely to reach the goal.

I use the phrase "threat of the electric shock" as an objective shorthand description of the fact that the shock has a certain probability of occurring. I use the term "fear", however, as a theoretical construct. The hypothesis is that in these situations—which are of the kind in which a human subject would show fear and in which the animal subject does indeed show some of the same symptoms, such as defecation, trembling and avoidance—there is the same intervening mechanism involved. Obviously, one must be very careful to distinguish the particular set of behavioural observations, which are the data, from the inference which one makes from them, which in this case is the hypothetical mechanism I refer to as "fear". This inference that some fear (or combined pain/fear) mechanism is involved can then guide a series of additional experiments, which will test the hypothesis.

If you do limit yourself strictly to the data themselves and do not make any hypothesis about them, you will be unlikely to relate experiments to one another in the way that I have done, and in particular will be unlikely to perform the experiment in which the animals press the bar to inject themselves. Apparently they press more if they are in a pain/fear situation than if they are not, exactly as one would expect from other experimental work in which a sudden reduction in the cues that have been associated with electric shock produces rapid learning. The theoretical construct of "fear" ties these experiments together.

The same hypothesis also guides physiological work: we have students looking for areas of the brain which are particularly involved in producing fear, and others looking for physiologically more direct measures of the fear. A hypothesis of this kind is therefore valuable for making sense out of the data, although one should be perfectly clear that it is only an hypothesis and that one is not observing the "fear" but using it as a construct with which to make sense out of a set of observations.

Hurwitz: In Professor Miller's Fig. 5 the effects on the rate of experimental extinction under amylobarbitone sodium and a placebo are shown. One noticeable feature of the results is that the animals receiving amylobarbitone sodium did not show much spontaneous recovery of the conditioned response, whereas the placebo controls showed both a marked waning of the response during each session and considerable recovery of response from session to session. At the beginning of each session the controls were in fact performing at a rate comparable to the amylobarbitone sodium treated group.

Many interpretations of the experimental extinction phenomenon have been advanced, so that one treads warily in committing oneself to one or other of these theories. The results cited by Professor Miller appear to be compatible with a point of view he expressed nearly thirty years ago, that the extinction of a response A is partly a product of the conditioning of a competing response B to the stimulus complex which had previously served as a conditioned stimulus for response A, the motive power for such counter-conditioning being an emotional reaction (frustration) generated by non-reward (Miller, N. E., and Stevenson, S. S. [1936]. *J. comp. Psychol.*, **21**, 205). In the present experiment the amylobarbitone sodium may be thought of as inhibiting frustration or some similar emotional effect so that extinction would be slowed down. The placebo control animals on the other hand would show the normal decrement in the conditioned response during an experimental session under non-reward. During the inter-session period the emotional effects would dissipate and a substantial recovery of response would then be noted in the next extinction session.

It will be seen that this interpretation of the results emphasizes motivational rather than learning factors.

Miller: You are quite right about this experiment. What happened was that the normal group showed extinction on one day and at the beginning of the next day would show a good deal of spontaneous recovery, followed by extinction again. The animals treated with amylobarbitone showed much less extinction and did not show the spontaneous recovery overnight. This indicates that the amylobarbitone sodium was doing the same sort of thing that the rest interval was doing; the process that the animals recovered from during the rest interval was the same process that the amylobarbitone sodium prevented them from being subjected to.

In my opinion, what is happening during experimental extinction is more complicated than what is happening during reward; it is not a single process but at least two processes and perhaps more, which I do not pretend to understand completely. The tentative hypothesis is that the drug protects the animal from an emotional effect of experimental extinction, and it is this emotional disturbance from which it recovers overnight. But the learning that running is no longer being rewarded is *not* affected either by the drug or by the overnight rest. The animal does not forget overnight, so to speak, that he was not rewarded.

EFFECTS OF DRUGS ON OPERANT CONDITIONING

L. COOK

Department of Neurology and Cardiology, Smith, Kline and French Laboratories, Philadelphia

MANY techniques have been used to evaluate the way in which drugs affect behaviour in animals, and there has been an impressive amount of such research in the past ten years. Much of this effort has been based on empiricism and on heterogeneous experimental procedures. Approaches range from observations of drug-induced symptoms in untrained animals to objective studies of drug effects on complex behaviour of highly trained animals. Frequently, experimental procedures are given catchy descriptive terms such as "hostility", "rage", or "conflict" because of a superficial resemblance to a counterpart in human behaviour. There is a growing feeling that investigators should be more concerned with the relevant variables in a procedure and should carefully specify the experimental contingencies when analysing the interaction of drugs and behaviour. A recent review (Cook and Kelleher, 1963) has discussed the following case in point. Meprobamate has been reported under certain conditions to enhance the attack behaviour of cats towards mice. Others have reported that meprobamate inhibits attack behaviour or rage, under other conditions. Although these results appear inconsistent on the basis of a superficial analysis of the behaviour, they are not so if the experimental contingencies influencing the quality of the drug effect are analysed.

Among the several techniques of experimentally controlling behaviour used in behavioural pharmacology are those termed operant conditioning. In general, these techniques develop and maintain behaviour by placing consequences on the behaviour. This experimental approach has been well described by Ferster and Skinner (1957). This paper describes some of our experience using these techniques in the analysis of the interaction of drugs and behaviour.

Conditioned avoidance behaviour has been extensively used in the evaluation of psychoactive drugs in animals. It has often been shown that chlorpromazine, other phenothiazine compounds and reserpine are consistently effective in blocking conditioned avoidance responses (reviewed in Dews and Morse, 1961). Cook and Kelleher (1962) indicated that the potency of phenothiazines in blocking these responses was correlated with their clinical potency. Many workers report that meprobamate has only slight effects on conditioned avoidance responses, or blocks only at relatively high doses (reviewed in Cook and Kelleher, 1963). Phenobarbitone and other barbiturates have been reported (Cook and Weidley, 1957; Verhave et al., 1958; Maffii, 1959) to have non-specific or weak effects on classical conditioned avoidance of the type where there are discrete trials, each with a stimulus, or to suppress this behaviour only at high neurotoxic or ataxic doses. Chlordiazepoxide appears to have an effect on this behaviour which is different from that of either chlorpromazine, meprobamate or phenobarbitone. In continuous ("Sidman") avoidance procedures, high doses of chlordiazepoxide increase the number of shocks delivered; however, the overall rate of responding is not decreased (Cook and Kelleher, 1962). Randall and co-workers (1960; Randall, 1960) indicated that chlordiazepoxide "affected only the regularity of responding, as indicated by the significant increase in shock rate beginning between 5 and 40 mg./kg. given orally, and higher doses of chlordiazepoxide (up to 80 mg./kg.) failed either to further increase shock rate or to depress overall rate of avoidance responding". A similar phenomenon was shown by Gray and his colleagues (1961) in a limited study of non-discriminated avoidance in rats.

In the evaluation of the interaction of drugs with specific aspects of experimentally controlled behaviour, it is often useful to establish the generality of these phenomena across species, particularly including human subjects. Several investigators have studied Pavlovian conditioning in humans. Results consistently showed (Alexander and Horner, 1961; Uhr *et al.*, 1961) that meprobamate had little effect on a Pavlovian conditioned galvanic skin response (GSR), even at relatively high doses. On the other hand, chlorpromazine (100–200 mg./kg. orally) produced a reduction of conditioned GSR. Similarly, Winsor (1958), using Pavlovian conditioning of vasoconstriction of the finger, showed that this conditioned response was not affected by pentobarbitone (50 mg.) or meprobamate (800 mg.); chlorpromazine (50 mg.) did block this conditioned vasoconstriction.

We have carried out a limited study to establish the interaction of chlorpromazine, meprobamate, phenobarbitone and chlordiazepoxide on conditioned avoidance in man. The technique was a non-discriminated avoidance procedure, using electric shocks applied to the forearm. Doses of these drugs were obviously within controlled clinical limits, and conclusions therefore are related to the range of doses employed. Fig. 1 illustrates the effect of an intramuscular injection of 37·5 mg. of chlorpromazine; suppression of avoidance behaviour was produced. Similar effects were produced by 25 or 75 mg. (i.m.) of chlorpromazine. Meprobamate (600 to 2,000 mg., orally), phenobarbitone (98 to 260 mg., i.m.) or chlordiazepoxide (20 to 300 mg., administered over 24 hours) all failed to inhibit this avoidance behaviour. General sedation was produced by all drugs tested; however, only chlorpromazine depressed avoidance behaviour, whereas the subjects who received the other drugs kept responding even though they appeared sedated. The effect of chlorpromazine on conditioned avoidance has generality between animals and man; this is also true with meprobamate and phenobarbitone. The lack of effect of chlordiazepoxide on conditioned avoidance behaviour in humans is consistent with the findings in animals that it affects avoidance differently from chlorpromazine.

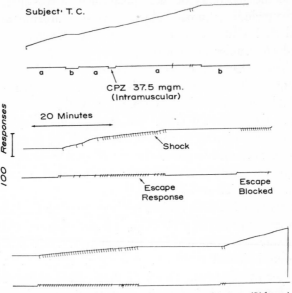

FIG. 1. Effect of chlorpromazine on continuous (Sidman) conditioned avoidance behaviour. Dose 37·5 mg., intramuscularly. Periods designated (a) represent avoidance (Sidman, 1953). Shock-shock intervals and response-shock intervals were both 30 seconds. Shock duration was 10 seconds, or until escape occurred. Pips on cumulative record indicate delivered shocks; pips on baseline represent escape responses. Onset of avoidance block occurred one hour post drug administration.

ENHANCEMENT OF RESPONSE RATES

Differences between the behavioural pharmacology of chlorpromazine and meprobamate or chlordiazepoxide can also be demonstrated with techniques other than conditioned avoidance behaviour. These include some operant schedules utilizing food motivated behaviour (positive reinforcement) as well as shock motivated behaviour (negative reinforcement).

A characteristic property of meprobamate and chlordiazepoxide is their ability to enhance behavioural responses in situations where behaviour is (a) weakly controlled by the environmental contingencies, or (b) suppressed by punishment or other environmental contingencies.

(a) Fixed-interval performance (squirrel monkeys)

The fixed-interval operant schedule is described by Ferster and Skinner (1957). We have incorporated this schedule into a three-component multiple schedule. In the presence of a visual Stimulus I, a ten-minute fixed-interval schedule was in effect. In the presence of a visual Stimulus II, a 30-response fixed-ratio schedule was in effect; that is, every 30th response was reinforced with food. Following each food reinforcement, the stimuli went off for a 2·5 minute time-out. Responses were not reinforced during the time-out periods (Cook and Kelleher, 1961). In the fixed-interval (FI 10) component the first response occurring after ten minutes is reinforced with food. Typical performance of animals trained on the fixed-interval (FI 10) schedule consists of a pause early in the interval, and then a gradual increase of response rates as the event of food reinforcement approaches.

As shown in Fig. 2, meprobamate produced a significant increase in responding in FI 10 components, especially as at e, f, g and h. These effects occurred at oral doses of 25, 50 or 100 mg./kg. Discrimination between stimuli remained intact, as shown by the maintenance of differential performance in the various stimuli. Fixed-ratio and time-out performances were not affected.

Chlordiazepoxide*, similarly to meprobamate, produced a significant increase of fixed-interval performance, after doses of 5, 10, 20 and 40 mg./kg. (oral). Fig. 3 shows the long duration of action of this drug. Again, as with meprobamate, the enhanced response rates were not generalized to all components of this procedure.

* Chlordiazepoxide, the generic name for "Librium", was formerly methaminodiazepoxide.

Fig. 4 presents dose-response relationships of chlordiazepoxide on this operant schedule. It shows that chlordiazepoxide produced increases of fixed-interval response rates after doses of 2·5, 5, 10, 20 or 40 mg./kg., given orally. It is also shown that no increases of the fixed-ratio response rates occurred after any of these doses.

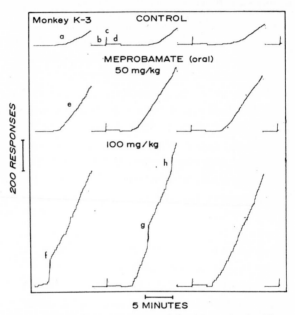

Fig. 2. Effects of meprobamate on behaviour maintained by a schedule of positive reinforcement in squirrel monkeys. The components are: fixed-interval—10 minutes (a); time-out—2·5 minutes (b and d); and fixed-ratio—30 responses (c). The recording pen reset to baseline when reinforcement occurred.

Instead, the fixed-ratio response rates were decreased at the doses which enhanced fixed-interval responses rates. This indicates that the level of responding and the schedule are determinants of the quality of drug action.

Chlorpromazine produced a qualitatively different effect from either meprobamate or chlordiazepoxide. Fig. 5 shows that

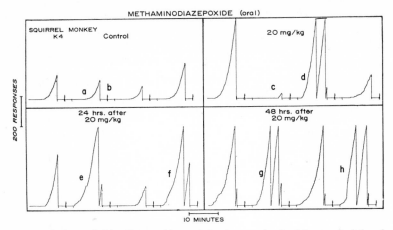

FIG. 3. Effects of chlordiazepoxide on behaviour maintained by a schedule of positive reinforcement in squirrel monkeys. The components are: fixed-interval —10 minutes (*a*); fixed-ratio—30 responses at *b*; and a time-out period of 2·5 minutes following each reinforcement (end of *a* and *b*). The recording pen resets at each food reinforcement or when 500 responses have cumulated. The effects of 20 mg./kg., orally, after 2, 24 and 48 hours, are shown.

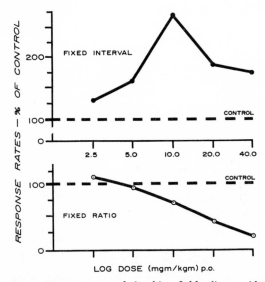

FIG. 4. Dose-response relationship of chlordiazepoxide on fixed-interval and fixed-ratio response rates in squirrel monkeys. Each point represents the average of three monkeys at each dose.

chlorpromazine completely decreased the FI 10 performance in this schedule (see *e, f, g, i* and *j*). It is interesting that occasionally responding in an FI 10 component occurs under chlorpromazine (as at *h*). As the dose of chlorpromazine is increased, pauses

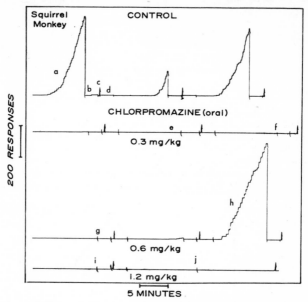

FIG. 5. Effects of chlorpromazine on behaviour maintained by a schedule of positive reinforcement in squirrel monkeys. The components are: fixed-interval—10 minutes (*a*); fixed-ratio —30 responses (*c*); and 2·5 minute time-out periods (*b* and *d*). The recording pen resets to the baseline when food reinforcement occurs.

precede the characteristic high fixed-ratio response rate. Again, discrimination between stimuli remains intact.

(*b*) *Tandem variable-interval—DRL (squirrel monkeys)*

Another operant schedule of positive reinforcement employed was a tandem variable-interval—DRL schedule.★ Responses were

★ DRL indicates a schedule of Differential Reinforcement of Low response rates and is described in Ferster and Skinner (1957).

reinforced with food intermittently on a variable basis (mean interval of 90 seconds); however, any response which was reinforced must have been spaced at least 7·5 seconds from the preceding response. The response rates generated under this

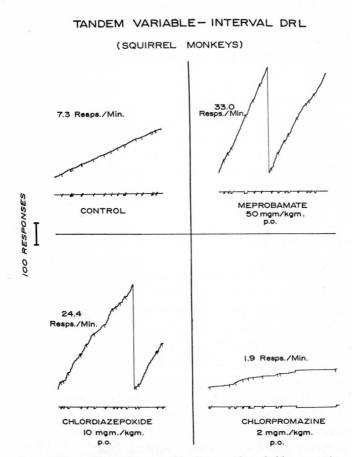

FIG. 6. Effects of meprobamate, chlordiazepoxide and chlorpromazine on behaviour maintained by a tandem variable-interval (90 seconds) —DRL (7·5 seconds) schedule in squirrel monkeys. Baseline recorder pen is depressed during time in the DRL contingency. Pips on cumulative record represent food reinforcement.

schedule are lower than response rates generated in a simple variable-interval (90 second) schedule. The DRL contingency is "holding the animal back" to an extent.* Fig. 6 shows that meprobamate (50 mg./kg., orally) and chlordiazepoxide (10 mg./kg., orally) enhanced the response rates in this operant schedule. Chlorpromazine (2 mg./kg., orally) decreased this performance; at no dose tested (0·5 to 4 mg./kg., orally) was an effect produced by chlorpromazine similar to that of meprobamate or chlordiazepoxide.

(c) Behaviour suppressed by punishment

The general approach used in this type of experiment is to make an aversive stimulus contingent upon the occurrence of a specific response; that is, ongoing behaviour is suppressed by punishing it. When electric foot-shock is employed as an aversive stimulus, the shock delivery is response-contingent. In some studies, investigators punished responses that required little or no training. Sacra, Rice and McColl (1957) selected cats that readily attacked mice, and then delivered an electric shock to the cats whenever they touched the mice; hence the attack behaviour was suppressed. They showed that meprobamate (19 mg./kg., i.p.), chlorpromazine (4·7 mg./kg., i.p.) and benactyzine (3·3 mg./kg., i.p.) attenuated this suppression. Naess and Rasmussen (1958) suppressed drinking responses in rats by punishing each response with electric shock. Meprobamate (40 mg./kg., i.p.) and amylobarbitone (5 mg./kg., s.c.) attenuated this punishment-produced suppression. Neither chlorpromazine (3 mg./kg., s.c.) nor benactyzine (4 mg./kg., s.c.) reversed this suppressed behaviour. These studies were consistent in showing that meprobamate attenuated the suppression; they did not show consistent results with benactyzine or chlorpromazine. Jacobsen (1957) and Geller and Seifter (1960, 1962a, 1962b) studied suppression by punishing con-

---

* Response rates seen under the variable-interval (90 sec.)—DRL (7·5 sec.) average 8 responses per minute. Response rates under a simple variable-interval (90 sec.) schedule average 20 responses per minute.

ditioned responses. These studies showed that meprobamate or chlordiazepoxide attenuated this type of suppressed behaviour, whereas chlorpromazine did not, or produced non-specific effects.

We have modified Geller's technique to some extent, and have found that our results confirm his findings. In addition, we have found that the interaction between the drug and this behaviour can be extended to include squirrel monkeys (*Simurari sciura*). Our studies employed a multiple variable-interval punishment schedule. The variable-interval component alternated with the punishment component. An eight minute variable-interval (average of 120 seconds) component alternated with a two minute period of tone. During the tone period, every response was reinforced with food; and 50 per cent of these responses were randomly punished by foot-shock (1·6 mA, one second duration). Each shock was delivered immediately after the food presentation. As shown in Fig. 7, monkeys exhibited stable characteristic performance during the variable-interval component (as at *a*); during the punishment component (indicated by a tone) responding was almost completely suppressed (as at *b*). Meprobamate (125 mg./kg., orally) produced the effects shown in the lower left recording. The number of responses in the punishment components was markedly increased, while response rates in the VI components were only slightly affected. At this dose the monkeys were depressed and ataxic. Similar effects were produced by chlordiazepoxide. The lower right recording in this figure shows the effects of 30 mg./kg. (i.m.) of chlordiazepoxide; depression and ataxia were also seen. Chlorpromazine failed to attenuate this type of suppression. Fig. 8 shows that chlorpromazine (2 mg./kg., orally), even at a dose which produced behavioural effects on the VI component, failed to increase the response rate during the punishment component.

These results indicate that performance which is generated and maintained by aversive stimuli (electric shock), as in conditioned avoidance procedures, is inhibited by chlorpromazine.

Chlordiazepoxide affects this behaviour in a characteristically different manner, and meprobamate has weak effects. The effect of chlordiazepoxide appears to be unique, in that it increases the

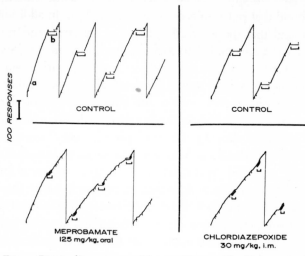

FIG. 7. Responding suppressed by punishment (shock) in squirrel monkeys. *Upper:* cumulative response records from control sessions on day before drug administration. *Lower:* cumulative response records, showing effects of meprobamate and chlordiazepoxide on this performance. The operant schedule was a multiple variable-interval (120 seconds) schedule (*a*), alternated with a punishment schedule (*b*). Pips on cumulative record indicate food reinforcement. Punishment component (underscored by brackets), was set up to deliver food for all responses, and to deliver shocks intermittently for about 50 per cent of responses. Number of responses during control punishment periods averaged from from 0 to 2 per component. Number of responses in same punishment components under meprobamate ranged from 20 to 45; and under chlordiazepoxide ranged from 40 to 60.

number of shocks delivered but does not decrease overall response rates. Drug effects in conditioned avoidance (non-discriminated) studies with human subjects appear to have some degree of correlation with those in animal studies.

Response rates which are held back (VI-DRL), or suppressed by

punishment (response-contingent shock), are enhanced by chlordiazepoxide and meprobamate. Under these conditions chlorpromazine does not enhance response rates; indeed, response rates
are generally decreased. It is obvious that qualitative differences

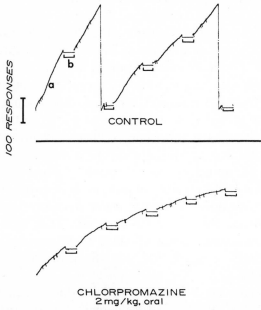

FIG. 8. Responding suppressed by punishment (shock) in
squirrel monkeys. Experimental conditions similar to Fig. 7.
Number of responses during control punishment periods
averaged from 0 to 2 per component. Under chlorpromazine, number of responses in same punishment
components averaged 0 to 1.

between chlorpromazine, meprobamate and chlordiazepoxide
can be measured using certain operant conditioning procedures.

RIBONUCLEIC ACID STUDIES

The experiments described above deal with the effects of drugs
on experimentally established stable behaviour. Indeed, the

stability of the behaviour was essential for the proper interpretation of the effects. Effects of pharmacological agents can also be measured using conditioned behaviour during its acquisition and extinction phases. These effects are described in the following experiments with ribonucleic acid (RNA) in rats.

Cameron and his co-workers (Cameron, 1958; Cameron, Solyon and Beach, 1961; Cameron and Solyon, 1961) have shown that chronic oral or intravenous administration of yeast ribonucleic acid had a "favourable effect in general upon memory retention failure in the aged", particularly in arteriosclerotic brain diseased patients. The RNA treatment improved retention in a counting test, and improved retention and speed of reconditioning in a conditioned response procedure. Other "favourable changes additional to those affecting the memory, were increased alertness, interest, initiative, and confidence". Montanari, Cutolo and Mazzoni (1961) reported improvement of psychogenic confusion and memory in patients under treatment for cerebrovascular disease and confusional disorders. Treatment consisted of daily oral administration of tablets containing the following ribonucleotides: cytidylic acid, adenylic acid, uridylic acid and guanylic acid.

Other investigators have reported on certain aspects of the relationship of RNA to behavioural processes in animals (Kreps et al., 1956; Hydén, 1960; Corning and John, 1961; Dingman and Sporn, 1961; John, 1961) but no direct evidence has been presented showing that the administration of purified RNA can produce an effect on the behaviour of animals. It is recognized that the type of behavioural study reported in this paper may not be directly related to the reported clinical findings; however, it was designed to study the interaction of administered purified RNA with certain basic elements of behaviour, the acquisition and extinction of a conditioned response in rats.

The conditioned escape response procedure employed was essentially that reported by Cook and Weidley (1957). The rats were individually placed, in the same position, in a chamber containing an electrified grid floor, with a pole suspended from the centre of the top of the chamber and a buzzer. In unconditioned response (UR) trials, the buzzer (CS) and electric shock through the grid floor (US) were presented simultaneously; in conditioned response (CR) trials, only the CS was presented. Each trial was terminated either by a response or at the end of 30 seconds. A response is defined as jumping on to the pole following the onset of the stimuli. Ribonucleic acid (dry powder yeast RNA) was given in daily intraperitoneal injections at a dose of 160 mg./kg., in a 10 per cent aqueous solution adjusted to pH 6·5–6·7. Fig. 9 (top) shows the effect of RNA on the rate of acquisition of conditioned escape performance after 53 consecutive daily injections (Group I). The RNA-treated group had a significantly faster rate of acquisition than the control saline-treated group (53 daily injections). This effect on rate of acquisition was confirmed in another group of rats (Group II) tested after 28 consecutive daily injections of RNA. In addition, extinction curves were also obtained in this group. As shown in Fig. 9 (bottom), the RNA group was more resistant to extinction than was the control saline group. Exact comparison of extinction rates is difficult since the level of performance was slightly better in the RNA-treated group at the start of extinction. However, the differences in extinction rate could at least indicate that the conditioned performance in the RNA group was stronger than in the saline group. Although these results do not reveal the mechanism of action of RNA on behaviour, they do show the manner in which acquisition and extinction of conditioned behaviour can be applied in pharmacological evaluation. It is not known whether RNA itself, one or more of its components, degradation products, or some biochemically resynthesized molecule is responsible for the effects described above. It is premature to conclude that the administered RNA directly affected learning or memory processes. Perhaps these measured behavioural changes are the

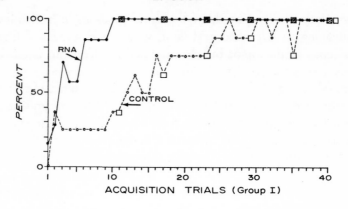

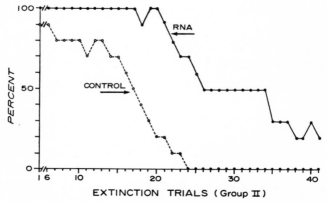

FIG. 9. Effects of ribonucleic acid on conditioned responses in rats. Dotted lines indicate average control group values; solid lines indicate average RNA group values.

Top: Effect of 53 daily injections of RNA on acquisition of conditioned responses (Group I). Circles indicate unconditioned response trials; squares indicate conditioned response trials. *Ordinate:* percentage of animals of each group exhibiting the response. *Abscissa:* individual trials, over a period of four days. Differences between groups (χ^2 test) were significant at P = 0.05 or less (one tailed).

Bottom: Effect on extinction after a total of 30 daily injections of RNA (Group II). Conditioned stimulus was presented without shock reinforcement. Percentage of rats of each group responding to the conditioned stimulus is on ordinate; individual trials, over a period of three days, are on abscissa. Differences between groups (χ^2 test) were significant at P = 0.05 level or less (one tailed).

result of the interaction of RNA with one or more of the experimental parameters utilized. However, the findings are generally consistent with some of the reported clinical results.

REFERENCES

ALEXANDER, L., and HORNER, S. R. (1961). *J. Neuropsychiat.*, **2**, 246.

CAMERON, D. E. (1958). *Amer. J. Psychiat.*, **114**, 943.

CAMERON, D. E., SOLYON, L., and BEACH, L. (1961). *In* Neuro-Psychopharmacology, **2**, 351, ed. Rothlin, E. Amsterdam: Elsevier.

CAMERON, D. E., and SOLYON, L. (1961). *Geriatrics*, **16**, 74.

COOK, L., and KELLEHER, R. T. (1961). *In* Neuro-Psychopharmacology, **2**, 77, ed. Rothlin, E. Amsterdam: Elsevier.

COOK, L., and KELLEHER, R. T. (1962). *Ann. N.Y. Acad. Sci.*, **96**, 315.

COOK, L., and KELLEHER, R. T. (1963). *Ann. Rev. Pharmacol.*, **3**, 205.

COOK, L., and WEIDLEY, E. (1957). *Ann. N.Y. Acad. Sci.*, **66**, 740.

CORNING, C. W., and JOHN, E. R. (1961). *Science*, **134**, 1363.

DEWS, P. B., and MORSE, W. H. (1961). *Ann. Rev. Pharmacol.*, **1**, 145.

DINGMAN, W., and SPORN, M. B. (1961). *J. Psychiat. Res.*, **1**, 1.

FERSTER, C. B., and SKINNER, B. F. (1957). Schedules of Reinforcement. New York: Appleton-Century-Crofts.

GELLER, I., and SEIFTER, J. (1960). *Psychopharmacologia*, **1**, 482.

GELLER, I., and SEIFTER, J. (1962a). *J. Pharmacol. exp. Ther.*, **136**, 284.

GELLER, I., and SEIFTER, J. (1962b). *Psychopharmacologia*, **3**, 374.

GRAY, W. D., OSTERBERG, A. C., and RAUH, C. E. (1961). *Arch. int. Pharmacodyn.*, **134**, 198.

HYDÉN, H. (1960). *Proc. IV Int. Congr. Biochem.*, **3**, 64. London: Pergamon.

JACOBSEN, E. (1957). *In* Psychotropic Drugs, p. 119, ed. Garattini, S., and Ghetti, V. Amsterdam: Elsevier.

JOHN, E. R. (1961). *Ann Rev. Physiol.*, **23**, 451.

KREPS, E., SMIRNOV, A., and CHETVERIKOV, D. (1956). Cited by PALLADIN, A. V., and VLADIMIRIV, G. E. *Proc. Intern. Conf. Peaceful Uses Atomic Energy, Geneva*, **12**, 402. New York: United Nations.

MAFFII, G. (1959). *J. Pharm. Pharmacol.*, **11**, 129.

MONTANARI, M., CUTOLO, E., and MAZZONI, S. (1961). *Arcisped. S. Anna Ferrara*, **14**, 573.

NAESS, K., and RASMUSSEN, E. W. (1958). *Acta. Pharmacol. (Kbh.)*, **15**, 99.

RANDALL, L. O., SCHALLEK, W., HEISE, G. A., KEITH, E. F., and BAGDON, R. E. (1960). *J. Pharmacol. exp. Ther.*, **129**, 163.

RANDALL, L. O. (1960). *Dis. Nerv. Syst.*, **21**, Suppl. 7.

SACRA, P., RICE, W. B., and McCOLL, J. D. (1957). *Canad. J. Biochem.*, **35**, 1151.

SIDMAN, M. (1953). *Science*, **118**, 157.

UHR, L., CLAY, M., PLATZ, A., MILLER, J. G., and KELLY, E. L. (1961). *J. abnorm. soc. Psychol.*, **63**, 546.

VERHAVE, T., OWEN, J. E., JR., and ROBBINS, E. B. (1958). *Arch. int. Pharmacodyn.*, **116**, 45.

WINSOR, T. (1958). *Arch. Surg.*, **76**, 193.

DISCUSSION

Stein: I am impressed by the profound effects that ribonucleic acid seems to have on the acquisition of the conditioned avoidance response. However, if RNA improves learning, why do the rats not learn to extinguish more rapidly?

Cook: I do not know why these RNA-treated rats failed to extinguish more rapidly than control rats. However, I am sure you agree that extinction is a complex phenomenon and that many variables are involved. One might expect *a priori* that the rats would learn to extinguish more rapidly. However, there are many ideas about the extinction phenomenon and the exact mechanism of RNA action, neither of which is understood. At present we feel that one cannot assume in which direction rates of extinction should be changed by RNA. I can only describe our results; the rate of acquisition under RNA treatment was enhanced, and the rate of extinction was prolonged. This experiment has been repeated several times, and this effect of RNA on extinction was consistent.

As I mentioned in my paper, we have also studied the effect of RNA on the extinction process more directly. We have used normal rats and have trained them for conditioned avoidance responses. Half the group was then given RNA for two weeks and half was given saline solution. During this treatment period no training was carried out and the animals remained in their home cages. At the end of the two-week treatment period both groups were started on extinction of the conditioned avoidance response. The RNA-treated group was more resistant to extinction than was the control group. This therefore confirms the effect of RNA in prolonging extinction, and in a more direct way, without the influence of different acquisition rates.

Bergel: Have you done a control experiment with a hydrolysate of your RNA?

Cook: No, we have not done this yet.

Actually, the RNA preparation was described by the manufacturers as being a tetranucleotide with a molecular weight of about 1300, a hydrolysis product of yeast RNA. Admittedly, it is unlikely that even a tetranucleotide, let alone undegraded RNA itself, would pass into the brain. It is quite probable that the RNA preparation we used is broken down to nucleotides or nucleosides and that these moieties themselves penetrate the brain where they may be active or are recombined to form RNA. We are currently studying the effect of administered nucleotides under similar experimental conditions, as well as higher molecular weight polynucleotides of RNA.

Another important aspect is that the animals we employed were young "normal" rats, which we assumed to be non-deficient; yet RNA affected their conditioned behaviour. The maximum effect of RNA we observe is usually during the first few conditioning trials during the acquisition phase. In addition, we find a consistent effect throughout the extinction phase. I believe that these results tend to pose the question of whether an effect of RNA is necessarily restricted to a "deficient" subject. Perhaps the reported clinical effect in seniles was obvious because the effect was magnified in these individuals. It is important to determine whether RNA has an effect on the behavioural capacities of normal people. We have no idea at the moment what is the mechanism of action or the active principle of RNA.

Weiskrantz: One simple hypothesis might be that these animals were in a chronic state of increased anxiety or jumpiness or something of the sort. Did your animals appear disturbed on gross observation?

Cook: We have administered the yeast RNA to normal untrained animals which were housed in their home cage. It was administered intraperitoneally (160 mg./kg. daily) for over a month and we saw no overt symptoms. Our trained personnel could not distinguish them from untreated rats. In addition, on autopsy, no gross pathology was observed in the peritoneal cavity.

Weiskrantz: Were the animals also studied in a learning situation in which there was a positive reinforcement rather than a negative reinforcement?

Cook: In the first attempt to study the effect of RNA on behaviour maintained by positive reinforcement, we did not observe a significant effect. This was a "matching the sample" experiment with rats. Hindsight suggests that we did not design the study properly, since we now feel that the maximum effect of RNA is on the first few experiences in an experiment. Since then we have been able to show that RNA does improve behaviour maintained by food (positive reinforcement) in rats. This study was designed to investigate the performance of animals in a multiple fixed–ratio/time-out schedule. Rats treated for two weeks with RNA left out extraneous time-out responding much faster than did saline-injected controls. These results were statistically significant. Therefore the effect of RNA is not limited to behaviour maintained by aversive events, but also extends to learning situations employing positive reinforcement.

Bureš: I want to stress the importance of the blood–brain barrier in the study of the rôle of RNA in the formation of the memory trace. We have recently used competitive inhibitors of RNA metabolism in an attempt to impair learning of a passive avoidance reaction in rats. Unfortunately we were not as successful as Dr. Cook. This may have been due to the inability of the drugs we used (azauracil and other drugs used in the treatment of carcinoma) to penetrate the blood–brain barrier. Direct injection of drugs into the cerebral ventricles would be more effective and should give better results in the study of the rôle of RNA in memory functions.

Dews: Dr. Cook illustrated (Fig. 5) an anomalous effect of chlorpromazine on fixed-interval responding, where the rate of responding increased very greatly. We have some fragmentary evidence that this is related to the experience of the animal, and is particularly likely to be seen if the animal has been on a fixed–ratio schedule. It is especially prominent if the fixed–interval component is observed in a multiple fixed–interval/fixed–ratio schedule. Did the squirrel monkeys have any previous experience of this kind?

Cook: These animals were on a multiple, fixed-interval/fixed-ratio schedule.

Hendry: You showed that chlorpromazine usually eliminates fixed-interval performance on a multiple FI/FR/TO schedule on which, of course, a different stimulus or signal is associated with each component. In this one case the animal broke through in the FI component and this breakthrough showed an interesting pattern of high rates alternating with very low rates, which is more characteristic of fixed-ratio performance, so that the results could be interpreted in terms of an effect on the perception of the animal. In other words, the animal thought that he was on FR, as it were, when in fact he was on FI. Professor Miller has shown that he takes hypotheses of this kind seriously and he has tested for the production of apparently motivational effects as a by-product of these perceptual effects. Dr. Cook, do you feel obliged to consider this type of explanation and to carry out the same kind of controls?

Cook: This question is related to the possible effect of chlorpromazine on perception or exteroceptive discrimination. The effect you refer to has been seen only very rarely, in about one in twenty monkeys; that is, on perhaps two occasions. I do not believe that chlorpromazine affects exteroceptive discrimination. In almost all our experiments, response rates decreased during the fixed–interval stimulus, and yet during the fixed–ratio the performance (high rates) was intact. Even though performance rates may be decreased or changed with chlorpromazine, the pattern of behaviour is usually appropriate to the stimulus present. This is consistently found on other schedules as well. The rates of responding under a specific stimulus may be altered, but the patterns of responding with different stimuli remain distinguished from each other. So we have enough experimental evidence to indicate that the animals still discriminate between exteroceptive stimuli.

To explain this breakthrough, I suggest an analogy with the effect of chlorpromazine on the gross appearance of monkeys, evaluated subjectively. Such monkeys sit for thirty or forty minutes and then suddenly make a lunge. Every once in a while you see the animal break through its depression and make a lunge.

The pattern in Fig. 5, of pauses separated by high rates, shows only a superficial resemblance to a high rate of fixed–ratio responding. I think there is insufficient evidence to conclude that merely the exteroceptive discrimination was affected so that the monkey "thought" he was on a fixed–ratio schedule. [See also discussion following p. 335.]

THE INFLUENCE OF DRUGS UPON MEMORY

MURRAY E. JARVIK

Department of Pharmacology, Albert Einstein College of Medicine, New York

THE possibility that drugs might affect memory has been suggested since antiquity. Greek mythology held that a drink from the river Lethe would erase the memories of a lifetime. Through the ages, elixirs and potions capable of causing forgetting have figured prominently in literature. For example, about 140 years ago Thomas de Quincey (1822) ascribed to opium the ability to cause unusual forgetting and remembering. His descriptions anticipated rather remarkably both Freudian repression theory and the reputed anamnesic properties of amylobarbitone.

The scientific study of memory began with the work of Ebbinghaus on man in 1885 and of Thorndike and Pavlov on animals at the turn of the century. Despite a massive accumulation of data since then, the physiological mechanisms underlying memory are almost as much a mystery to us as they were to the ancients. If physicochemical reactions are involved in learning and remembering, it is likely that drugs will be useful in the analysis of these processes. Yet the number of investigations devoted to the influence of drugs upon memory has been surprisingly meagre. Some of the recent investigations will be described in this paper.

The word "memory" is avoided by many psychologists who feel that it has a mentalistic flavour. Even though its meaning, like that of other psychological abstractions, has been contaminated by ambiguous lay usage it is perhaps better to filter out a meaning that can satisfy the scientist rather than resort to a circumlocution or neologism. After all, the word memory has signified a common construct for hundreds of years.

Memory may be defined in its broadest sense as the process by which the effects of an experience upon an organism persist and manifest themselves at a later time. If a set of stimulus conditions occurring at one time is found to be related to a set of responses produced subsequently, we may say a memory exists. This concept of memory is more general than that of the engineer who refers to memory as the place in his computer where data are stored. Frequently, people interested in biochemical coding mechanisms will regard memory and retention as synonymous. A broader view encompasses not only retention but also retrieval, analogous to what is commonly called remembering, and involving, for example, recall and recognition. The broadest view of memory (Woodworth, 1938; Woodworth and Schlosberg, 1954) includes three stages and we may refer to them as the three r's: registration, retention, and retrieval. This conception traces information from its entry into the organism, through its storage, to its final manifestation in outward behaviour.

Of particular interest to us is the possibility that a fixation process may be involved in retention. The hypothesis that a neural process perseverates after the termination of a stimulus and gradually becomes consolidated through time is clearly stated by Mueller and Pilzecker (1900). The vicissitudes of this hypothesis have been described by Glickman (1961) and evidence both supporting it (Deutsch, 1962) and opposing it (Coons and Miller, 1960; Adams and Lewis, 1962) has appeared in the recent literature. The rôle of this hypothesis in explaining certain drug effects upon retention will be considered later in this paper.

IMPAIRMENT OF MEMORY BY DRUGS

General impairment

If the duration of a drug's action greatly overlaps registration, retention and retrieval, then an indirect approach must be made to determine whether there is a differential effect upon these

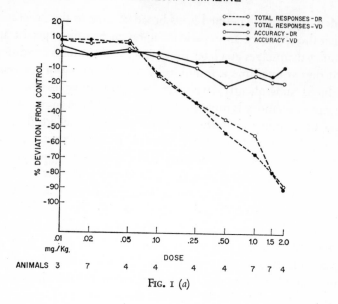

FIG. I (a)

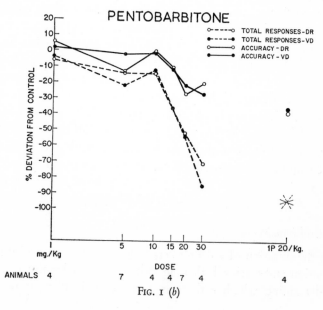

FIG. I (b)

stages. We were faced with this problem in attempting to measure the impairment or enhancement of short-term memory of a few seconds' duration by centrally acting drugs which had durations of action of several hours. Our measure of short-term memory has been the delayed response test, using monkeys as

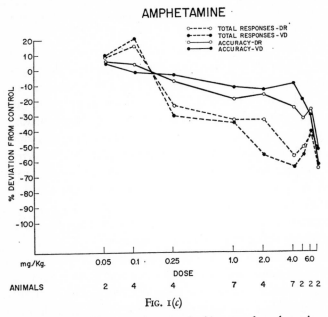

FIG. 1(c)

FIG. 1. Effects of chlorpromazine, pentobarbitone, and amphetamine upon performance on a visual discrimination (VD) and delayed response (DR) test in monkeys.

subjects. Pharmacological interference with retention alone would indicate a lability of the retention process or an impermanence of the trace.

Initially we used a mechanized two-second delayed alternation test in which the animal worked for a liquid reward. The monkey had to press a right and a left panel alternately every 2 seconds to receive a drop of orange drink. Dr. Stephan Chorover and I found that lysergic acid diethylamide (LSD-25) administered intramuscularly before the test markedly impaired performance (Jarvik and Chorover, 1959), but the effect might have been equally upon registration, retention or retrieval. Subsequently Dr. Martin Adler and I (1961) found that performance on a visual discrimination test was affected to approximately the same extent on a two-second delayed response test by 80 per cent nitrous oxide.

Dr. Adler and I then conducted the same test with varying doses of three longer-acting drugs, namely, chlorpromazine, pentobarbitone, and amphetamine. Fig. 1 shows that the impairment induced by pentobarbitone at doses from 10–30 mg./kg. was approximately equal for both visual discrimination and delayed response accuracy. With amphetamine and chlorpromazine there was slightly greater impairment of delayed response performance than of visual discrimination. Although the differences were small they were consistent and a sign test indicated that animals gave significantly lower performances on delayed response than on visual discrimination with chlorpromazine and amphetamine but not with pentobarbitone.

At this point for several reasons modifications were made in the delayed response test. In order to obtain more consistent performance the incentive was changed from a liquid reward to shock avoidance; animals were now tested in their home cages to reduce variability induced by daily handling; two delays, of 1 second (short) and 8 seconds (long), were presented in random sequence; immediate visual discrimination was no longer required so that the animal did not have to make an overt response at the time that the visual stimuli appeared. In the previous test, performance following only one delay had been compared with visual discrimination performance. The first drug tested with the new technique was ethyl alcohol (in collaboration with Dr. Elizabeth van Laer). Administering large amounts of liquid to monkeys posed some formidable problems, so we allowed the animals to administer to themselves a 6 per cent alcohol solution in an orange drink and measured their intake. Animals were grossly intoxicated by doses ranging from 1·0 to 5·0 g./kg. Preliminary tests suggested that drug effects might be magnified by running animals with an extinction procedure, and both control and drug results were obtained from such a test. In the scatter-grams in Fig. 2 each point is the average performance on a given day

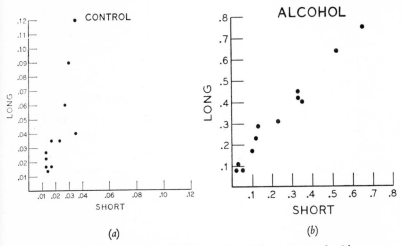

FIG. 2. Errors made by monkeys following short delays compared with errors following long delays with and without alcohol. Note that alcohol changes the slope of the regression line towards 1·0.

for a group of 6 animals. If alcohol produced continuous inter-ference during the delay interval, we should expect relatively greater impairment in responses following a long delay than following a short delay. Although monkeys made more errors of omission when intoxicated, the average ratio of errors follow-ing short delays to those following long delays is actually closer to 1·0 under alcohol than under control conditions. It appears that either alcohol reduces interference and thus relatively im-proves retention, or that in reducing accuracy it wipes out whatever is responsible for the initially poor performance on long delays. In any case, it is clear that alcohol does not impair retention under the conditions of this particular delayed response test.

Subsequently we thought that it would be useful to obtain

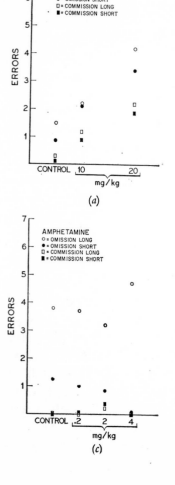

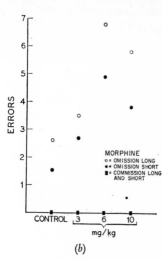

FIG. 3. Effects upon monkeys of pentobarbitone, morphine, and amphetamine on delayed response test with short (1 second) and long (8 second) delay. Note the tendency of errors to increase with dose.

more control data and to reduce variability by changing the procedure. Therefore, the animals were run consistently either with or without drug on a VR3 reinforcement ratio (i.e. one error in three was punished at random). Some interesting effects and differences were obtained with pentobarbitone, morphine, and amphetamine. The dose–response curves in Fig. 3 show that all drugs caused an increase in errors of omission following the

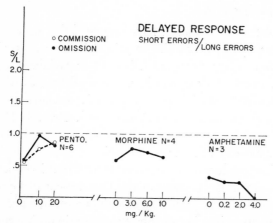

FIG. 4. Ratios of errors following short delays to those following long delays with different doses of pentobarbitone, morphine, and amphetamine in monkeys.

long delay. Pentobarbitone (N = 6) and morphine (N = 4) caused an increase in errors of omission following the short delay as well, but amphetamine (N = 3) produced a decrease in errors of omission following the short delay. The errors of commission were increased by pentobarbitone just as they were by alcohol, but not by morphine or amphetamine. If we plot the ratios of short over long errors (Fig. 4), then pentobarbitone and morphine show no change or actually less of a difference between the errors following the two intervals. This indicates that the same type of process is probably occurring with these two drugs as with

ANL. BEH.—3

alcohol. This tendency of the ratio of the two kinds of errors to approach 1·0 with increasing doses is especially evident with pentobarbitone. With amphetamine, on the other hand, there is a decrease in ratio with increasing dose which indicates that this drug possibly had an effect upon retention, acting to impair it. These studies are now being extended.

Impairment of registration

A number of investigators have suggested that central depres-sant drugs may impair learning in animals (Settlage, 1936; Headlee and Kellogg, 1941; Ader and Clink, 1957; Steinberg and Sum-merfield, 1957). A drug which has been credited for more than fifty years with the ability to produce amnesia is hyoscine (Gauss, 1906; Goodman and Gilman, 1955). Recently Hardy and Wakely (1962) reported that hyoscine did produce a very slight impairment of memory in patients. A series of informal observations made with us by Mrs. Ruth Cohn in collaboration with Dr. Seymour Romney of the Department of Gynecology and Obstetrics were aimed at examining the reputed amnesic effects of hyoscine in an obstetrical setting. Twenty-seven patients were given 0·65 mg. hyoscine hydrobromide and 12 patients were given 0·65 mg. hyoscine methyl nitrate (kindly supplied by Strasenburgh Laboratories as "Skopolate"). The latter drug is a quaternary compound which apparently pene-trates the central nervous system with difficulty but produces typical peripheral cholinergic blockade. While under the influ-ence of these drugs patients were given three simple stimuli: the sound of a small bell, the illumination of a flashlight, and the smell of lavender water. When tested the next day 9 out of 27 patients receiving hyoscine showed no recall of these stimuli whereas 2 out of 12 patients receiving hyoscine methyl nitrate showed no recall. All 39 patients received in addition the usual ward regimen consisting of fairly large doses of quinalbarbitone and chlorpromazine. This presumably accounts for the forgetting by the two patients who received hyoscine methyl nitrate. An undrugged group of 15 post-partum patients tested in the same way showed 100 per cent recall.

A variety of centrally acting compounds have been shown capable of impairing learning. Cholinergic blocking compounds such as hyoscine and a variety of other newer drugs (Biel *et al.*, 1962) have been shown to interfere with perception and thinking. While drugs may impair learning or acquisition under appropriate conditions and doses, many explanations for such effects are possible. Impairment of perception, of motivation, or of ability to respond may all affect learning detrimentally. So far as I know, drugs which specifically affect one or another component of behaviour have not yet been reported, with the possible exception of the neuromuscular blocking agents.

Impairment of retention

The question of whether memory traces are susceptible to impairment by drugs is of great theoretical importance, for such interference with retention would imply a certain lability of the storage mechanism. If susceptibility of the trace to impairment by a drug showed a negative temporal gradient, that is, if the interfering effect of the drug decreased as time from registration increased, it would provide evidence supporting a theory of memory trace consolidation.

Results obtained in our laboratory (Pearlman, Sharpless, and Jarvik, 1961) indicate that anaesthesia applied within minutes after a learning experience is capable of interfering with a subsequent expression of such learning. A temporal gradient of effect was obtained for both diethyl ether and intravenous pentobarbitone, but the duration of the pentobarbitone effect was greater than that of the ether. Essman and Jarvik (1961) and Abt, Essman and Jarvik (1961), using variations of the technique in mice, obtained essentially similar results with diethyl ether.

With the same behavioural technique that Pearlman, Sharpless, and I had used, Heriot and Coleman (1962) were able to demonstrate a temporal gradient of effect with electroconvulsive shock. Pare (1961) showed a temporal gradient of impairment when quinalbarbitone was injected into rats at different times following massed training on a Thompson visual discrimination apparatus. Subjects injected 5 seconds or 2 minutes after the last trial showed a significant increase in errors, whereas those injected an hour later did not perform differently from controls.

Experiments are in progress in our laboratory to determine possible mechanisms whereby general anaesthetics may reduce fear. A one-trial learning situation is particularly suitable for such investigations since the time between learning and treatment may be fairly accurately measured. In the apparatus we are now using, a mouse or rat is put into a box with four metal plates on the floor. Whenever the animal touches two plates simultaneously it completes a circuit which either activates a transistor or gives the animal an electric shock. Our usual procedure is to put an animal into this box for one minute and then either give it a shock and remove it, or remove it without giving a shock. Later the animal is retested for one minute. We are at present examining effects of punishment and anaesthesia in this situation and are finding that high temperatures seem to augment the reduction of fear produced by ether without materially affecting the "shock, no drug group" (Table I). The surprising

Table I

MEAN ACTIVITY OF MICE ON TESTING TRIAL

Group	Temperature > 80°F			Temperature < 70°F		
	N	Median	Mean ± SD	N	Median	Mean ± SD
No shock, no drug	16	23·5	24·3±6·1	30	20	21·3±6·6
No shock, ether	8	21·5	23·4±6·1			
Shock, no drug	123	4·0	5·4±5·6	81	4	6·9±7·4
Shock, ether immediate	93	17·4	17·2±8·1	26	11	11·3±8·5
Shock, ether 1 hour	44	18·5	18·0±8·6	24	9	11·3±7·2

fear-reducing action of ether in this situation at one hour is now under study. It should be noted that ether alone does not produce conditioned suppression of activity. Animals rendered unconscious by being put into an atmosphere of nitrogen do not show loss of fear. On the other hand, animals given electroconvulsive shock do show loss of fear if they are convulsed immediately after being punished but not if they are convulsed an hour later (Table II).

Table II

EFFECTS OF ELECTROCONVULSIVE SHOCK ON ACTIVITY IN TESTING TRIAL

Group	3 Hour			24 Hour		
	N	Median	Mean± SD	N	Median	Mean± SD
No shock, no ECS	29	17·0	16·2±6·6			
No shock, ECS	39	16·0	15·4±6·0			
Shock, no ECS	116	4·0	6·4±9·1	32	2·0	4·3± 6·3
Shock, ECS, immediate	133	14·0	13·4±7·9	32	18·0	16·3±22·6
Shock, ECS, 1 hour	61	5·0	8·5±7·7	30	5·0	6·1± 8·9

Findings of memory impairment in animals led us to ask whether general anaesthetics might produce similar effects in man. Dr. Jerome Jaffe of our department and Drs. Louis Orkin and Howard Zauder of the Department of Anesthesiology and I have initiated a project to determine whether patients given a short picture memory test (2 minutes, 24 items) just before receiving thiopentone anaesthesia would subsequently remember less if anaesthesia followed immediately than if it were delayed for 10 minutes. Subjects had to distinguish 24 new from 24 old pictures on day 2. Preliminary results obtained with 27 patients given immediate anaesthesia showed that 24 hours later they forgot 46 per cent of the pictures whereas 11 patients given anaesthesia 10 minutes after the pictures forgot only 21 per cent. The difference in errors of omission was significant at the 5 per cent level.

It was found that there was a marked serial position gradient in which the last pictures in the list were forgotten most often, but

Table III

MEAN NUMBER OF ERRORS ON RETESTING ONE DAY AFTER IMMEDIATE
AND DELAYED THIOPENTONE

		Omission				Commission
	N	1–6	7–12	13–18	19–24	Total	
Immediate	27	2·0±1·8	2·4±1·9	3·0±1·9	4·1±1·6	11·4±6·3	3·1±3·6
Delayed	11	0·6±0·8	1·5±1·6	2·0±1·6	2·3±1·9	6·5±5·2	4·8±5·2

this effect was found in both groups so that its significance remains in doubt. These experiments are being repeated and extended with different lists and intervals of time. It must be pointed out that many of the patients receiving immediate anaesthesia were able to remember a good deal of the material and also were able to describe a great deal of what happened to them immediately before anaesthesia. Whatever retrograde amnesia occurred was far from overwhelming and apparently required a delicate test to reveal it.

Impairment of retrieval

If an animal is trained without a drug but tested while under its influence, some impairment of retrieval may be demonstrated. The effects of drugs upon well-learned tasks have been investigated by a number of contributors to the present symposium and will be discussed by them. This method is commonly used in drug screening.

The results we considered under the heading "general impairment" dealt with delayed responses and we were primarily interested in retention. However, one might equally view these experiments as effects of drugs upon retrieval. The animals received prolonged training in the delayed response task before they were given drugs, and they had to remember not only the pre-delay stimulus but also the essentials of the training procedure (i.e., learning sets) which were acquired in the non-drugged state.

It is clear that retrieval may be adversely affected by drugs. Its impairment might be due to difficulty in extracting information which has been stored or in translating it into action or in the ability to use whatever releasing stimuli are being fed into the organism.

FACILITATION OF MEMORY BY DRUGS

Weiss and Laties (1962) in their review of enhancement of human performance by caffeine and the amphetamines remark on their surprise that only a handful of studies have dealt with enhancement of learning by drugs. One reason may be that rates of acquisition of conditioned responses by animals or of information by people show large individual differences. An animal can be used only once in a learning task unless some kind of reversal procedure is employed. Since few drugs have been suggested as facilitators of learning, research in this area is apt to be risky and expensive, as it is in the empirical screening of any compound.

Some work yielding positive results has been done in recent years. McGaugh and Petrinovich (1959) confirmed an old study of Lashley's (1917) which showed that strychnine could facilitate maze learning in rats. McGaugh has shown that injections of picrotoxin and strychnine after a trial could facilitate learning and he ascribes this to an acceleration of consolidation. The study by Pare (1961) lends weight to this argument since he demonstrated that caffeine would facilitate learning more if it was administered shortly after a learning experience than if it was delayed for an hour.

Summerfield and Steinberg (1957) have demonstrated in man that nitrous oxide given after a learning experience could result in greater retention than an equivalent control period of air. They attributed this apparent facilitation to a reduction in interference. We obtained only an impairment in performance on a delayed response with monkeys. However, if it were possible to administer the nitrous oxide during the delay interval only, facilitation could conceivably result.

LACK OF DRUG EFFECTS ON MEMORY

Many of the experiments failing to show drug effects upon registration, retention, or retrieval have gone unpublished because negative results may always be attributable to inadequacies in experimental procedure. Potent centrally acting drugs are used daily in clinical medicine without notable effects upon memory. It is clear that subtle memory changes are not detectable without refined procedures.

Dr. Elizabeth van Laer and I have been interested in determining what ether anaesthesia would do to a memory connected with a positive incentive. For this purpose rats were trained to run alternately to one side and then to the other in a T-maze (for a water reward, with half an hour between trials). When the animals had reached a high level of proficiency they were anaesthetized immediately after a first trial and re-run 45 minutes later. The results of 4 replications (Table IV) indicate that little impairment of accuracy was produced by the ether but running times were markedly increased.

Table IV

EFFECT OF POST-TRIAL ETHER ANAESTHESIA UPON
DELAYED ALTERNATION ACCURACY IN RATS

$N=21$

Experiment	I	II	III	IV
% Correct Alternations				
Control	81	86	76	80
Ether	71	62	48	80
Running Times (Mean)				
Control	7·7	7·3	8·3	5·8
Ether	8·2	16·5	18·8	18·4

The differences between these results and those of Pearlman, Sharpless and Jarvik (1961) may be due to differences in situational factors such as the use of a maze instead of a Skinner box, positive instead of negative incentive, tested instead of naive animals.

Further work is now being done to determine whether a stronger disruptive treatment such as electroconvulsive shock might in fact influence the accuracy of animals in the delayed alternation situation.

MOLECULAR BASIS OF THE TRACE

The programme of research in our laboratory has as its ultimate aim the elucidation of brain mechanisms which may be involved in trace formation, storage and translation into behaviour. It is clear that engram formation must involve some kind of plastic change in the nervous system. If there is growth of a neuronal structure it is likely that protein synthesis is somehow involved. Flexner and his colleagues (1962) have indicated that 83 per cent inhibition of brain protein synthesis by puromycin does not interfere with certain kinds of learning in mice. The involvement of protein synthesis in learning is not completely ruled out by this experiment since the remaining synthesis may be adequate to handle learning, or the particular kinds of learning used might not be sensitive to the puromycin effects.

Nucleic acid synthesis has also been invoked as an explanation of learning (Hydén, 1961). Nucleic acids are known to be rather stable carriers of genetic information. The turnover rate for nuclear DNA is essentially zero which makes it a stable information storage medium, but the evidence that nucleic acids play a rôle in learning and memory is, so far, rather circumstantial. Dingman and Sporn (1962) found that a purine analogue, 8-azaguanine, would interfere with registration in a maze-learning situation while sparing retention and retrieval. The authors point out that the action of this substance could conceivably have been due to some mechanism other than nucleic acid antagonism. The differential susceptibility of poorly learned and overlearned tasks to drugs is well known but the explanation for such effects on a molecular basis has not yet been forthcoming.

We have been collaborating with Dr. Samuel Barondes of the United States Public Health Service, National Institutes of Health, in an investigation of the effects of intracerebrally injected actinomycin D which is known to be a rather specific inhibitor of ribonucleic acid synthesis. Preliminary experiments have shown that at least 55 per cent inhibition of brain RNA synthesis can be obtained in mice with intracerebral injections of actinomycin D. Parallel experiments indicated that mice with such injections trained in the transistorized activity box were still able to learn. Current work indicates that much higher levels of inhibition of RNA synthesis can be attained and behavioural studies are in progress to determine whether learning is impaired. The development of a relatively simple rapid learning test for mice has considerably expedited the study of chemical and pharmacological influences upon memory, and we are eagerly pursuing the problem.

Acknowledgments

I should like to thank Herbert Alpern, Jay Carley, James Guyer and Robert Stern for skilled assistance in conducting these experiments. I am grateful to Dr. Gerald Edlist for help in performing the human anaesthesia studies.

REFERENCES

ABT, J. P., ESSMAN, W. G., and JARVIK, M. E. (1961). *Science*, **133**, 1477.
ADAMS, H. E., and LEWIS, D. J. (1962). *J. comp. physiol. Psychol.*, **55**, 299.
ADER, R., and CLINK, D. W. (1957). *J. Pharmacol. exp. Ther.*, **121**, 144.
BIEL, J. H., NUHFER, T. A., HOYA, W. K., LEISER, H. A., and ABOOD, L. D. (1962). *Ann. N.Y. Acad Sci.*, **96**, 251.
COONS, E. E., and MILLER, N. E. (1960). *J. comp. physiol. Psychol.*, **53**, 524.
DE QUINCEY, T. (1822). *Confessions of an English Opium Eater*. London: Taylor and Hessey.
DEUTSCH, J. A. (1962). *Ann. Rev. Physiol.*, **24**, 259.
DINGMAN, W., and SPORN, M. B. (1962). *J. Psychiat. Res.*, **1**, 1.
ESSMAN, W. B., and JARVIK, M. E. (1961). *Psychopharmacologia*, **2**, 172.
FLEXNER, J. B., FLEXNER, L. B., STELLAR, E., DE LA HABA, G., and ROBERTS, R. B. (1962). *J. Neurochem.*, **9**, 595.
GAUSS, C. J. (1906). *Arch. Gynak.*, **78**, 579.

GLICKMAN, S. E. (1961). *Psychol. Bull.*, **58**, 218.

GOODMAN, L. S., and GILMAN, A. (1955). The Pharmacological Bases of Therapeutics. New York: MacMillan Co.

HARDY, T. K., and WAKELY, D. (1962). *Anaesthesia*, **17**, 331.

HEADLEE, R. R., and KELLOGG, W. N. (1941). *Amer. J. Psychol.*, **54**, 353.

HERIOT, J. T., and COLEMAN, P. D. (1962). *J. comp. physiol. Psychol.*, **55**, 1082.

HYDÉN, H. (1961). *Sci. Amer.*, **205**, 62.

JARVIK, M. E., and ADLER, M. W. (1961). *J. Pharmacol. exp. Ther.*, **131**, 108.

JARVIK, M. E., and CHOROVER, S. (1959). *Psychopharmacologia*, **1**, 221.

LASHLEY, K. G. (1917). *Psychobiol.*, **1**, 141.

MCGAUGH, J. L., and PETRINOVICH, L. (1959). *Amer. J. Psychol.*, **72**, 99.

MUELLER, G. E., and PILZECKER, A. (1900). *Z. Psychol.*, **1**, 1.

PARE, W. (1961). *J. comp. physiol. Psychol.*, **54**, 506.

PEARLMAN, C. A., SHARPLESS, S. K., and JARVIK, M. E. (1961). *J. comp. physiol. Psychol.*, **54**, 109.

SETTLAGE, P. H. (1936). *J. comp. physiol. Psychol.*, **22**, 339.

STEINBERG, H., and SUMMERFIELD, A. (1957). *Quart. J. exp. Psychol.*, **9**, 138.

SUMMERFIELD, A., and STEINBERG, H. (1957). *Quart. J. exp. Psychol.*, **9**, 146.

WEISS, B., and LATIES, V. G. (1962). *Pharmacol. Rev.*, **14**, 1

WOODWORTH, R. S. (1938). Experimental Psychology. New York: Holt.

WOODWORTH, R. S., and SCHLOSBERG, H. (1954). Experimental Psychology. New York: Holt.

DISCUSSION

Summerfield: I entirely agree with your definition of memory, Dr. Jarvik, and your distinction between the processes of registration, retention and retrieval. However, so far as experiments with drugs are concerned, it is necessary to add a fourth stage which precedes the other three. In principle, it is possible to give a drug so that it has its effect in the period before a learning task is begun and, therefore before your three stages come into play. Of course, there is the problem of distinguishing effects on each of these four stages, because of the time courses of the action of drugs.

Why do you consider it paradoxical that central nervous depressants have an improving effect on memory, while central nervous stimulants like amphetamine have the reverse effect? When Dr. Steinberg and I did the experiments on learning and retention in man to which you referred in your paper, we used nitrous oxide in a 30 per cent mixture with oxygen. Nitrous oxide was chosen because of its short time course, which makes it possible to distinguish effects on these different stages. We found that this central nervous depressant depressed the stage of registration, but that over a short period of time it enhanced retention. Why, therefore, do you find your results paradoxical?

Jarvik: I thought that your results were surprising but, naturally, after your explanation they seemed perfectly logical. One would in general expect a stimulant drug to enhance performance, whatever it may be, and a depressant drug to interfere with it. However, if the depressant is interfering with something which itself is interfering with performance, one would end up with an enhancement. It is quite possible that my results could also be explained in this way.

Summerfield: In your experiment on the effects of ethyl alcohol on long and short delay, might the effect depend on the length of time involved in registration and retrieval? With a long delay, the effect of ethyl alcohol on registration may have been masked compared with the short interval. Overall, therefore, there may not have been too much difference between the two parts of the results. I have recently obtained some results in man which support this kind of interpretation.

This was with nitrous oxide, which in many ways is similar to alcohol. In a task which involved reading out numbers, there was more impairment of performance, the higher the dose. This could be interpreted as an effect on *registration*. But in a further task which involved short-term memory as well, there was an additional effect of *increasingly* greater impairment as the dose was increased. This suggests an effect of the drug on *retention* as well as on registration.

Jarvik: It is quite possible that the effects of ethyl alcohol were on either the registration or the retrieval processes. These effects were so marked that, even if there were also an effect on retention, whether it were an impairment or an enhancement, it would not show up. The ideal way to answer this question is to repeat the experiment the way you did it with nitrous oxide but to interpose the drug between the registration and the retrieval periods, that is, to give it during the retention interval. But this is rather difficult to do with ethyl alcohol, particularly when the delay intervals are only a few seconds. The onset and duration of action of the drug are too long, and we therefore had to use a rather indirect and unsatisfactory method instead. Perhaps some other quick-acting drugs would throw greater light on this problem.

Joyce: It is very exciting to see that the results of Dr. Jarvik's animal experiments bear out the conclusions of work that he has now carried out in human beings. A few years ago we did some work on the synergism between ethyl alcohol and phenobarbitone in man (Joyce, C. R. B., Edgecombe, P. C. E., Kennard, D. A., Weatherall, M., and Woods, D. P. [1959]. *J. ment. Sci.*, **105**, 51). We found that ethyl alcohol increased the speed with which a simple typing task was done, and that it also increased the frequency of errors. Phenobarbitone, on the other hand, slowed down this kind of behaviour and reduced the number of errors; errors which were made tended to be corrected. However, when half doses of both drugs were given to the same subjects they behaved as if they had had even larger doses of ethyl alcohol. In other words, the effect of the two drugs together was to increase the effect of one of the drugs alone.

This brings me to a point about Dr. Jarvik's experiments in which some patients were given the picture memory task and were then immediately induced with thiopentone, while others were given the same task and were left ten minutes before they were induced. It is the practice in Britain and, from personal observation, in the United States as well, to give a number of drugs pre-operatively apart from the inducing agent. On Dr. Jarvik's own evidence, morphine and probably hyoscine or atropine also are likely to have effects upon memory. Although it is likely that his "immediate" and "delayed" groups were given similar pre-anaesthetic medication, nevertheless the time relationships must clearly have been different. I doubt if this matters very much, but I should like to be assured that it does not.

Jarvik: It is quite true that the patients all received pre-anaesthetic medication and moreover it did vary somewhat from patient to patient. Patients were selected at random and even the anaesthetist giving the test did not know whether he was going to wait ten minutes or not. However, this is a flaw in the experiment and we hope it will work itself out by further replications. It was by chance that the proportion of patients receiving a particular pre-anaesthetic medication in one group was the same as in the other, since there was no selection for this factor. It is, of course, likely that pre-anaesthetic medication has some effect on learning. Drugs such as hyoscine, morphine and the barbiturates, which are commonly used in pre-anaesthetic medication, are known to interfere with learning. Ideally, one would like to use patients who have not received any pre-anaesthetic medication, but I am not in a position to control this. Despite this, I think that the differences are due to the thiopentone and not to the other medication.

THE STRUCTURE OF SOCIAL BEHAVIOUR AND DRUG ACTION

M. R. A. CHANCE AND A. P. SILVERMAN

Department of Pharmacology and Medical
Biochemistry, University of Birmingham, and
Ethology Laboratory, Uffculme Clinic, Birmingham

STEINBERG (1962) has said that " . . . the screening of psycho-active drugs is at present still being carried out against a background of many unsolved problems." Nor is this surprising in view of the absence of much relevant fundamental work. Especially is this so for the study of the action of drugs on social behaviour. Until recent ethological studies began to systematize the observations of social behaviour, upon which alone a scientific analysis could be based, no approach other than those based upon fragmentary use of concepts borrowed from psychology, neurophysiology, or frank anecdote has been attempted. Ethologists who have been studying courtship behaviour by simple identification and description of the components of behaviour (acts and postures) have been able to reveal the structure of social behaviour in a number of different orders of vertebrates.

In effect, they show that mating behaviour takes place only within an agonistic context of aggression and flight appropriate to the antagonism between males, which either separates them into territories or arranges them in an order of rank. Seasonal changes in fertility, if not in the actual breeding season, are the rule in nature. The antagonism of the males at the start of the breeding season is initially directed at all intruders, including the females. In this context courtship can be seen as a way of behaving which gradually reduces the agonistic components of behaviour to a point where the sexes are able to come together. Seen in this context a new dimension is added to our way of thinking about sexual behaviour. It is no longer a single, separate category of acts but is only isolable for study after its relation to other forms of social interactions has been understood.

In nature males court at a time and in circumstances when another male or female in any stage of reproductive behaviour may be encountered, to say nothing of the possibility of meeting a predator. Hence, it is reasonable to assume that the repertoire of social behaviour, available not only to other mammals but also to ourselves, will be based on mechanisms established in evolution to meet the requirements of this widespread pattern. The appropriate drives have been found organized into complexes with specific patterns of arousal, dependent in part also on the participation of that species either at present or in the evolutionary past, in epideictic (population density dependent) displays (Wynne Edwards, 1962) which are concentrated close to the breeding occasions. The discoveries which brought this to light, however, were initially the result of direct observation of behaviour in the wild. Recently, the systematization of these observations, initially the province of naturalists, has led to the branch of behaviour studies known as ethology, and ethological method may be demonstrated by the studies of Grant (1963a, b) and Grant and Mackintosh (1963) on the social encounters between rats.

Attention to the biological context of the behaviour of an animal studied in a laboratory has not been a conspicuous feature of psychopharmacological studies up till now. This is not perhaps surprising in view of the way the methods of pharmacology are at present so largely modelled on those of physiology and biochemistry. Pharmacology, however, is the study of the action of chemicals in a living organism, in part or in whole, and hence it will have to take more notice of the relevant biological facts if in future it is to encompass its task adequately.

In this instance, to be able to observe and describe the behaviour of rats it is essential to take into account their nocturnal habits and, unless one is prepared to stay up at night, their waking hours must be made to coincide with ours by putting them to sleep with bright light at night and keeping them awake in the daytime in dim, red light. If, then, one introduces a strange male rat into a cage where another has lived for a few days (see Chance and Mead, 1955), one effectively reproduces, in the restricted space of a cage, the intrusion of one male into the territory of another. Previous isolation for suitable periods increases the intensity of social interaction and concentrates it under the experimenter's control at the start of the encounter.

Two observers, each trained to recognize the forty or so identifiable postures, record the sequence of acts appearing in the behaviour of one of the rats on one track of a double-track tape recorder, in conjunction with a paper-strip pen recorder.

It is possible to plot the frequency with which one act is preceded and followed by another in the behaviour of one rat and thus to analyse the motivational relationships between these acts, or to discover the response of one rat to a particular act of the other. Here we are only concerned with the order of acts in the behaviour of one animal.

Suitably displayed in tabular form, the most frequently repeated sequences are easily distinguished. The sequence "Sniff" at the ano-genital region, "Follow" the retreating male or female (the sequence is the same between males as between males and females) and "Mounting" comprises the recognizable components of the male mating behaviour. The agonistic components are, however, less easily distinguished. If we assume that a bite is the final aggressive act and escape the final consummatory act of flight motivation, then neither of these is seen prominently between males in a cage, the former because only cine-photos make it visible, when it is seen as a very fast nip which is rarely sufficiently intense to elicit a squeak, and flight, because retreat to the space below the food hopper takes place, if only infrequently, and leads, with little consistency, to the separation of the rats. Consummatory acts are by definition those which bring about drive reduction, hence those acts which are infrequently followed by a return to the sequence leading up to them or, more generally, lead to the cessation of all social activity, would qualify as consummatory acts of social drives.

Inspection soon revealed that when a situation developed where one rat lay on its back, straddled by another, this condition was fulfilled, and a crouching rat with another grooming its neck was a rather similar situation (Figs. 1 and 2). However, whereas the social behaviour was completely interrupted following the rat lying on its back with the other straddling it, the acts which each rat performed following the crouching situation were acts appearing in exactly the same proportion as acts appear in the total social encounter. That is to say, the rat's next act could be any one act from its repertoire, and the probability of which particular act it was depended on the frequency of distribution of all the acts in the encounter. This means that the crouching rat was giving no sign to the one that was grooming its neck, whereas the one lying on its back and "submitting", as we say, was effectively presenting a sign stimulus to the one straddling it. The sequence of acts leading to these two terminal situations is shown in Fig. 3. The animals first turn their head away and then turn their body away from the other animal before proceeding to crouch. These postures indicate that the rats are flight-motivated and if the whole encounter is carried on in a large enclosure, "Crouch" disappears in this situation and is replaced by true flight and escape. Hence, there is a bifurcated flight pathway with one part of it leading to social submission, in which the two animals remain next to each other, and another escape pathway which separates the animals completely, and these are two distinct pathways of response. Change in the use that any rat will make of these two pathways can, for example, be made by assessing the changes in total frequency with which the postures comprising each response pathway occur in an encounter of fixed duration, say, of ten

Fig. 1. The consummatory postures at the end of the social pathway. Full aggressive posture, top rat; full submissive posture, bottom rat.

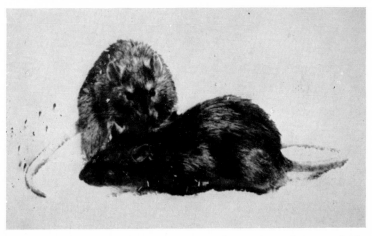

Fig. 2. Terminal posture of a blocked escape pathway. Aggressive grooming by facing rat; crouching by rat in front.

To face p. 68

minutes; and the amount of change can be assessed using a χ^2 comparison of the actual and the expected frequencies. Previous experience influences the extent to which one pathway is preferred to the other. Keeping male rats in groups rather than in isolation increases the amount of submissive behaviour during encounters. Previous mating experience further enhances the use made of submission by male rats. Grant (1963*a*, *b*), who made

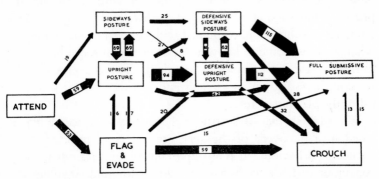

Fig. 3. Diagram of flight pathways in a balanced set of introductions showing the number of responses per pathway. The diagram demonstrates an escape pathway leading from *Attend* through *Flag* and *Evade* to *Crouch*, and a social submission pathway leading from *Attend* through reciprocating *Sideways* and *Upright* postures to *Full Submission*. (From Grant, 1963*a*.)

The printed numbers refer to the number of times each pathway is used, constructed by mapping the number of responses between *Attend* and the eight flight motivated postures.

these observations, also showed that behaviour differences between strains of rats were reflected in the same way.

From what has already been said, it will be clear that the drives subserving sociability form a complex. Aggression does not, except at high intensities, disperse animals of the same species but rather brings them together; in a variety of ways it is held in balance with flight tendencies and this balance is manifested in ambivalent postures, such as the upright and sideways of the rat. The mating drive also brings animals together and so probably does a tendency towards social investigation which has not yet been fully analysed in the present context. All these modulate the approach tendencies, though they may themselves be in conflict with each other for the control of the final motor pathway, but above all, sociability depends on a sufficient availability of social submission. Otherwise the flight tendency will be expressed in escape and the animals dispersed. While the submission pathway undoubtedly reflects a suitable balance of withdrawal and approach tendencies, it is a distinct pathway of response. This complex of submission, combined with aggression and mating, is what we must come to know as the structure of social behaviour (probably not yet completely revealed). The complex of submission, investigation, aggression and mating can, for short, be called the SIAM structure.

We suggest that this structure, upon which sociability is based, is a discovery of the very greatest consequence for the science of behaviour. It is as important for understanding social behaviour as is the carbohydrate system for understanding the energy system of the cell, or the cholinergic system for neurophysiology.

Continuing the analogy with the carbohydrate cycle, we would suggest that just as riboflavine deficiency produces different symptoms in the rat and in ourselves, so would a defect in the structure of sociability produce different effects in the final behaviour of the rat and ourselves. It has come to be realized that riboflavine, as well as other B vitamins, can be measured in the appropriate circumstances on the growth rate of the rat; in an analogous way, we may well expect that the same defect in our behaviour and in that of the rat may eventually be assessable in the rat in a specific way, once we have understood how to isolate the appropriate part of the structure of social behaviour.

If one accepts this analogy, then it bears very distinctly on how the action of drugs may be assessed on the behaviour of animals. As Steinberg (1962) notes in her admirably lucid review of the present state of our knowledge " . . . for practical reasons, most of the work with drugs must be done on animals, mainly rats and mice, whose brains and behaviour differ much more from those of man than do, for example, their circulatory systems." Many experimenters will probably agree that it is wrong to look for superficially similar behaviour in man and animals as a way of bridging the gap between our behaviour and theirs, but it is equally untenable to take the apparent differences as evidence of wide divergencies in processes underlying the behaviour of man

FIG. 4. Defensive sideways postures of hamster (left), guinea pig (centre) and mouse (right). (From Grant and Mackintosh, 1963.)

and animals. Such a divergence was never assumed, for example, when the rat was used for discovering the nutritional significance of vitamins. In just the same way, behaviour manifestly different in final outcome is, nevertheless, based on strictly homologous processes common to man and animal.

At this point we wish to emphasize the nature of this system which, despite the differences in behaviour, can be identified in a number of different species. For example, the three postures shown in Fig. 4 are the same postures, as judged by their position in the pathways of response, in three different species, and yet their difference *as postures* is self-evident. In the circumstances it is easy enough to see how a too-ready assumption of the meaning of any one posture is fraught with pitfalls. Without reference to a sufficient study of the social behaviour, psychopharmacological literature has become littered with facile assumptions about the meaning of postures.

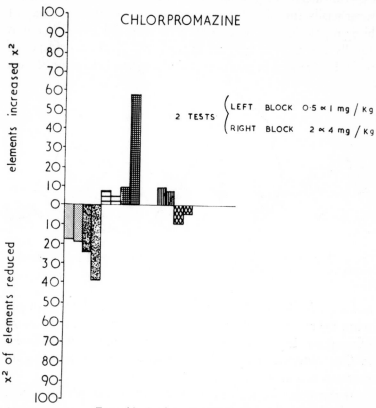

FIG. 5 (a). See legend and key on p. 75.

The existence of the SIAM structure of behaviour in the rat (Submission, Investigation, Aggression and Mating) is amply confirmed by the effects of drugs (Silverman, 1962). Using the method already outlined, the animals injected with drugs are compared in encounters with saline controls by a χ^2 test, comparing the total occurrences of each of the thirty to forty elements or postures. This statistic not only measures the overall difference

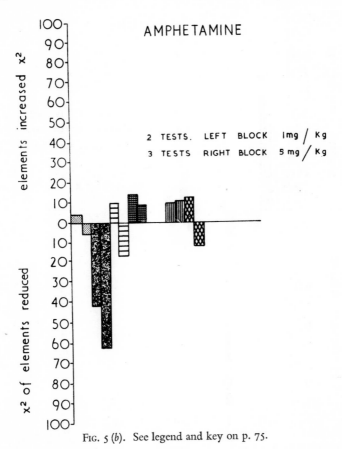

FIG. 5 (b). See legend and key on p. 75.

in the behaviour of the two groups of rats as several non-parametric tests would do, but each element contributes an independent fraction to the total χ^2. Because such a contribution may range from nil to a value high enough to make the whole test significant on its own, it becomes possible to measure the effects of the drug on each individual element separately. Of the postures recorded a few are too infrequent to be considered separately and are,

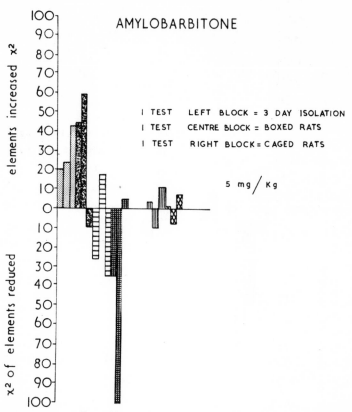

FIG. 5 (c). See legend and key on p. 75.

therefore, combined into a residual group, and this leaves a χ^2 with approximately 30 degrees of freedom. If a drug has had an effect on the rat's motivation it would be shown in three ways. First, several elements will be individually and significantly increased or decreased and the drug's effect on motivation can be deduced

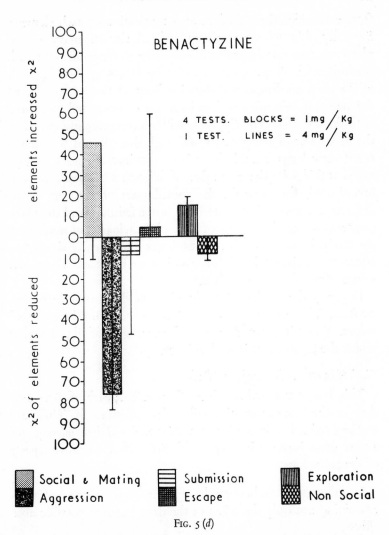

FIG. 5 (d)

FIG. 5. Histograms showing the effects of drugs on the drive systems of behaviour. The abscissae plot the different drive systems. The ordinates represent differences, either increases or decreases, from the control values.

from a consideration of the known motivation of each element. Secondly, although the motivation of each element may be complex, elements may be grouped according to the tendency which predominates. A histogram can then be drawn up showing each of the main tendencies and showing how far the total χ^2 for all the elements belonging to it is increased or decreased compared with the controls. Thirdly, there will be corresponding effects on the behaviour of the partners, although they do not themselves receive any drugs, but this factor is not considered here. It may be noted at this point that a number of different variables have been investigated, for example, the contribution of observer error, differences between introduced and home animals, and the effect of previous experience. All of these play their part in modifying the results but none of them contributes a sufficiently significant effect to obviate what is now going to be stated about the effects of the drugs themselves.

In Fig. 5 the abscissa plots the different drive systems of behaviour. The ordinate represents χ^2 differences from the expected values. Each histogram represents the aggregate of all postures in which the given drive is predominant.

G.K.26 (a reversed ester of pethidine)

This drug was tested at a dose of 4 mg./kg.; each of three tests showed the same qualitative effects (not illustrated). These are marked reduction in *mating*, *aggression* and *social submission* and a very great increase in *escape*, with little effect on other aspects of the behaviour.

In subsequent studies we have been more concerned with examining not only the effect of the drug but also possible dose effects.

Chlorpromazine

The effects of this drug are illustrated by two blocks in each histogram, the left-hand block being the average of two tests, one at 0·5 mg./kg. and the other at 1 mg./kg., and the right-hand block representing the average of two tests, one at 2 mg./kg. and the other at 4 mg./kg. These tests have been selected as representative of the results from ten comparisons in six different tests. At both levels there is a slight reduction in *mating* behaviour and *aggression* is even more reduced by both doses. *Submission* is very little interfered with but the larger doses increase very markedly the *escape* activity and there is a simultaneous further decrease in *attack* and increase in *flight*, but hardly amounting to a disruption of the social elements.

Amphetamine

The left-hand block in each histogram is the mean of two tests at 1 mg./kg., and the right-hand block of two tests at 5 mg./kg. Detailed examination of rats given amphetamine shows that physical exploration is uniformly, but not greatly, increased, as measured by frequency of postures but, at the same time, duration of the postures is so long that there is no doubt that the amount of exploratory motor activity is very much increased, but it is stereotyped and may not be functioning as a true form of exploration. This type of histogram shows something of a chlorpromazine-like effect in that *aggression* is always reduced and *escape* has a tendency to increase. However, a further effect involves making the distinction between social investigation and mating, on the one hand, and aggression and submission on the other. Aggression and submission are truncated in that while low intensity postures may be increased, the higher intensity and consummatory postures are greatly reduced. In contrast the reverse happens with the components of the mating drive. Amphetamine-injected rats seem to indulge in apparently aimless activities.

Amylobarbitone

This drug demonstrates that the success of the test largely depends upon the correct experimental conditions. At 5 mg./kg., amylobarbitone increases *aggression* and, to a lesser extent *social exploration*, *mating* and *submission*, and reduces *escape*. However, these effects are masked in the usual conditions of the experiments, because there seems to be a maximum to the amount of social behaviour which rats can display in a restricted time. With the usual pre-experimental isolation period of seven days, this maximum is usually reached by the saline controls, leaving little room for a consistent increase by rats given barbiturate. If the period of isolation is shortened to three days, or if the rats are introduced in solid-walled boxes instead of cages, the social activity of the saline controls is reduced. In these conditions the total activity of rats injected with amylobarbitone sodium is increased, and the changes outlined become clear.

Benactyzine (1 mg./kg.)

We see that there is increase in *mating* and *social exploration*, together with a decrease in *aggression*. If however, the dose is increased to 4 mg./kg., *mating* is now reduced, *aggression* and *submission* remain reduced and *escape* increases.

A summarized presentation has been made which, by combining the elements of behaviour with common motivation, gives a single (linear) scale of measurement for changes in each cluster of acts, but this is based on pathway analysis which is essential for the delineation of the behaviour structure. Information is already available from the behaviour of the partners but is omitted here.

In placing before you what we believe will prove to be a discovery of lasting significance for studies of behaviour, namely that social behaviour has a structure which was laid down during the evolution of the vertebrates, we hope we have shown that the methods of ethology can contribute to the future of psychopharmacological research, by providing a firm basis for the construction of tests of drug action.

Acknowledgments

We wish to thank Professor Harold Stewart for supplying G.K. 26, the Mental Health Research Fund for the purchase of essential equipment, the Management Committee of All Saints Hospital, Birmingham, for support, and Christine Summerhill for technical assistance.

REFERENCES

STEINBERG, H. (1962). *In* Recent Advances in Pharmacology, 3rd. ed., pp. 77–78, by Robson, J. M., and Stacey, R. S. London: Churchill.

CHANCE, M. R. A., and MEAD, A. P. (1955). *Behaviour*, **7**, 2.

GRANT, E. C. (1963a). *Behaviour*, **21**, 260.

GRANT, E. C. (1963b). *Anim. Behav.*, in preparation.

GRANT, E. C., and MACKINTOSH, J. H. (1963). *Behaviour*, **21**, 246.

SILVERMAN, A. P. (1962). M.Sc. Thesis, Birmingham University.

WYNNE-EDWARDS, V. C. (1962). Animal Dispersion in Relation to Social Behaviour. Edinburgh: Oliver and Boyd.

DISCUSSION

Joyce: Dr. Chance, could you set my mind at rest about some elementary arithmetic involved in your interesting block diagram (Fig. 3) of the SIAM system. It looked to me as though the animals were starting by producing about 130 to 150 responses and ending up on the right-hand side of the diagram with 300 responses involved. You have shown that some drugs may interfere with one pathway rather than another, and if this interference occurs at one side of the diagram it will presumably produce a spurious interference with pathways involved on the other side. The diagram as a whole seems extremely valuable because it allows equivalent elements of behaviour in different species to be identified, and so quantitative estimates of drug effects on these elements can be made.

Chance: The diagram is a selection of the eight most frequent flight-motivated postures from a system of much greater complexity. There should, of course, be other thinner lines feeding into the system which would make up the difference. The situation may be easier to handle in the future with electronic computers.

I want to revert to a point in the discussion of Professor Miller's paper. The implications of what we have found with amylobarbitone are very closely allied to his conclusions. It may be that in our experiments the approach tendencies are enhanced by amylobarbitone, which in the appropriate situation overcomes the normal tendency for the negative elements to balance the approach element.

Our method is, in a sense, in front of your methods, Professor Miller, because we have watched these animals in open spaces and have seen what they actually do, rather than put them in confined spaces where one cannot see what they do. The way you analyse the activities does not help you to analyse them into separate pathways. In the early stages, I think you were interested in the question of whether you should remove the animals which crouched from the experimental setting. On statistical grounds you considered that this was not justified. We agreed with you at that time, but I think now we see that we are, in fact, dealing with a different form of response when the rats crouch.

Miller: I am very sympathetic to this approach of studying animals in their natural situation and trying to analyse their behaviour in it objectively, as a background to experimental work. In psychology we often tend to go directly into experiments without having isolated the appropriate units to study by natural history observations. We are studying one additional aspect of the fear pattern, crouching. One drug, dexamphetamine, greatly reduces the crouching, and hence facilitates avoidance learning in a shuttle box situation.

We had some control over the effects of amylobarbitone on the approach tendency. In the first part of our tests, before we introduced the fear-arousing stimulus, the amylobarbitone seemed to slow down the speed of running. This seems to indicate that the amylobarbitone did not merely increase the strength of approach to both food and water. But this initial slowing could be a complex effect. For example, it could be produced by interference with the motor side of the response so that the net effect was slowing down, although the animal might really have a stronger approach tendency. It would be interesting to use other techniques, such as strength of pull, or resistance to quinine, so that the technique for measuring approach would not be confounded by possible motor effects. Such additional tests are especially desirable since amylobarbitone increases the quantity of food that animals eat, and presumably therefore also increases hunger.

Irwin: We have carried out our social behaviour studies somewhat differently from Dr. Chance. We were interested in whether or not a correlation existed in rats between their locomotor drive state, as measured in revolving treadwheels, and their tendency to engage in social–interactional behaviour when paired with another animal. Previous studies (Irwin, S., Slabok, M., and Thomas, G. [1958]. *J. Pharmacol.*, **125**, 73) had shown the locomotor treadwheel counts of animals to remain relatively constant over many months of their life-span, although wide differences in counts were observed between individuals. In the present study, female rats were paired according to the similarity of their treadwheel counts and were housed separately in groups of four. At weekly intervals the drug was administered subcutaneously and the animals were placed in an observation unit for 20 minutes measurement and recording of various components of their social and non-social behaviour. One animal routinely received saline solution; the other, on alternate weeks, saline or drug. Very briefly, we found a positive correlation between the treadwheel counts of animals and the amount of time they engaged in active (total body movement) non-social behaviour; also, a significant negative correlation between individual treadwheel counts and the time devoted to interactional behaviour. Thus, for example, animals active in the treadwheel exhibited low interactional scores; surprisingly, the converse was true of animals relatively inactive in the treadwheel—they spent a considerable amount of time in social-interactional behaviour. It became of interest, therefore, to determine how drugs which increased (methamphetamine) or decreased (perphenazine) locomotor drive would affect the ratio between social and non-social behaviour. When tested, the expected change in non-social dynamic activity occurred, but the slope and intercept of the regression line between this behaviour and the time spent in social-interactional behaviour was the same as with saline administration. The shift in activity drive by the drugs produced a concomitant change in interactional behaviour; for example, the amount of time spent in social activity was actually increased by the administration of a phenothiazine tranquillizer and decreased by a stimulant. In both instances, the changes in interactional behaviour seemed to be secondary to the primary actions of the drugs on locomotor drive. With imipramine and morphine, however, a direct effect on social behaviour was seemingly observed. Imipramine reduced the durations of both the active, non-social and the interactional behaviour; morphine, in doses having no effect on the duration of active non-social behaviour, completely abolished the interactional component. A complete dissociation of the non-social from the social behaviour was thus obtained. The technique in general seems to be a useful one for differentiating drug effects on social behaviour.

DISCRIMINATION AND THE FRONTAL LOBES OF MONKEYS

L. WEISKRANTZ

Psychological Laboratory, University of Cambridge

I HAVE been specifically asked to talk about some methodological and other general aspects of drug action in order to widen the discussion. The title of my paper might seem incompatible with this rôle, but I do not think it is, because the problem of the interaction of the frontal lobes with drugs emphasizes certain methodological problems common to the study of interactions between *any* two treatments, especially where these are supposedly antagonistic to each other.

Most psychotropic drugs are, after all, administered clinically because it is hoped that they will antagonize certain behavioural states. Generally in the clinical situation we do not know precisely what caused the behavioural state or what, in fact, it *is* exactly, but we can at least assume that with further study we shall know more precisely how to describe it, how to classify it, and also what caused it. To what extent can the study of these antagonisms themselves help in furthering such a description and classification?

It is a difficult business and one which is full of traps. Let us take an example where we know exactly what is wrong with someone and see what we infer from the effects of various treatments. Let us suppose that someone limps—he has a pulled tendon, or some such medical condition. Let us suppose, however, that our experimenter does not know this; in fact, let us assume that all he has discovered is that this person does not run a distance of 100 yards in anything like the time a normal person does. Being enterprising, the experimenter will see if there is anything he can do to make the person run the distance in the normal time. He may electrify the 100 yards distance and finds that the man runs much faster; he may even approach normal speed. At this point the experimenter might stop and conclude that the man suffered from lack of motivation or uncommonly heavy torpor with respect to running. He may even conduct further experiments and show that rewarding him with a large sum of money on each occasion when he runs fast also increases the mean running speed, thereby confirming the hypothesis.

Now substitute a frontal lobe lesion for the pulled tendon and a delayed reaction test for running 100 yards. In monkeys the one leads to abnormally low performance in the other—a fact which has been known for twenty-five years or so (Jacobsen, 1936). (The delayed reaction test is one in which the animal is shown food being placed under one of two containers, but is not allowed to displace either container until after a delay period—typically 5 to 10 seconds—has elapsed. During the delay period an opaque screen is lowered between the animal and the containers. When the screen is raised, the animal must remember which of the two containers hides the food. Usually about 50 such tests are given in succession in a single session, the position of the baited container being varied randomly.) For the electrification of the track, substitute any number of treatments which have been shown to help the monkey with a frontal lesion to improve its delayed response performance—among them, keeping it in the dark during the delay period (Malmo, 1942), allowing it a pre-delay reward (Finan, 1942), changing the baiting situation from a spatial to a non-spatial one (Mishkin and Pribram, 1956), and finally, administering barbiturates, notably pentobarbitone sodium (Nembutal) (Wade, 1947; Pribram, 1950; Mishkin et al., 1953). Each treatment is associated with a different but definite hypothesis as to what it is that ails the monkey, such as that it is lacking something that the particular variation provides.

But, just as in the case of our limping man, it might be argued that these variations of the task might cause *any* monkey, whether or not it has its frontal lobes intact, to improve its performance. It would take too long to go through the various arguments in support of that claim at this stage, but it is obvious that we might reach quite erroneous conclusions from such experiments. In fact, the general nature of the trap is as follows: whenever a performance is subject to control by several variables, it may be falsely assumed that two treatments may be antagonistic when one affects one variable and the other another variable, which in combination leads to what appears to be cancellation of the effect of one by the other.

Well, it may be retorted, why not study control monkeys under the same variations? Surprisingly, that has not often been done, but in those cases where it has been done, sometimes the controls improve, and sometimes they do not. In those cases where the controls do not improve, it is sometimes difficult to know whether they were not already performing so well that no further improvement could have been detected. Where there is just slight improvement in the controls we get into difficult questions of whether the amount of improvement in the controls was really equivalent to the amount of improvement in the frontal monkeys, just as we might wonder if the increase in the speed of running of normal persons on an electrified track is equivalent to the increase of a lame person.

In order to prove that two treatments are antagonistic, our results should have the following characteristics:

(1) Treatment A should produce some effect on behaviour;
(2) Treatments A plus B should produce no effect on behaviour; and
(3) Treatment B should produce no effect on the same behaviour that was affected by treatment A.

I am not saying that these are the defining properties of antagonism, but simply that such conditions are informative. So we should like to have a treatment that has no effect on delayed response in the normal animal, yet counteracts the effects of frontal lesions on this task. We wish two further conditions to be met: first, that the normal animal is tested in a sufficiently sensitive way so that it could conceivably improve under the effect of the treatment; and secondly, the drug ought to produce *some* effects

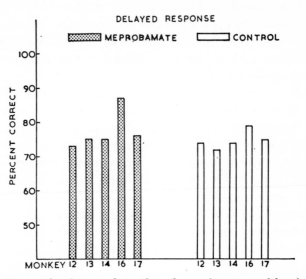

FIG. 1. The absence of an effect of meprobamate on delayed response of intact monkeys. The mean percentage of correct responses is based on at least five testing sessions for each animal under each of the two conditions. Reconstructed from Gross and Weiskrantz (1961).

on normal animals (but not, as we just said, on delayed response) so that we might make some guesses about the general type of behaviour pattern involved.

Gross and I have already published results (1961) which show that meprobamate has no effect on delayed response in normal animals (Fig. 1). Testing was carried out on a sliding scale of difficulty, so that the normal animals were not prevented from improving simply by virtue of performing at high asymptotic levels of accuracy. We also showed that the same dose of the drug in the same animals in the same testing sessions *did* impair auditory discrimination performance (Fig. 2). My colleague, Dr. Baltzer, showed when he was with us last year that simultaneous visual discrimination tasks are affected by the drug in a

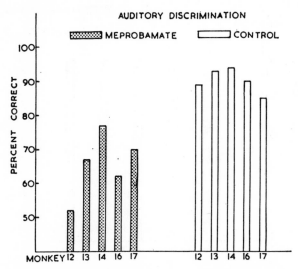

FIG. 2. The effect of meprobamate on auditory discrimination performance of intact animals. Means based on same number of sessions as for delayed response, Fig. 1. The decrement for animals 14, 16, 17 is significant at $P < 0.05$, for 12 and 13 at $P < 0.001$. From Gross and Weiskrantz (1961).

similar manner (unpublished material). These results fit in with a general hypothesis about one of the effects of "tranquillizers" which we have discussed elsewhere (Weiskrantz, 1957). It happens that one of the hypotheses about frontal lobe performance which we have tested is that the frontal monkey suffers from an excessive sensory bombardment and that he samples too quickly and too furiously, rather like a manic patient does. Gross, Baltzer and I consequently wished to see whether a treatment which is known to impair sensory discrimination performance might thereby help the frontal animal in delayed response tests. That it appears to do so is shown in Fig. 3. As I have already said, earlier research has also suggested similar effects of barbiturates, although the reliability of some of these is highly questionable. We also

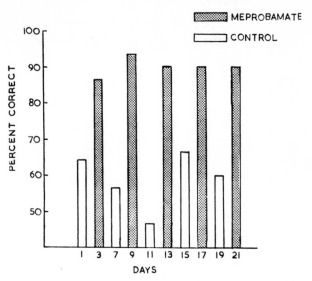

FIG. 3. The effect of meprobamate on delayed response performance of a monkey with bilateral frontal cortical resection. Sessions occurred in order indicated on abscissa. Control was isotonic saline.

tested pentobarbitone sodium on other animals, and found an effect comparable to that of meprobamate (Figs. 4 and 5). But we still do not know if pentobarbitone is without any effect on the normal and I rather doubt that it is. In addition, we do not know whether any of these drugs interferes with discrimination performance by frontal animals; I doubt whether any of them does.

Even if all of these possibilities were filled in with unequivocal

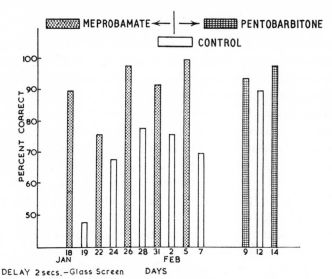

FIG. 4. Effects of meprobamate and pentobarbitone sodium on delayed response of a frontal monkey (not the same animal as in Fig. 3). Control was isotonic saline.

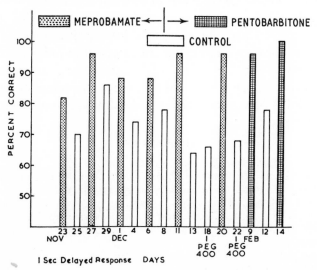

FIG. 5. Effects of meprobamate and pentobarbitone sodium on delayed response of another frontal monkey. Control was isotonic saline, except where marked "PEG 400", which refers to the blank meprobamate vehicle.

results we should still not have reached any final goal, since there is no final goal, but only an asymptote. It is still conceivable, for example, that the drug affects some other behaviour which we do not directly measure and which happens to be correlated with performance on some task which we do measure; general locomotor activity might be such an example. In general, when our measure is performance in some kind of behavioural task, one might say that we can only understand changes in performance by studying as wide a sample of tasks as possible, and as analytically as possible (we have a nice model of this in Professor Miller's paper), because there is no such creature in the behavioural sciences as a single pure test of any function. But that is yet another story, and I have not the space to present evidence from other analytical experiments which we are carrying out on frontal animals. Meanwhile I hope that I have demonstrated that there are interesting methodological questions about the interaction of effects of different treatments, whether or not the treatments happen to involve drugs. I have also given an example of where the effects of a drug on behaviour are not studied in their own right, but are exploited in order to test a hypothesis about the effects of a neurological interference. Incidentally, I hope I have said something interesting about the frontal lobes of monkeys and, independently, about meprobamate.

REFERENCES

FINAN, J. L. (1942). *Amer. J. Psychol.*, **55**, 202.
GROSS, C. G., and WEISKRANTZ, L. (1961). *Quart. J. exp. Psychol.*, **13**, 34.
JACOBSEN, C. F. (1936). *Comp. Psychol. Monogr.*, **13**, No. 3.
MALMO, R. B. (1942). *J. Neurophysiol.*, **5**, 295.
MISHKIN, M., and PRIBRAM, K. H. (1956). *J. comp. physiol. Psychol.*, **49**, 36.
MISHKIN, M., ROSVOLD, H. E., and PRIBRAM, K. H. (1953). *J. Neurophysiol.*, **16**, 155.
PRIBRAM, K. H. (1950). *J. Neurophysiol.*, **13**, 373.
WADE, M. (1947). *J. Neurophysiol.*, **10**, 57.
WEISKRANTZ, L. (1957). *In* Psychotropic Drugs, p. 76, ed. Garattini, S., and Ghetti, V. Amsterdam: Elsevier.

Session 2: Neurophysiological and Biochemical Correlates of Behavioural Effects of Drugs

CHAIRMAN: Professor W. S. Feldberg

AMPHETAMINE AND NEURAL REWARD MECHANISMS

L. STEIN

Wyeth Laboratories, Philadelphia

THE distinguishing feature of operant behaviour is that it can be controlled by its consequences, or the contingencies of reinforcement (Thorndike, 1913; Skinner, 1938). Because of the importance of reinforcement processes, one must always consider the possibility that they have been influenced when one attempts to analyse a powerful and specific effect on operant behaviour.

The effects of psychoactive drugs are no exception to this rule. In this paper, I shall try to account for some of the behavioural effects of amphetamine* by a suggestion that the drug acts on a brain mechanism for reward.

SUBSTRATES OF REINFORCEMENT

Work on the identification of brain systems for reward and punishment really began only nine years ago. In 1954 Delgado, Roberts and Miller (following early work by Hess, 1954) reported the first experimental proof that electrical stimulation of the brain could serve as a punishment; coincidentally, in the same

---

* Or methamphetamine. For the present purposes I have treated the two drugs as interchangeable.

year Olds and Milner (1954) described for the first time the
unexpected finding that electrical brain stimulation could serve as

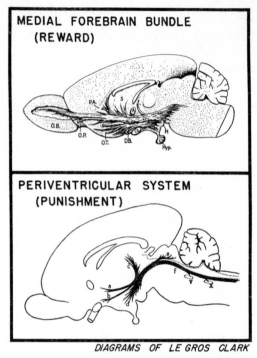

FIG. 1. *Upper.* Diagram representing medial forebrain
bundle (the presumed substrate of reward mechanism)
in a generalized and primitive mammalian brain. Some
abbreviations are: A., Anterior commissure; D. B., Nucleus of the diagonal band; M., Mammillary body;
S., Septum. *Lower.* Similar diagram representing the
periventricular system of fibres (presumed substrate of
punishment mechanism). Some abbreviations are: b.,
Anterior hypothalamus; c., Thalamus; d., Posterior
hypothalamus; e., Tectum (Le Gros Clark *et al.*, 1938).

a reward. Later work has confirmed and extended both findings
and has permitted some limited appreciation of the organization
of the reinforcement systems in the brain. Largely as a result of

the efforts of Olds (1962) it now seems almost certain (although direct evidence is lacking) that the hypothalamic medial forebrain bundle and its connexions play a central rôle in the mediation of reward and that the periventricular system of the diencephalon and midbrain has a critical part in the mediation of punishment. Le Gros Clark published excellent diagrams of both systems twenty-five years ago (Fig. 1).

Needless to say, each of these structures comprises only one part of a more complex system. Nevertheless, for convenience, I shall refer to a medial forebrain bundle reward system and a periventricular punishment system. The medial forebrain bundle may be thought of as part of a "go" mechanism that facilitates operant behaviour and the periventricular system as part of a "stop" mechanism that inhibits operant behaviour. Furthermore, there is reason to believe that the "go" and "stop" mechanisms are mutually inhibitory, like antagonistic spinal reflexes. Hence activation of one mechanism can depress the other. Similarly, a sudden deactivation of one mechanism can release the other from inhibition and cause a brief period of heightened activity by a rebound effect.

ANTICIPATION OR EXPECTATION OF REINFORCEMENT

Because future events cannot affect present occurrences, the facilitating action of a reinforcing stimulus must be brought forward in some way to influence the behaviour that precedes it. The correct operant must obviously be energized before reinforcement if it is to be successful. Subjectively, it seems as if it were the "anticipation" or "expectation" of reinforcement, and not its actual occurrence, that directly engages or motivates the operant behaviour. According to such a view, the reinforcing stimulus itself plays a critical but indirect part; its rôle is to establish and maintain the expectation.

To be of scientific value, the concept of expectation must be stripped of its teleological connotations and placed on a mechanical or physiological basis. One way to do this is to assume that the expectation of reinforcement is a conditioned reflex. The argument cannot be presented in detail here, but the idea is an old one and its history has been described elsewhere (see discussion in Mowrer, 1960). Briefly, my version (Stein, in press) runs as follows. Pairing an operant response with reward may be viewed as an instance of Pavlovian conditioning. Response-related stimuli (environmental as well as internal) are the conditioned stimulus and the reward is the unconditioned stimulus. By virtue of the pairing, the medial forebrain bundle "go" mechanism is conditioned to response-related stimuli. Thus, on future occasions, any tendency to engage in the previously rewarded behaviour initiates facilitatory feedback by an activation of the "go" mechanism, and thereby increases the probability that the response will run off to completion. In the case of punishment, periventricular activity is conditioned to stimuli associated with the punished operant. This decreases the probability that the operant will be emitted in the future because feedback from the "stop" mechanism will tend to inhibit the behaviour.

SOME BEHAVIOURAL EFFECTS OF AMPHETAMINE

Although clinical pharmacologists generally classify amphetamine as a stimulant of behaviour, experiments on animals frequently seem to contradict the clinical impression. There are reports not only of failures to obtain stimulation, but often of instances of depression. Such evidence has moved some writers to suggest that it might be profitable to give up the use of "stimulation" and "depression" as general terms in behavioural pharmacology (Cook and Kelleher, 1962).

I propose to take a step backwards, in the case of amphetamine at least, and to reintroduce the idea of behavioural stimulation. But the usage is intended to be conceptual, not descriptive.

Indeed, a single instance of reduction of response under amphetamine lowers the value of the term for descriptive purposes, though it does not detract from its conceptual value if the decrease can be shown as a special case. Also, I would wish to substitute the term "facilitation" for "stimulation". I think it is more accurate to speak of amphetamine as facilitating or enhancing the tendency to respond, rather than stimulating or instigating it.

Experimental findings seem to be consistent with the idea that moderate or optimum doses of the amphetamines have a facilitating effect on operant behaviour, if account is taken of the following: (i) that amphetamine depresses food and water intake, apparently by reducing hunger and thirst; (ii) that some minimum tendency to respond is required for amphetamine facilitation; and (iii) that the facilitating effect of amphetamine will be less conspicuous when the tendency to respond is very great. These points will be taken up in turn.

1. Anorexic and thirst-inhibitory effects of amphetamine

Millions of dollars-worth of amphetamine are sold every year to lessen the craving for food and to reduce weight. These sales figures are fully confirmed by animal studies which show that amphetamine decreases the intake of food (Wentink, 1938; Tainter, 1944) and also the intake of water (Andersson and Larsson, 1956). Such observations suggest that amphetamine will have conflicting effects on behaviour maintained by food or water reinforcement; that is, the drug will exert two opposing effects that will tend to cancel each other out. One effect will be the general facilitation of response tendency proposed above and documented below, while the other will be an inhibitory effect that may be likened to satiation. Whether one effect or the other predominates in a specific case will no doubt depend on the dose, the species, and many other features of the situation (see discussion below).

If reinforcers other than food or water are used, it is a relatively easy matter to demonstrate that amphetamine enhances the tendency to respond. For example, when behaviour is maintained by negative reinforcement, as it is in shock avoidance, amphetamine reliably increases the rate of response over a wide range of conditions (Sidman, 1956; Verhave, 1958; Teitelbaum and

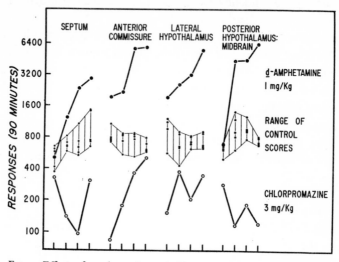

Fig. 2. Effects of amphetamine and chlorpromazine on self-stimulation in a variable-interval schedule. Each vertical line of points shows test scores of one rat; four rats in each electrode group. Note logarithmic scale of ordinate.

Derks, 1958; Hearst and Whalen, 1963). Amphetamine also substantially increases the output of behaviour maintained by positive reinforcement if electrical stimulation of the brain, rather than food or water, is used as the reward (Olds, 1959; Stein and Seifter, 1961; Stein, 1962a, 1962b; Horovitz, Chow and Carlton, 1962). Under the drug, rats exposed to cold respond at higher rates for heat reinforcement (Weiss and Laties, 1963) and monkeys respond at much higher rates for flashes of light

(Fox, 1962). It would be of interest to know if amphetamine also augments sexually reinforced operant behaviour.

Fig. 2 shows drug effects on self-stimulation at four different brain sites (four rats used per site). Electrical reinforcements were programmed every 30 seconds on the average but at unpredictable intervals (30-second variable-interval schedule; Ferster and Skinner, 1957). Current levels were individually adjusted so that each rat would emit about 750 responses in a 90-minute test. Large increases in rate may be observed after amphetamine in 14 cases, although rats with septal electrodes appear somewhat

Table I

EFFECTS OF FOUR PSYCHOACTIVE DRUGS ON SELF-STIMULATION
(30-second variable-interval schedule: 90-minute test)

Drug	Dose (mg./kg.)	Mean responses± S.E. of mean (N= 16 rats)	Percentage of control
Saline (Control)	—	781± 48	—
Dexamphetamine sulphate	1	3,209±484	411
Chlorpromazine hydrochloride	3	237± 32	30
Pentobarbitone sodium	8	847±255	108
Hyoscine hydrochloride	0·4	752± 78	96

less responsive to the drug than the others. Chlorpromazine (3 mg./kg.) had a strongly depressive effect on self-stimulation at all locations. Tests with a number of different drugs suggest that the amphetamines specifically enhance self-stimulation and that the phenothiazines and reserpine specifically block it (Olds, 1962; Stein, 1962a, 1962b). Table I compares average effects of amphetamine and chlorpromazine in the variable-interval self-stimulation test with average effects of two other drugs. It may be seen that pentobarbitone at a dose that is quite active against punishment (Geller and Seifter, 1962) and hyoscine at a dose that severely depresses water consumption (Stein, 1963) had no important average effect on self-stimulation. In a few cases, however, self-stimulation was substantially depressed or enhanced by pentobarbitone (note the large standard error of the mean for pentobarbitone).*

2. *A minimum tendency to respond is necessary in order to obtain amphetamine facilitation*

This idea was suggested first by Dews and Morse (1961) to account for data of Verhave (1958). Verhave failed to obtain increases in response with methamphetamine if tests were made on baselines of extremely low rate. In one test the low rates were achieved by programming no consequences to the lever press response for several days; in the other test, which was regular Sidman (1953) avoidance, methamphetamine was given very early in training, before "the avoidance contingency had started to take effect" (Verhave, 1958). Strongly depressing the tendency to respond by prolonged extinction or discrimination training may also eliminate the facilitating effect of amphetamine (Dews, 1955; Carlton, 1963).

3. *Strongly engaged behaviour is less susceptible than mildly engaged behaviour to facilitation by amphetamine*

Studies on performance maintained by different schedules of reinforcement in pigeons led to the suggestion that "control rate of responding is an important factor, that sustained rates of responding are not susceptible to increase, but that very low rates or intermittent responding are readily increased" (Dews and Morse, 1961). So susceptible are low rates to augmentation by amphetamine that often striking augmentations have been demonstrated even when the reinforcer was food. Amphetamine has long been known to augment the low rates of response emitted in extinction (if extinction is not prolonged, or if partial reinforcement precedes extinction; Skinner and Heron, 1937); similarly it has proved effective in programmes that maintain low

---

* All drug doses mentioned in this paper are expressed in terms of the salt.

or erratic rates by infrequent reinforcement (Dews, 1958) or by differential reinforcement of low rates (Sidman, 1956; Kelleher et al., 1961). An unpublished experiment by Finocchio extends this idea to include cases involving negative reinforcement. A monkey was trained on a multiple schedule (Ferster and Skinner, 1957) to avoid shocks both on a Sidman programme and, alternately, on a fixed-ratio programme (specifically, in the fixed-ratio programme, a tone signalled the delivery of a shock after one minute unless 100 responses were emitted). Methamphetamine (0·25–2 mg./kg.) sharply increased the relatively low control rates generated by the Sidman programme, but neither increased nor decreased the very high avoidance rates generated by the fixed-ratio programme. The failure to observe an increase in the fixed-ratio avoidance rate coincides with the idea that high rates are less susceptible to augmentation by the amphetamines than low rates. The failure to observe a decrease was taken to be contrary to the tentative suggestion of Dews (1958) that very high rates (or short inter-response times) *per se* will be decreased by amphetamine.[*]

In a recent study of self-stimulation in rats, it was found that amphetamine may increase low and high rates alike, although low rates usually showed proportionately greater increase. In this study, a high baseline rate of self-stimulation was generated by reinforcing every response (regular reinforcement schedule) and a low rate by presenting the same electrical reinforcement on an aperiodic basis (30-second variable-interval schedule). A representative result, from a rat with a hypothalamic electrode, is shown in Fig. 3. The low rate of response under aperiodic reinforcement was increased 380 per cent by 1 mg./kg. of dexamphetamine; the same dose produced an increase of 20 per cent in the regular reinforcement test, despite a control rate of 105 responses per minute. On the average, aperiodically

[*] Similarly, Sidman (1956) has observed that amphetamine increases short inter-response times ("bursts") in a free avoidance situation.

reinforced rates were increased by 308 per cent and regularly reinforced rates by 73 per cent.

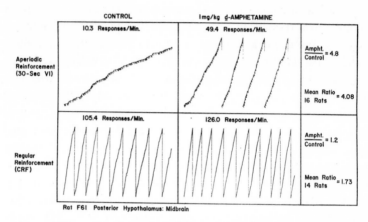

Fig. 3. Effects of amphetamine sulphate on high (regular reinforcement) and low (30-second variable-interval reinforcement) baseline rates of self-stimulation. Each record shows performance in a 90-minute test. Diagonal lines on variable-interval response curves indicate deliveries of the electrical reinforcement. Average augmentation ratios (amphetamine rate/control rate) of all animals tested are given at the right.

POSSIBLE MECHANISM OF AMPHETAMINE FACILITATION

It was suggested earlier that there might be a system in the brain, centred on the medial forebrain bundle, whose activity serves to facilitate ongoing operant behaviour. If this were so, it would be reasonable to speculate that amphetamine facilitates behaviour by acting on this system. Speculations about mechanisms of action of drugs should account for features that limit, as well as produce, the drug action. Specifically, in the case of amphetamine, the proposed mechanism should explain (a) why facilitation is not observed when the tendency to respond is extremely low and (b) why moderate response tendencies are more readily augmented than strong tendencies.

These limiting features perhaps may be accounted for by the assumption that amphetamine acts specifically through reduction of reward thresholds. In that case, a minimum input would still be required to activate the sensitized reward mechanism despite lowering of the threshold. The greater susceptibility of moderate response rates to facilitation by amphetamine could be explained by the well-established neurophysiological fact that response to moderate input benefits more from a reduction in threshold than does response to a strong input.

Data obtained in self-stimulation experiments support the idea that amphetamine lowers reward thresholds (Miller, 1960; Stein and Ray, 1960). In the experiment of Stein and Ray the animal indicates its own threshold by its pattern of response. The animal works in a box with two widely-spaced levers in one wall. Each response at one lever delivers a brief electrical stimulus and also sets the current down one step. When the current is driven below a maintaining or reinforcing value, the animal operates the second lever which resets the current to the top step and starts the next cycle. The current level at the time of reset is taken as the threshold level.

Relatively large doses of the amphetamines (1 mg./kg. or more) appear to have a distinct "threshold-lowering" effect, since they cause resetting to occur at lower current steps; some animals, especially those with electrodes in the posterior hypothalamus, may respond to lower doses of amphetamine (Stein and Ray, 1960; Stein, 1962b). Chlorpromazine, in low doses, causes resetting at higher intensities; higher doses (more than 2–3 mg./kg.) generally cause all response to cease. Finally, it may be briefly noted that a low dose (5 mg./kg.) of the antidepressant drug, imipramine, which has no effect of its own, will potentiate the response to amphetamine profoundly (Stein, 1962b).

In another experiment the regular self-stimulation procedure is used, but the current is set just below the reinforcement threshold (Stein and Seifter, 1961). Even small doses (0·25 mg./

kg.) of the amphetamines are active in this test. Typically, amphetamine initially induces a high rate of self-stimulation, which declines to the very low control level more or less gradually as the drug wears off (Fig. 4).

One interpretation of the increase in rate is that amphetamine, by lowering reinforcement thresholds, temporarily converts

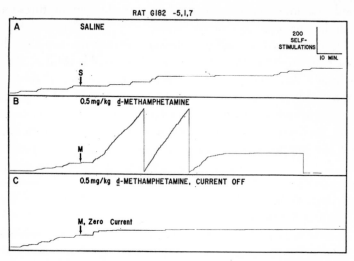

FIG. 4. Facilitating effect of methamphetamine on self-stimulation for subthreshold reinforcement (panel B). Saline injections have no effect on the extremely low baseline rate (panel A). If the current is turned off when methamphetamine is injected, the facilitating effect is abolished (panel C).

the subthreshold stimulus into a superthreshold stimulus. An alternative interpretation is that amphetamine induces a nonspecific psychomotor stimulation. The rival interpretations were tested by evaluating the effect of methamphetamine with and without the subthreshold stimulus. Fig. 4 and Table II show that no increase will be obtained if the current is turned off; therefore the delivery of the subthreshold stimulus is essential. This result favours the interpretation that amphetamine lowers reward

Table II

SUMMARY OF DATA OF SELF-STIMULATION EXPERIMENT ILLUSTRATED IN FIG. 4
(Total responses in a 1-hour test)

| Rat | d-Methamphetamine (0·5 mg./kg.) | | Saline |
	Current on	Current off	Current on
G182	1,000	47	81
G201	986	61	73
G181	973	100	55
E105	884	132	37
G187	849	210	243
Mean	938·4	110·0	97·8

thresholds, since a non-specific psychomotor stimulation should occur with or without the subthreshold stimulus.

DUPLICATING AMPHETAMINE EFFECTS BY REWARDING ELECTRICAL STIMULATION

One stringent way to test the idea that amphetamine acts on a neural reward mechanism would be to try to duplicate the facilitating effects of the drug with low intensity electrical stimulation of reward areas. Presumably, the electrical stimulation will lower reward thresholds just as the drug is assumed to do. The similarity between drug and stimulation is not perfect, however, because the stimulation may also activate the reward mechanism directly. Nevertheless, since a positive result would be informative, we compared amphetamine and brain stimulation in two experiments, one based on positively reinforced and the other on negatively reinforced behaviour.

1. Positive reinforcement: daily extinction test

An extinction procedure was used because of the powerful effect of amphetamine on extinguished behaviour (Skinner and Heron, 1937). Conventional extinction designs usually require comparisons between groups of animals. To facilitate study of this problem a "daily" extinction test was devised that allows an animal to act as his own control.

Hungry rats are trained to press a lever to obtain food only in the presence of a tone. If they respond within 10 seconds food is delivered; otherwise, the tone ends automatically. Inter-trial responses are never reinforced (and if necessary postpone the presentation of tones to ensure that at least three seconds elapse between a response and a tone). Tones are programmed every 30 seconds on the average but at unpredictable intervals. When performance is perfect, the extinction procedure is introduced. Each day, rats are first given 20 reinforced trials followed immediately by 50 extinction trials. This procedure is repeated day after day until the number of responses in extinction stabilizes.

Control records shown in Fig. 5 exemplify the baseline. Important features are: first, the rapid cessation of responding in extinction and the stability of total extinction output; and secondly, the overnight recovery of perfect responding in the initial 20 reinforced trials. The most important datum for present purposes is the total number of responses in the 50 extinction trials.

Nine rats were used for amphetamine tests and 15 rats (37 electrodes) for brain stimulation tests. Brain stimulation was given on an uncontingent (response-independent) basis in 0·15-second trains every 1·5 or 3 seconds throughout the test. After extinction data were collected, each electrode was evaluated for positive reinforcement in a self-stimulation test. Ten electrodes yielded more than 1,000 responses per hour (strong reward) and 15 electrodes gave less than 150 responses per hour (non-reward).

Amphetamine and strongly rewarding brain stimulation (with one exception) invariably augmented extinction responding (Fig. 6); the effect in some cases was quite pronounced (Fig. 5). Non-rewarding electrodes, on the other hand, had no definite effect, or perhaps a slight tendency to reduce extinction respond-

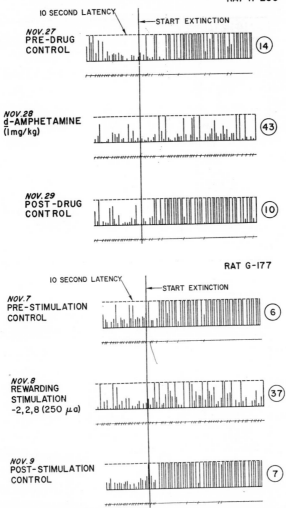

FIG. 5. Records of performance in extinction test of two rats, showing latencies of each response in sequence for three consecutive daily sessions. Each vertical line indicates a trial. Short lines to left of vertical extinction marker give latencies of initial 20 reinforced responses. Longer lines to right of vertical marker show extinction latencies. Average inter-trial interval is 30 seconds. Line with diagonal pips below each latency record also indicates responses. Circled number at right indicates total number of responses in extinction. Note pronounced augmenting effect on extinguished responding by amphetamine or rewarding background stimulation.

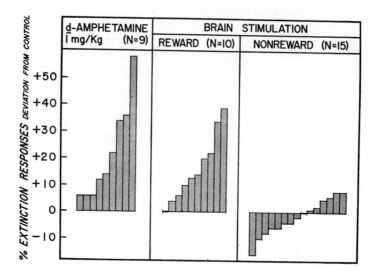

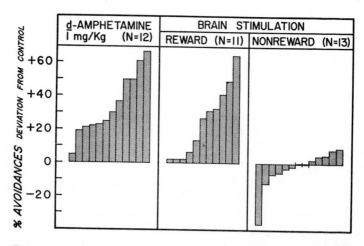

FIG. 6. Summary data showing augmenting effects of amphetamine and rewarding brain stimulation on the tendency to respond in extinction (upper) or shuttle box avoidance (lower). Each bar stands for one case and shows the absolute deviation from control induced by the drug or brain stimulation.

ing (Fig. 6). Amphetamine and rewarding brain stimulation differed, however, in their effects on inter-trial responding. Amphetamine did not increase (and even slightly decreased) inter-trial responding, perhaps because of the prolonged extinction of this behaviour (see p. 98). On the contrary, rewarding brain stimulation more than doubled the output of inter-trial responses (Table III). The difference between amphetamine and

Table III

AVERAGE EFFECTS OF AMPHETAMINE OR REWARDING BRAIN STIMULATION IN DAILY EXTINCTION TEST

Group	No. of rats	Extinction responses (Percentage responses to tones)	Inter-trial responses (Total responses between tones)
Amphetamine	9	41·4	74·9
Brain stimulation	10	35·4	198·9
Control	19	19·3	94·2

brain stimulation in this case may be explained by the direct activating effect that the electrical stimulation may have had on reward fibres, although other interpretations are possible.

2. *Negative reinforcement: shuttle box avoidance test*

On first analysis the greatest difficulty facing the present reward theory of amphetamine action is the clear augmenting effect that amphetamine has on avoidance behaviour (Sidman, 1956; Hearst and Whalen, 1963). Not only does the theory seem to fail to explain this important effect, but, on the basis of common sense, it even seems to be contradicted by it. According to common sense, a drug that sensitizes a mechanism for positive reinforcement might well have a detrimental effect on behaviour maintained by negative reinforcement.

The solution I prefer at present, after considering a number of alternatives, is based on a theory of avoidance behaviour suggested recently by Olds (in press). Fanciful as the theory may initially seem, it nevertheless has the dual advantage of comporting with the data and contradicting common sense.

The scheme may be paraphrased as follows. During exposure to the warning stimulus in discriminated avoidance, brain mechanisms for punishment are activated and mechanisms for reward (by reciprocal inhibition) are therefore suppressed. If an operant response terminates the warning stimulus, the reward mechanisms will suddenly be released from inhibition and, by a rebound effect, will go through a brief period of increased activity. This burst of positively reinforcing activity serves to reward the avoidance response. If avoidance behaviour really is maintained by the activity of a positive reinforcement mechanism, then the present theory of amphetamine action may explain why avoidance is facilitated by the drug. By lowering reward thresholds, amphetamine will augment avoidance just as it does self-stimulation and other rewarded behaviour.

A shuttle box avoidance procedure was used to test these ideas. Warning lights at both ends of the shuttle box signal to the rat that it must cross to the opposite side within 7·5 seconds or receive a punishing periventricular brain shock. A successful avoidance response averts the shock and turns the lights out for a 15-second period of safety before the next trial. Otherwise, the lights stay on and a brief train of punishing stimulation is delivered every 7·5 seconds. Typically, delivery of the first punishing brain shock elicits a leap to the other side which terminates the trial.

Avoidance learning is quite slow in this situation and performance levels tend to stabilize at a low value even after extensive training. One important retarding factor here is "freezing". Rats understandably are reluctant to approach the opposite warning light or to return to a place where punishment was received. In any case, the low baseline levels are desirable as the aim is to potentiate avoidance behaviour.

When baselines of avoidance were established, the effects of amphetamine (12 rats) or stimulation of various brain points (29 electrodes, 19 rats) were studied. In stimulation tests, a brief priming stimulus is delivered simultaneously with the onset of the warning lights. The priming stimulus terminates automatically after 0·2 sec. and hence is independent of the rat's behaviour. In a typical experiment, sets of 50 control trials (no stimulation) alternate with sets of 50 test trials. After avoidance data are

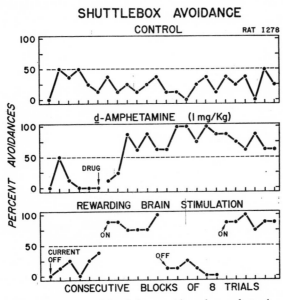

FIG. 7. Facilitation of shuttle box avoidance by amphetamine and rewarding brain stimulation.

collected, each priming electrode is analysed for positive reinforcement by a self-stimulation test. Eleven electrodes yielded more than 1,000 responses per hour (strong reward) and thirteen electrodes gave less than 150 responses per hour (non-reward).

As in the extinction test, amphetamine and rewarding brain stimulation had similar augmenting effects on avoidance (Figs. 6 and 7). When the priming stimulus was non-rewarding, no such increase in avoidance was observed (Fig. 6).

It may be thought that the rewarding stimulus facilitates avoidance merely by providing an additional warning cue. However, if a brief but clearly audible buzzing noise was substituted for rewarding brain stimulation no appreciable facilitation

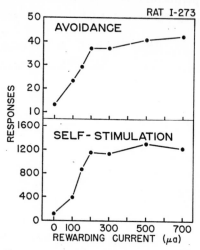

Fig. 8. Intensity functions obtained from the same rewarding electrode in avoidance and self-stimulation tests. High degree of correspondence is evidence of a mechanism common to both situations.

of avoidance was obtained. The negative findings with non-rewarding priming stimuli, which should provide extra cues too, also argue against this idea.

Some other explanations may be ruled out. Observation of animals and latency data indicate that rewarding priming stimuli did not evoke reflex (short-latency) responses. Positive results in later experiments, where the interval between trials was independent of the rat's behaviour, proved that avoidance responses were not reinforced by a shortening of the interval between rewarding priming stimuli. Spontaneous inter-trial crossings were increased both by amphetamine and by rewarding stimulation; this effect is expected if it is correct to view the spontaneous crossings as generalized avoidance responses (but see also Hearst and Whalen, 1963).

Finally, intensity studies emphasize the motivational significance of the priming stimulus. If the power of a brain stimulus to facilitate avoidance depends in part on its reward value, then variations of current will produce correlated changes in avoidance performance and self-stimulation. The most striking example of this obtained so far is given in Fig. 8.

SOME EVIDENCE ON THE CHEMICAL BASIS OF AMPHETAMINE ACTION

Recent work on a chemical structural problem will now be described. Does the central action of amphetamine depend on its phenethylamine structure? As a first step, various doses of phenethylamine were tested for amphetamine-like activity in the brain self-stimulation test. Phenethylamine seemed virtually inactive compared with amphetamine, but an extremely high dose (30 mg./kg.) had a small short-lived effect. This result could be explained if phenethylamine were active but was rapidly metabolized. Since it was known that phenethylamine is an excellent substrate for monoamine oxidase and that amphetamine is resistant to the enzyme and even inhibits it (Alles, 1959), additional tests were made on phenethylamine after the action of monoamine oxidase had been inhibited by iproniazid (100 mg./kg.). Under these conditions phenethylamine had a powerful augmenting effect that seemed to resemble the action of amphetamine in all respects (Fig. 9). These findings suggest, first, that the behavioural facilitation produced by amphetamine is based on its phenethylamine structure, and secondly, that the α-methyl group of amphetamine is important because it protects the drug from the action of monoamine oxidase. The potentiation of iproniazid may depend on more than a simple protective action, however, because iproniazid also potentiates amphetamine in this test (Stein, 1962a).

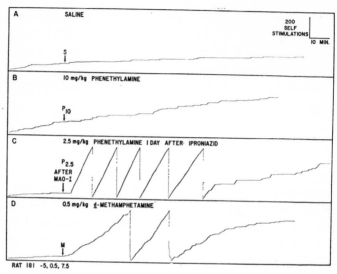

FIG. 9. Amphetamine-like facilitation of self-stimulation for subthreshold reinforcement by phenethylamine after pretreatment with 100 mg./kg. of iproniazid (panel C). 10 mg./kg. of phenethylamine given prior to iproniazid had no important effect (panel B). See Fig. 4 and text for further explanation.

Acknowledgment

I am indebted to Alfred T. Shropshire and Karey L. Sledge for meticulous technical assistance in the conduct of these experiments.

REFERENCES

ALLES, G. A. (1959). Trans. 5th Conf. on Neuropharmacology, p. 181, ed. Abramson, H. A. New York: Josiah Macy, Jr. Foundation.
ANDERSSON, B., and LARSSON, S. (1956). *Acta. physiol. scand.*, **38**, 22.
CARLTON, P. L. (1963). *Psychol. Rev.*, **70**, 19.
COOK, L., and KELLEHER, R. T. (1962). *Ann. N.Y. Acad. Sci.*, **96**, 315.
DELGADO, J. M. R., ROBERTS, W. W., and MILLER, N. E. (1954). *Amer. J. Physiol.*, **179**, 587.

DEWS, P. B. (1955). *J. Pharmacol. exp. Ther.*, **115**, 380.

DEWS, P. B. (1958). *J. Pharmacol. exp. Ther.*, **122**, 137.

DEWS, P. B., and MORSE, W. H. (1961). *Ann. Rev. Pharmacol.*, **1**, 145.

FERSTER, C. B., and SKINNER, B. F. (1957). Schedules of Reinforcement. New York: Appleton-Century-Crofts.

FOX, S. S. (1962). *J. comp. physiol. Psychol.*, **55**, 438.

GELLER, I., and SEIFTER, J. (1962). *J. Pharmacol. exp. Ther.*, **136**, 284.

HEARST, E., and WHALEN, R. E. (1963). *J. comp. physiol. Psychol.*, **56**, 124.

HESS, W. R. (1954). Das Zwischenhirn: Syndrome, Lokalisationen, Functionen (2nd ed.). Basel: Schwabe.

HOROVITZ, Z. P., CHOW, M., and CARLTON, P. L. (1962). *Psychopharmacologia*, **3**, 455.

KELLEHER, R. T., FRY, W., DEEGAN, J., and COOK, L. (1961). *J. Pharmacol. exp. Ther.*, **133**, 271.

LE GROS CLARK, W. E., BEATTIE, J., RIDDOCH, G., and DOTT, N. M. (1938). The Hypothalamus. Edinburgh: Oliver and Boyd.

MILLER, N. E. (1960). *Fed. Proc.*, **19**, 846.

MOWRER, O. H. (1960). Learning Theory and Behavior. New York: Wiley.

OLDS, J. (1959). *In* Neuro-Psychopharmacology, **1**, 20, ed. Bradley, P. B., Deniker, P., and Radouco-Thomas, C. Amsterdam: Elsevier.

OLDS, J. (1962). *Physiol. Rev.*, **42**, 554.

OLDS, J. (in press). *Electroenceph. clin. Neurophysiol.*, Suppl. No. **24**.

OLDS, J., and MILNER, P. (1954). *J. comp. physiol. Psychol.*, **47**, 419.

SIDMAN, M. (1953). *J. comp. physiol. Psychol.*, **46**, 253.

SIDMAN, M. (1956). *Ann. N.Y. Acad. Sci.*, **65**, 247.

SKINNER, B. F. (1938). The Behavior of Organisms. New York: Appleton-Century-Crofts.

SKINNER, B. F., and HERON, W. T. (1937). *Psychol. Rec.*, **1**, 340.

STEIN, L. (1962a). *In* Psychosomatic Medicine, p. 297, ed. Nodine, J. H., and Moyer, J. H. Philadelphia: Lea and Febiger.

STEIN, L. (1962b). *In* Recent Advances in Biological Psychiatry, vol. 4, p. 288, ed. Wortis, J. New York: Plenum.

STEIN, L. (1963). *Science*, **139**, 46.

STEIN, L. (in press). *In* Pleasure Integration and Behavior, ed. Heath, R. G. New York: Hoeber.

STEIN, L., and RAY, O. S. (1960). *Psychopharmacologia*, **1**, 251.

STEIN, L., and SEIFTER, J. (1961). *Science*, **134**, 286.

TAINTER, M. L. (1944). *J. Nutr.*, **27**, 89.

TEITELBAUM, P., and DERKS, P. (1958). *J. comp. physiol. Psychol.*, **51**, 801.

THORNDIKE, E. L. (1913). Educational Psychology, Vol. 2. The Psychology of Learning. New York: Teachers College, Columbia University.

VERHAVE, T. (1958). *J. exp. Anal. Behav.*, **1**, 207.

WEISS, B., and LATIES, V. G. (1963). *J. Pharmacol. exp. Ther.*, **140**, 1.

WENTINK, E. (1938). *J. exp. Psychol.*, **22**, 150.

DISCUSSION

Miller: I should like to add to Dr. Stein's remarks about amphetamine. This drug reduces the crouching behaviour very strikingly and makes it much easier to learn, especially in the shuttle box procedure. It reduces crouching behaviour whether or not the animals are in the shuttle box, so the reduction is probably the cause, rather than the result, of improved avoidance learning.

Stein: I do not think amphetamine has an effect on learning, Professor Miller, because when you test later, after the drug has worn off, the performance is back to baseline.

Miller: We found that too, but amphetamine does reduce the crouching.

Stein: I agree, and find this observation compatible with my hypothesis. I assume that two antagonistic mechanisms, a rewarding "go" system and a punishing "stop" system, jointly and continuously influence the tendency to respond. Freezing and crouching are observed, presumably, when the "stop" mechanism predominates. I assume, furthermore, that amphetamine may increase the output of the "go" mechanism by reducing its activation threshold. If control were shifted away from the "stop" mechanism by this means, freezing and crouching would be reduced or eliminated under the drug.

It is significant that when you break up the crouching with amphetamine, it is the avoidance response that appears rather than some other response, such as turning round in the box. I am tempted to take this as evidence that the avoidance response is maintained by and dependent on feedback from the rewarding "go" mechanism. The effect of amphetamine on avoidance is so striking that it would not be surprising if the drug exerted its effect in more than one way. Hence, amphetamine may not only allow the avoidance response to get started by counteracting freezing, but it may also increase the probability that the avoidance response will run off to completion by increasing the feedback from the "go" mechanism.

Hilton: Dr. Stein, towards the end of your paper you presented an hypothesis which you said was fanciful and, therefore, perhaps rather more attractive. I think it may also be wrong! I recently spent a few weeks in Dr. Gutman's laboratory in Prague, where they have for some time been interested in the behavioural responses of rats, and were then investigating the hyperglycaemic response to a painful stimulus. Dr. Vrbová and I trained a group of animals to do a shuttle box task, in which the unconditioned stimulus was a shock via the grid on which the rat was standing: a light was the conditioned stimulus to which the rat learnt "avoidance". We found that during the period when they were learning to "escape", the rats always developed the hyperglycaemic response during a trial. When they were "avoiding", that is, responding to the light alone, they no longer showed the hyperglycaemic response. This seemed to indicate that when the avoidance reaction was established, the whole defence mechanism was by-passed. Other evidence giving support to this idea was obtained when lesions were made in the hypothalamus of the trained rats, in order to destroy the region concerned in the integration of the defence reactions. The animals retained their avoidance reactions, even though they no longer responded in the slightest to the unconditioned, noxious stimulus. It looks as though the avoidance reaction is mediated by central nervous structures other than those which integrate behaviour patterns characteristic of the defence reaction.

Stein: Although fanciful, the hypothesis that avoidance behaviour is maintained by a positive reinforcement mechanism is probably right— and I wish it were mine! I am still trying to trace the history of this idea. Woodworth and Schlosberg in 1954 (Woodworth, R. S., and Schlosberg, H. [1954]. Experimental Psychology. New York: Holt) suggested that the avoidance response is maintained by "the positive incentive value of safety" (p. 676). O. H. Mowrer ([1960]. Learning Theory and Behavior. New York: Wiley) expressed a similar view, substituting the term "relief" for "safety". The ingenious rebound notion described in my paper was originated, as I have already indicated, by J. Olds (*Electroenceph. clin. Neurophysiol.*, Suppl. **24**, in press).

The findings you describe, Dr. Hilton, in no way contradict this theory and perhaps even support it. You showed that rats no longer exhibit signs of stress (or distress), like the hyperglycaemic response, when the avoidance response is fully developed. This is in agreement with a theory of avoidance which assumes that eventually a positive, and not a negative or punishing, brain mechanism motivates and maintains the behaviour. Perhaps the experience, in human terms, is like the satisfaction of being indoors in a storm or, better, like the thrill of narrowly averting danger on a roller coaster or fast car.

Jarvik: Dr. Stein, would you care to comment on some rather peculiar effects of amphetamine on activity in mice which we found, using the activity box which I have described? If we put mice into this box and gave them approximately 5 mg./kg. dexamphetamine sulphate intravenously, their activity increased, as one might expect, to about double the baseline value. On the other hand, if we gave the animal a shock during the one minute they were in the box, the activity decreased precipitously until they were not moving at all. If, however, we combined shock and amphetamine, their average activity was greater than the activity of those receiving amphetamine alone. In this case, we have a non-adaptive reaction to the situation. The animals were getting shocks all the time. This is in contrast to the double grill-box situation, where amphetamine breaks up a crouching response which is a rather adaptive reaction. I wonder if this phenomenon fits into your scheme?

Stein: The finding that amphetamine antagonizes the suppressing effects of punishment on spontaneous activity is in line with the theory. This is because amphetamine is assumed to sensitize a (reward) mechanism whose action would counteract the suppressing effects of punishment. The further finding that shock *increased* activity under the drug is not in line with the theory. One possibility might be that the increase in counts you obtained in the shock-drug condition was an artifact due to reflex jumping to the shocks, and did not reflect an increase in spontaneous activity.

Irwin: Dr. Stein was referring to the effect of amphetamine on animals with different baselines, and was indicating that a certain minimum degree of responsiveness is necessary in order to get stimulation. On the other hand, he mentioned that with a fixed-ratio schedule, particularly where a high requirement for bar-pressing is present, the animals are rather unresponsive. Perhaps I could explain some of the factors that affect such responsiveness.

The initial baseline or control level of activity exhibited by an animal has been shown to be fairly well correlated with its response to drugs. There appear to be several laws or rules which govern such responsiveness, varying with the measure under study. Some time ago, Wilder (Wilder, J. [1957]. *J. nerv. ment. Dis.*, **125**, 73) introduced what he called a "law of initial value". This law states that, given a standard stimulus or drug and a standard period of measurement, the higher the initial value, the smaller is the response to function-raising stimuli and the greater the response to function-depressing stimuli; the converse occurs when the initial value is low. This "law" appears to apply to a wide variety of measures, particularly to those of a physiological or biochemical nature; it would also seem to apply to the fixed-ratio schedule. However, it by no means describes all phenomena and is generally less applicable to measures of mental behaviour. At least two other types of "laws" or rules governing the response to drugs exist (Irwin, S. [1964]. *In* Clinical Pharmacology: Animal and Human Techniques, ed. Nodine, J., and Siegler, P. Chicago: Year Book Medical Publishers. In press).

With certain measures, as with the effects of drugs on the pain theshold or on the level of wakefulness, the response to drugs seems to be a purely additive arithmetical function of the initial level. With still other measures, as with drug effects on locomotor activity, a divergence occurs in which hyperactive animals are very much more responsive to stimulant or depressant drug effects than hypoactive animals. Thus, animals that exhibit very low levels of locomotor activity, as measured in revolving treadwheels, are quite unresponsive to the locomotor stimulant effects of amphetamine, no matter how high the dose of drug administered. On the other hand, animals at a higher baseline level of activity before the drug is given are quite sensitive to either stimulants or depressants.

Yet another important factor affecting the response to drugs is the condition of behavioural arousal of the individual before and/or during drug administration, for the greater the state of arousal, the greater is an individual's sensitivity to stimulant drugs and his resistance to depressant drugs. The phenomenon of "aggregate toxicity" would seem to be an example of this, whereby the toxicity of amphetamine is greatly increased by increasing the number of animals housed together; conversely, increasing the level of arousal is known to diminish the toxicity of depressants.

If one keeps these considerations in mind—the baseline level of the activity to be modified, the particular law governing its response to drugs, and the state of behavioural arousal of the individual (as may be inferred, in part, from the arousal-provoking quality of the experimental situation)—one can often predict within reasonable limits how an individual, and not simply a group, is going to respond to a drug.

E.E.G. CORRELATES OF DRUG EFFECTS

P. B. BRADLEY

Department of Experimental Neuropharmacology, University of Birmingham

A VARIETY of alterations in the electrical activity of the central nervous system show correlations with behaviour. There are two main ways in which we can examine these electrophysiological phenomena. We can record the spontaneous electrical activity of the brain whilst the subject, either animal or man, is showing normal patterns of behaviour and attempt to correlate the two. Or, we can examine the potentials evoked by particular stimuli, to which the subject has been trained to give a particular behavioural response, and examine the relationship between these two phenomena. Leaving aside human studies for the time being, as the techniques required are somewhat different, both types of study in animals are dependent on the use of techniques for the chronic implantation of electrodes (Bradley and Elkes, 1953), but the advances made in the development of such techniques in the last ten years, partly due to the availability of new materials, have made such methods relatively easy to use and it is not intended to discuss them in detail. The need for having leads between the animal and the recording apparatus, however, must of necessity, restrict and modify the behaviour and the use of telemetering devices would be of advantage in behavioural experiments with animals.

Considering the spontaneous electrical activity of the brain, probably the best known changes in cortical activity are those which occur during the transition from sleep to wakefulness and also during the reverse process, and these patterns of activity are now well established (Jasper, 1941). They correlate well with the behavioural state both in animals and in man, and Lindsley (1952) has described the correlation between the EEG and various criteria for psychological states related to wakefulness (Table I).

Drugs which cause alterations in the level of wakefulness produce appropriate changes in the EEG. Thus, sedatives and other central depressant drugs cause slowing of electrocortical potentials whilst central stimulants, such as amphetamine, cause desynchronization and behavioural excitement. The use of combined electrophysiological and behavioural techniques for the study of the actions of these drugs has made it possible for their sites of action in the brain to be determined (Bradley and Elkes, 1957). Such investigations have led to the hypothesis that these two groups of drugs, the central depressants and central stimulants, produce their effects by direct actions on the brain stem reticular formation, the region of the brain responsible for controlling levels of wakefulness and sleep.

This system will not be described in detail here, but it is note-worthy that the earlier views, that the maintenance of the wakeful state was an active process and that sleep and loss of consciousness were due to the cutting off of a diffuse ascending facilitatory influence from the brain stem, may have to be modified, as it is now probable that both synchronizing and desynchronizing centres exist in the brain stem (Magnes et al., 1961). It is therefore possible that the balance between the levels of activity of these two centres might be the factor which ultimately determines the state of wakefulness. In addition, there are observations which show that the EEG does not always reflect the behavioural state; for example, the paradoxical stage of sleep which has been des-cribed both in animals and man (Dement, 1958; Jouvet et al., 1959), in which the EEG shows a desynchronized pattern of activity in deep sleep, and secondly, a pharmacological dissociation between the electrocorticogram and behaviour which appears when certain drugs are administered. This was first described by Wikler (1952), who found that when he administered atropine to

Table I

PSYCHOLOGICAL STATES AND THEIR EEG, CONSCIOUS AND BEHAVIOURAL CORRELATES
(FROM LINDSLEY, 1952)

Behavioural continuum	Electroencephalogram	State of awareness	Behavioural efficiency
Strong, excited emotion (Fear) (Rage) (Anxiety).	Desynchronized: Low to moderate amplitude; fast, mixed frequencies.	Restricted awareness: divided attention; diffuse, hazy; "Confusion".	Poor: (lack of control, freezing-up, disorganized).
Alert attentiveness.	Partially synchronized: Mainly fast, low amplitude waves.	Selective attention, but may vary or shift. "Concentration", anticipation, "set".	Good: (efficient, selective, quick reactions). Organized for serial responses.
Relaxed wakefulness.	Synchronized: Optimal alpha rhythm.	Attention wanders—not forced. Favours free association.	Good: (routine reactions and creative thought).
Drowsiness.	Reduced alpha and occasional low amplitude slow waves.	Borderline, partial awareness. Imagery and reverie. "Dream-like states."	Poor: (unco-ordinated, sporadic, lacking sequential timing).
Light sleep.	Spindle bursts and slow waves (larger). Loss of alphas.	Markedly reduced consciousness (loss of consciousness). Dream state.	Absent.
Deep sleep.	Large and very slow waves (synchrony but on slow time base). Random, irregular pattern.	Complete loss of awareness (no memory for stimulation or for dreams).	Absent.
Coma.	Isoelectric to irregular large slow waves.	Complete loss of consciousness, little or no response to stimulation; amnesia.	Absent.
Death.	Isoelectric: Gradual and permanent disappearance of all electrical activity.	Complete loss of awareness as death ensues.	Absent.

unanaesthetized dogs, sleep patterns appeared in the EEG whilst the animals were behaviourally excited. We have shown that a similar dissociation occurs in the cat when atropine or physostigmine is used (Bradley and Elkes, 1957) and more recently also in the rat (Bradley, 1964). It might be thought that these observations argue against the use of electrophysiological techniques in behavioural studies of drug action, but in my view, they argue strongly in favour of combining these techniques wherever possible.

Reference has already been made to the changes which take place in the pattern of electrocortical activity accompanying the transition from sleep to wakefulness. If this transition is abrupt, that is, in response to a sensory stimulus of sufficient intensity, then the concomitant electrical changes are also abrupt. This response, the arousal response, can also be elicited by direct electrical stimulation of the brain stem reticular formation, if suitable stimulus parameters are used. We have used this response to assess quantitatively the effects of different drugs on the arousal system of the brain and to determine independently their effects on electrocortical arousal and behavioural alerting (Bradley and Key, 1958). This was done by injecting the drugs in incremental quantities and determining the threshold for arousal produced either by electrical stimulation of the brain stem reticular formation or by sensory stimulation after each injection. In this way graphs of the threshold changes could be plotted against the dose of the drug and it was found that these graphs were characteristic for each drug and consistent in different experiments. Since these results have been published for some time, only a summary of the principal findings will be given here. The results obtained supported the earlier hypothesis that the barbiturates produce their central action by depressing the brain stem reticular formation and that the central stimulant drug, amphetamine, has a facilitatory action on this system. They have also been extended to include other types of central depressant and stimulant drugs. Experiments of this type have made it possible for the sedative action of the barbiturates to be distinguished from the actions of the phenothiazine tranquillizers, which appear to depress afferent influences on the brain stem arousal system (Bradley and Key, 1959). Similarly, the excitant effects of amphetamine could be distinguished from those of the hallucinogenic drug LSD-25, which also has an action related to afferent influences at the brain stem level. In all four of these groups of drugs the graphs for the behavioural and electrophysiological responses followed virtually the same course, but in the case of atropine and physostigmine the curves for the two responses diverged and provided a quantitative demonstration of the dissociation between behaviour and the EEG.

The drugs whose effects appeared to be most interesting in these experiments were chlorpromazine and LSD-25, because it was obvious that the changes in both the electrophysiological and the behavioural responses reflected changes in the animals' reactions to environmental conditions and in many ways paralleled the clinical reports of the effects of these drugs. Thus, it was thought necessary to look more closely at the effects of these drugs in relation to responses to sensory stimulation.

It is well known that the continued repetition of the same sensory stimulus results in a diminution of the response and its eventual loss due to the process of habituation. This has been shown to be true for the electroencephalographic arousal response (Sharpless and Jasper, 1956). Thus, when the same stimulus, which in the present experiments was a sound, is repeatedly presented to the animal the arousal response diminishes and is eventually lost. In the case of stimuli at threshold intensities, habituation is indicated by a rise in the threshold for arousal, until a point is reached where even high intensities of stimulation fail to evoke an arousal response, both electrophysiologically and behaviourally (Fig. 1). This loss of arousal by repetition of biologically insignificant stimuli has been compared to satiation of an animal to salivary conditioning. It has been suggested that in both cases the drive dimension has been altered. When the animal is conditioned to a particular sound stimulus, however, by pairing it with a mild electric shock, the effects of habituation are overcome and the threshold remains at a steady low level

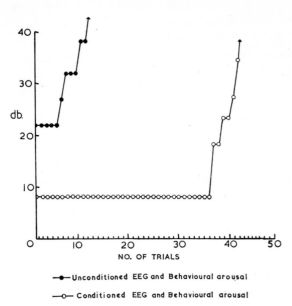

FIG. 1. Changes in the threshold for EEG and behavioural arousal produced by repeated presentation of an auditory stimulus.

Full circles: non-conditioned tone of 40 c./sec., showing habituation. Open circles: conditioned tone of 600 c./sec., showing extinction after 30–40 trials.

over a large number of presentations of the unreinforced conditioned stimulus (sound), before extinction begins to take place (Fig. 1). At this point a further single reinforcement is sufficient to provide stability of the arousal threshold for this stimulus. This effect is specific to the parameters of the conditioned stimulus used and a slight change in these parameters, for example in the frequency of the sound, results in the reappearance of habituation.

Experiments were carried out with animals in which recording electrodes had been implanted some months previously in order that the thresholds for both EEG activation and behavioural arousal could be determined independently. However, in all cases these thresholds followed the same course. The effects of chlorpromazine and LSD-25 on the thresholds for arousal produced by both conditioned auditory stimuli and non-conditioned stimuli (using different tones) were examined in these animals (Key and Bradley, 1960). Chlorpromazine, in increasing doses, produced a similar elevation of both thresholds and at the same time reduced the period of activation of the EEG. Thus, the drug had similar effects on the threshold for the conditioned response as well as for the non-conditioned response, and this finding implied that the effects of chlorpromazine on sensory-induced arousal are not masked by habituation. In some respects it appeared that the effects produced by chlorpromazine simulated the process of habituation. In the case of LSD-25, the experiments were carried out using three different auditory stimuli, one of which was non-conditioned, the second had been previously conditioned and the third was fully habituated—that is, it had been presented a sufficient number of times for complete loss of the arousal response to occur (Fig. 2). The drug was then given. The threshold for the conditioned response remained unaltered. That for the non-conditioned stimulus fell to about the same level as for the conditioned response and the fully habituated response returned, not at its former threshold level, but at a new low level, roughly equivalent to that for the other two responses.

The effects of LSD-25 on these afferent-induced arousal responses were therefore in many ways opposite to those of chlorpromazine and while the latter drug appeared to simulate the process of habituation, LSD-25 simulated the effects of positive conditioning and overcame the effects of habituation. We have referred to the fact that habituation occurs rapidly to biologically insignificant stimuli. An originally novel stimulus loses its significance for the organism on repeated presentation. In these terms,

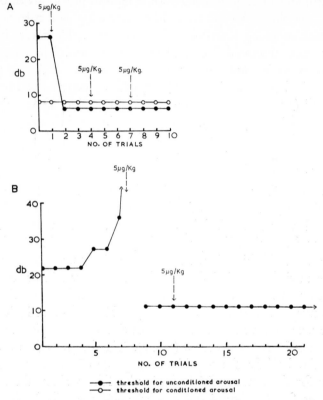

FIG. 2. The effect of *d*-lysergic acid diethylamide on A: arousal produced by non-conditioned (full circles) and conditioned (open circles) auditory stimuli, and B: a habituated arousal response (from Key and Bradley, 1960).

chlorpromazine would appear to lower the significance level for a wide range of sensory stimuli, even those to which the animal had previously been conditioned, while LSD-25 increases the significance level of stimuli over a wide range to that normally achieved by positive conditioning. It therefore seems probable that these two drugs interfere selectively with the mechanisms concerned in the filtering and integration of sensory information in the brain. This idea is supported by the results of further experiments

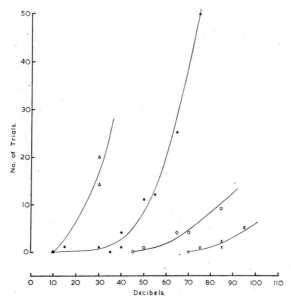

FIG. 3. The effects of chlorpromazine and d-lysergic acid diethylamide on the rate of habituation of the electrocortical arousal response evoked by 1000 c./sec. pure tone at different levels of intensity (from Key, 1961a).

● : control
○ : 5 mg./kg. chlorpromazine
× : 10 mg./kg. chlorpromazine
△ : 15 μg./kg. LSD-25

(Key, 1961a) in which the rate of habituation of arousal responses at different stimulus intensities was measured in control animals which had been given injections of normal saline and in animals to which small quantities of LSD-25 and chlorpromazine had been administered (Fig. 3). The effect of chlorpromazine was to potentiate the rate of habituation, whereas LSD-25 retarded this process, and this was consistent with the results of previous experiments. Since most of the experiments which have been described so far were carried out with auditory stimuli, different tones being used where more than one stimulus was required, it was possible that some of the effects observed may have been due to changes in the animals' ability to discriminate between the different tones used, and therefore, in a separate series of experiments, the effects of both LSD-25 and chlorpromazine on sensory discrimination and sensory generalization were examined (Key, 1961b). It was found that neither drug, in the doses used, had any appreciable effect on sensory discrimination in so far as the stimulus parameters were concerned. Furthermore, the generalization gradients of the responses (in this case conditioned avoidance responses) were unchanged by these drugs, although the generalization curves were shifted in opposite directions by LSD-25 and chlorpromazine. Thus, the amount of generalization, in terms of the range of stimuli to which the animal responded, was increased by LSD-25 and diminished by chlorpromazine (Fig. 4).

It is possible that these findings may have some relevance to the actions of these drugs in man, where distortions of perception occur when they are administered and it is known that sensory generalization and discrimination are related to perceptual processes. If habituation and conditioning may be considered to be forms of learning, then it is probable that these two drugs will affect learning and possibly memory as well. This aspect of their actions is being investigated at present.

In this paper an attempt has been made to demonstrate how, by the combination of electrophysiological and behavioural techniques for the study of the actions of drugs on the central nervous system, we can learn not only more about the actions of the drugs concerned, but also more about the functioning of the central nervous system, as manifested by the behaviour of the

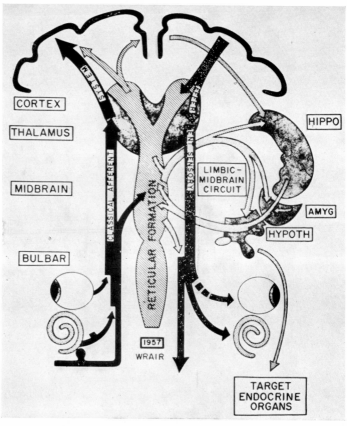

FIG. 5. Brain systems involved in learning (from Galambos, 1958).

To face p. 129

organism in relation to its environment. A great deal still needs to be done to elucidate the precise physiological mechanisms by which sensory information is filtered and integrated in the brain and the extensive amount of purely electrophysiological data

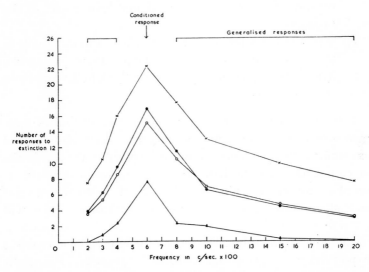

FIG. 4. The effect of LSD-25 and chlorpromazine on the extinction of a conditioned avoidance response and similar responses evoked through sensory generalization (from Key, 1961b).

● and ○: control curves
▲: after 5 mg./kg. chlorpromazine
×: after 15 μg./kg. LSD-25

available does not help in this respect as much as one would hope. However, it is possible from a consideration of some of these data to suggest a number of systems which may be involved, and four of these are shown in Fig. 5 (Galambos, 1958). These are:

(1) The classical afferent pathways via the specific thalamic nuclei to the corresponding cortical projection areas.

(2) The descending, efferent sensory systems arising from the cortical and subcortical regions and making synaptic connexions with ascending pathways at all levels.

(3) The reticular, or non-specific, pathway receiving collaterals from the specific sensory tracts and passing to the cortex by way of the intra-laminar and mid-brain nuclei of the thalamus.

(4) The mid-brain limbic circuit in which activity arising in the mid-brain passes to the hippocampus, amygdala, hypothalamus, septal nuclei and then back to the mid-brain reticular formation.

It has been suggested that learning involves all four of these main systems and there is some evidence from electrophysiological experiments that the hippocampus is involved in the acquisition of learned responses. Such diagrams must represent a gross over-simplification and they indicate only some of the interconnexions and interactions between the various pathways. They will certainly have to be modified and augmented by the results of further investigations but they serve a useful purpose in enabling hypotheses to be set up and tested experimentally. The results of the experiments outlined in this paper point to the involvement of the reticular non-specific system, although the controlling influence of this system may not be at the brain stem level but may be exerted via the cerebral cortex and the descending efferent system. Work which is in progress may throw some light on this possibility.

REFERENCES

BRADLEY, P. B. (1964). This volume p. 338.
BRADLEY, P. B., and ELKES, J. (1953). *Electroenceph. clin. Neurophysiol.*, **5**, 451.
BRADLEY, P. B., and ELKES, J. (1957). *Brain*, **80**, 77.
BRADLEY, P. B., and KEY, B. J. (1958). *Electroenceph. clin. Neurophysiol.*, **10**, 97.
BRADLEY, P. B., and KEY, B. J. (1959). *Brit. J. Pharmacol.*, **14**, 340.
DEMENT, W. (1958). *Electroenceph. clin. Neurophysiol.*, **10**, 291.

GALAMBOS, R. (1958). Trans. 1st Conf. on The Central Nervous System and Behavior, p. 289, ed. Brazier, M.A.B. New York: Josiah Macy, Jr. Foundation.

JASPER, H. H. (1941). In Epilepsy and Cerebral Localisation, ed. Penfield, W., and Erickson, T.C. Springfield: Thomas.

JOUVET, M., MICHEL, F., and COURJON, J. (1959). C.R. Soc. Biol. (Paris), 153, 1024.

KEY, B. J., and BRADLEY, P. B. (1960). Psychopharmacologia, 1, 450.

KEY, B. J. (1961a). Nature (Lond.), 190, 275.

KEY, B. J. (1961b). Psychopharmacologia, 2, 352.

LINDSLEY, D. B. (1952). Electroenceph. clin. Neurophysiol., 4, 443.

MAGNES, J., MORUZZI, G., and POMPEIANO, O. (1961). Ciba Found. Symp. The Nature of Sleep, p. 57. London: Churchill.

SHARPLESS, S., and JASPER, H. (1956). Brain, 79, 655.

WIKLER, A. (1952). Proc. Soc. exp. Biol. (N. Y.), 79, 261.

DISCUSSION

Hilton: Dr. Bradley will not mind if I say that the scheme of the reticular activating system which he used as an illustration for his paper (Fig. 5) was probably rather fanciful even when it first appeared. Some of its features are no doubt correct, but the general concept is a bit old-fashioned. I feel particularly doubtful about the idea of a non-specific, ascending, reticular activating system—a sort of sausage running right through the middle of the brain stem, which has no function except to initiate features of arousal when some stimulus sends impulses into it. A major part of the brain stem is known to be involved in highly specific activities of the animal; and that behaviour for instance, which has been called the defence reaction—comprising the responses which culminate in flight or attack—has the largest representation of all, extending from the mid-brain forward into the hypothalamus. With moderate stimulation of these parts of the brain stem, one gets the behaviour which has been termed alerting, arousal or startle. But it seems, from work carried out by Abrahams, Malcolm, Zbrozyna and myself, that these brain stem regions can really be regarded as a reflex centre for the defence reaction, in all its complexity (Abrahams, V. C., Hilton, S. M., and Zbrozyna, A. [1960]. *J. Physiol.* [*Lond.*], 152, 54P; 154, 491; Abrahams, V. C., Hilton, S. M., and Malcolm J. L. [1962]. *J. Physiol.* [*Lond.*], 164, 1).

This reflex centre is thus seen to occupy a major part of what has been called the reticular activating system: its function is not simply to produce arousal, but to integrate all the component features of the response. The basic idea behind this conclusion is not so original; it was known many years ago that these behavioural responses are produced as stereotyped reactions when this system is cut off from higher parts of the brain by decortication or decerebration (Goltz, F. M. [1892]. *Pflügers Arch. ges. Physiol.*, **51**, 570; Bard, P., and Rioch, D. McK. [1937]. *Bull. Johns Hopk. Hosp.*, **60**, 65).

With particular reference to Dr. Stein's comment in his paper to the effect that the function of the periventricular grey matter was a closed book until the initiation of recent behavioural studies, I should add that detailed investigation of this problem has been continued over the years; Bard and Cannon started in the 1920's to work out the function of the periventricular area of the hypothalamus in relation to fear and rage reactions (Bard, P. [1928]. *Amer. J. Physiol.*, **84**, 490; Cannon, W. B., and Britton, S. W. [1925]. *Amer J. Physiol.*, **72**, 283). Hess added considerably to this work (Hess, W. R., and Brügger, M. [1943]. *Helv. physiol. pharmacol. Acta*, **1**, 33). A lot of information of this sort has been accumulated over the years by physiologists as well as psychologists, which all seems to fit into one consistent pattern; perhaps it is time that this idea of a non-specific reticular activating system was dropped.

Bradley: I am sorry if I gave the impression that Fig. 5, which was taken from Galambos, was the answer to all our problems. I did state that it was an oversimplification but I think that there is a fair amount of evidence, from anatomical and electrophysiological studies, that all four systems probably exist. As far as your objection to the non-specific system is concerned, I was, of course referring to the ascending activation effects, as opposed to the specific afferent pathways. An afferent stimulus reaching this system produces a non-specific effect and there is some degree of convergence. It is well known that in the brain stem a number of other functions are subserved, including reflex functions, one of which you have studied and found these very interesting effects. There was insufficient time, however, to cover all these aspects in my paper.

Stein: Dr. Hilton correctly points out that the periventricular system has been explored for many years and that reactions characteristic of emotional disturbance have long been observed. On the basis of these early observational data, however, one could not easily infer whether or not the reactions observed reflected a "true" emotion capable of motivating behaviour. In fact, Masserman (Masserman, J. H. [1941]. *Psychosom. Med.*, **3**, 1) concluded that hypothalamic stimulation produces only a "sham rage" when he failed to obtain evidence that it could be conditioned. To my knowledge, the first convincing experimental proof that direct brain stimulation may have the *behavioural* properties of punishment was obtained by Delgado, Roberts, and Miller at Yale (Delgado, J. M. R., Roberts, W. W., and Miller, N. E. [1954]. *Amer. J. Physiol.*, **179**, 587). These investigators showed for the first time that electrical stimulation of certain brain points could serve to (a) motivate an avoidance response, (b) punish (inhibit) positively motivated behaviour, and (c) establish, through conditioning, aversive properties in an originally neutral stimulus.

Hendry: I was struck by Dr. Bradley's illustration (Fig. 4) which showed that chlorpromazine and LSD-25 had antagonistic effects on responses. He showed that LSD-25 increased the response strength in extinction, but also increased the range of stimuli which elicited the responses, or in the presence of which the response was given, whereas chlorpromazine had the opposite effect. This looks like a classic result of manipulating motivation, as in a strictly psychological experiment, and Dr. Bradley did not comment on this similarity. Does he object to interpreting drug effects as unitary effects upon a psychological entity such as drive or motivation?

Bradley: The effects of these two drugs were not antagonistic as you suggest, but opposite in direction. It is quite true that they can be explained in purely psychological terms such as drive or motivation and I certainly have no objection to such an explanation. However, it is not likely to help us to understand the underlying physiological mechanism, which is what we are really interested in. I agree that we might consider psychological concepts in interpreting the results.

THE EFFECT OF PHYSOSTIGMINE AND ATROPINE ON THE MECHANISM OF LEARNING

J. Bureš, O. Burešová, Z. Bohdanecký and T. Weiss

Institute of Physiology, Czechoslovak Academy of Sciences, Prague

Since attempts to find direct electrophysiological correlates of conditioning have brought rather disappointing results, a less straightforward electrophysiological approach to the neurophysiology of learning becomes more and more important. Learning ability is correlated with characteristic electrical phenomena in certain brain structures. EEG patterns incompatible with learning may indicate the neural circuits subserving specific behavioural functions. Characteristic EEG changes induced by physostigmine or atropine are very suitable for this purpose.

Clear-cut hippocampal theta activity (4–8/sec. waves of almost sinusoidal shape) can be evoked by intraperitoneal injection of physostigmine (1 mg./kg. physostigmine salicylate) in rats, as in other mammals (Sailer and Stumpf, 1957; Bradley and Nicholson, 1961). In electrophysiological experiments performed in curarized or freely-moving rats with electrodes implanted in the dorsal hippocampi and in the frontal neocortices, theta waves in the hippocampus were found to appear 3–7 minutes after administration of physostigmine (Fig. 1). In the tenth minute practically the whole hippocampal record was covered by regular theta activity, which lasted for 30–50 min. (Fig. 2). No enduring orienting or attentive behaviour (which usually accompanies the hippocampal theta activity under physiological conditions) could be observed during the physostigmine-induced hippocampal theta waves.

Another type of dissociation between the EEG and behaviour can be evoked by atropine. Atropine sulphate (6 mg./kg.) induces

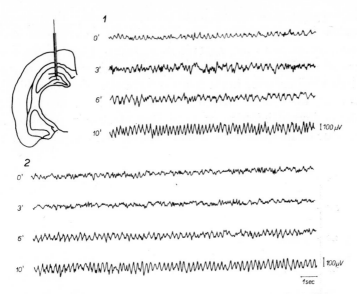

FIG. 1. The effect of physostigmine (1 mg./kg. intraperitoneally) on hippocampal electrical activity in curarized rats. Development of theta activity during the first ten minutes after injection is illustrated by two typical cases (1, 2). (From Bureš, Bohdanecký and Weiss, 1962.)

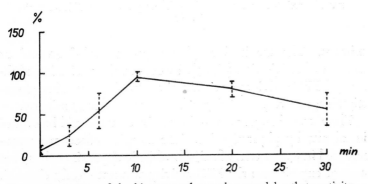

FIG. 2. Percentage of the hippocampal record covered by theta activity at different intervals after physostigmine administration. The interrupted vertical bars correspond to the 95 per cent confidence limits ($N = 15$).

an irregular slow wave, high voltage sleep-like EEG pattern which is not, however, accompanied by behavioural sleep (Funderburk and Case, 1951; Wikler, 1952). These results were confirmed in our electrophysiological experiments in rats with electrodes implanted in the reticular formation, the dorsal hippocampus, the caudate nucleus and the frontal neocortex. After intraperitoneal injection of 6 mg./kg. of atropine sulphate an increase of the peak to peak EEG voltage occurred in about 15

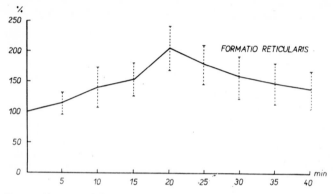

FIG. 3. Changes of the peak to peak amplitudes of reticular electrical activity at different intervals after atropine administration. The interrupted vertical bars correspond to the 95 per cent confidence limits (N= 12).

minutes. The maximal amplitude was recorded 20 and 25 minutes after injection (Fig. 3). Moreover, the restitution of the normal EEG activity was slower after atropine than after physostigmine, recovery not being complete even after 45 minutes.

The above changes were quite consistent and could be evoked in all rats by physostigmine. The atropine effects were pronounced in 85 per cent of animals while in approximately 15 per cent of experiments the EEG activity was not clearly changed. No electrophysiological recording was made, therefore, in the animals used in the behavioural part of the study, as it was supposed that the statistically determined time course of the drug effect would be the same as in the electrophysiological experiments.

A simple one-trial learning procedure originally described by

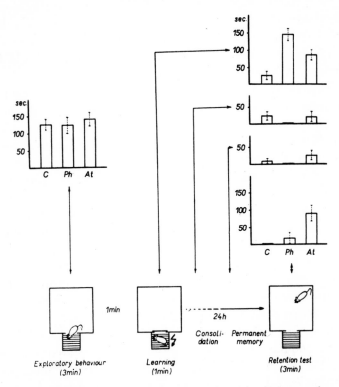

FIG. 4. The effect of physostigmine (Ph) and atropine (At) on exploratory behaviour and different phases of learning of a passive avoidance reaction.

C: control groups injected with saline. The dotted vertical bars indicate the standard errors of the means. For details, see text.

Kurtz and Pearl (1960), the so-called passive avoidance reaction, was used throughout. A naive rat was placed in an apparatus (Fig. 4) consisting of a large compartment (40 × 40 cm.) connected by an opening (6×6 cm.) to a small compartment (10×10 cm.) with an electrifiable grid floor. Most animals rapidly find the entrance into the small compartment and spend there 120–140 sec. of the 3-minute exploratory period. This is the unconditioned behaviour. The opening between the two compartments is then closed with a perspex shutter and the rat is put into the small compartment, where it receives intermittent electric shocks for 1 minute. This is the learning procedure.

Twenty-four or 48 hours later the animal is allowed to explore the apparatus again for 3 minutes. Normal rats enter the small compartment only exceptionally. This is the retention test. The time between learning and the retention test can be divided into two parts: the consolidation period, during which the memory traces can be impaired by an electro-shock, and the permanent memory period.

Results are illustrated in Fig. 4 by columns indicating the time spent in the small compartment. The exploratory behaviour of naive animals is influenced neither by physostigmine (0·5 mg./kg.) nor by atropine (6 mg./kg.). All other data express the results of the retention test in different groups of animals in which the drugs were given in such a way as to maximally influence the above phases of the experimental procedure.

Physostigmine and atropine did not influence the consolidation process and the permanent memory. Learning and retrieval were significantly affected, however. Ten minutes after physostigmine injection (0·1–1·0 mg./kg.) the rats were unable to learn the passive avoidance reaction. But when the drugs were given before the retention test, retrieval was impaired more by atropine than by physostigmine.

The effect on retrieval could be observed only with liminal learning, however. Even slight overlearning of the passive avoidance reaction, for example by repeating the 1 minute shock period twice within 30 minutes, prevented any impairment of retrieval by 6 mg./kg. of atropine. This may explain why so little effect of atropine on conditioned reflexes is reported in studies using firmly established conditioned reactions.

A dose of atropine which almost suppresses retrieval does not prevent learning. This was clearly shown in experiments (Fig. 5A) in which the retention test under atropine was followed on the

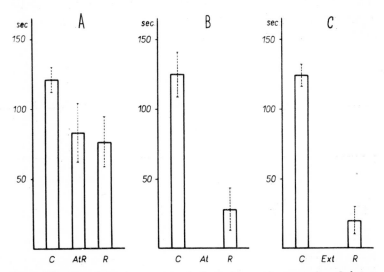

FIG. 5. The effect of atropine on retrieval of a passive avoidance reaction. Columns indicate the time spent in the small compartment during the first exploration or during the retention test performed 24 or 48 hours later.

At: application of atropine. Ext: forced extinction by 3 min. confinement in the small compartment without shocks. R: retention test. For details see text.

next day by a second retention test under normal conditions. Since retrieval was no better, it seems that unpunished entering of the small compartment under atropine probably induced some extinction of the original passive avoidance reaction. Such a conclusion is supported by control experiments which indicate that neither atropine alone (Fig. 5B) nor forced extinction (3 minutes in the small compartment, Fig. 5C) on day 2 could account for the loss of retention on day 3 described above.

The effect of both drugs on extinction of an overlearned passive avoidance reaction was tested in another group of experiments. The original learning procedure was repeated three times with 30-minute intervals between trials. On the next day the animal was confined in the small shock compartment for 30 minutes. The effect of this extinction procedure was clearly seen in the retention test performed 24 hours later (Fig. 6). The passive

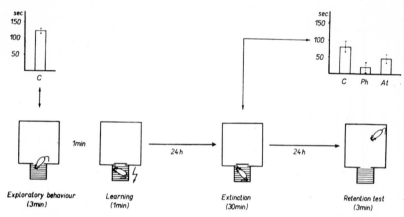

FIG. 6. The effect of physostigmine (Ph) and atropine (At) on extinction of an over-learned passive avoidance reaction. Columns indicate time spent in the small compartment during the original exploration or during the retention test. C: control group.

avoidance reaction was nearly extinguished in the control group, but it remained well preserved in animals in which the extinction trial was performed under the influence of physostigmine and atropine.

It is well known that the EEG patterns of alertness and sleep induced by physostigmine and atropine are not accompanied by corresponding behavioural correlates. This dissociation of electro-physiological and behavioural phenomena does not indicate, however, that these drugs have no behavioural effects at all, as recently pointed out by Sadowski and Longo (1962). The diffuse system of cholinergic receptors affected by physostigmine and atropine evidently plays an important rôle in more subtle neural functions like learning and retrieval. Probably both physostigmine and atropine cause a functional blockade of this system either by hyperactivity or inactivation, with different side effects on related non-cholinergic circuits. Their different effects on learning and retention of the passive avoidance reaction indicate that these two processes are subserved by somewhat different neural mechanisms which may be separated more or less selectively by pharmacological means.

The marked effect of physostigmine on the electrical activity of the hippocampus may throw some light on recent hypotheses about the behavioural rôle of this structure. According to Adey, Walter and Hendrix (1961), consistent phase shifts between leads from different hippocampal and entorhinal regions characterized the correct and incorrect responding of a cat in a discrimination situation. As the physostigmine-induced theta activity considerably increases hippocampal synchronization without affecting overlearned conditioned reflexes, phase comparison can be scarcely considered essential for retrieval in rats. Our findings do not support the assumption of Grastyán (1959) about the hippocampal inhibition of the orienting reflex. In spite of continuous hippocampal theta activity the rats display various behavioural patterns, from clear-cut orienting and searching behaviour to deep inhibition. The physostigmine-induced impairment of learning cannot therefore be explained by the animal's inability to inhibit the orienting behaviour.

Similar arguments can be used in interpreting the effects of atropine. Although high voltage, slow wave activity in the cerebral cortex usually accompanies inhibition of conditioned reflexes (Morrell, 1961), this EEG pattern is not necessarily connected with an impairment of behaviour. It is evident that the EEG changes induced by physostigmine and atropine do not affect the entire neuronal population of the corresponding areas and that the remaining neurones may subserve even complex behavioural functions. This invalidates hypotheses of the mechanism of learning based on macroelectrode recording only.

In conclusion, the importance of experimental techniques which make possible independent examination of the effects of drugs on various stages of learning and memory trace formation must be stressed. When the effect of the drug on retention is tested, the degree of overlearning must also be taken into account. Overlearned behaviour is probably maintained by an increase in the number of interconnected parallel circuits, the totality of which is more resistant to elimination of the same relative number of neurones than the non-redundant circuits of threshold learning.

REFERENCES

ADEY, W. R., WALTER, D. O., and HENDRIX, C. E. (1961). *Exp. Neurol.*, **3**, 501.
BRADLEY, P. B., and NICHOLSON, A. N. (1961). *C.N.R.S. Coll. Physiologie de l'hippocampe*, p. 445. Paris: Centre National de la Recherche Scientifique.
BUREŠ, J., BOHDANECKÝ, Z., and WEISS, T. (1962). *Psychopharmacologia*, **3**, 254.
FUNDERBURK, W. H., and CASE, T. J. (1951). *Electroenceph. clin. Neurophysiol.*, **3**, 213.
GRASTYÁN, E. (1959). *Trans. 2nd Conf. The Central Nervous System and Behavior*, p. 119, ed. Brazier, M.A.B. New York: Josiah Macy, Jr. Foundation.
KURTZ, K. H., and PEARL, J. (1960). *J. comp. physiol. Psychol.*, **53**, 201.
MORRELL, F. (1961). *Physiol. Rev.*, **41**, 443.
SADOWSKI, B., and LONGO, V. G. (1962). *Electroenceph. clin. Neurophysiol.*, **14**, 465.
SAILER, S., and STUMPF, C. (1957). *Naunyn-Schmiedeberg's Arch. exp. Path. Pharmak.*, **231**, 63.
WIKLER, A. (1952). *Proc. Soc. exp. Biol. (N.Y.)*, **79**, 261.

DISCUSSION

Feldberg: Dr. Bureš, can you be certain that in your experiments peripheral actions of physostigmine and atropine do not interfere? Is everything you record due to their central action?

Bureš: I cannot answer this quite confidently, but there are several indications which support this claim. One is that we have found a good correlation between the time course of the effects on the EEG and the effects on behaviour. When we look at the time for the development of the hippocampal theta activity induced, for example, by physostigmine, we see the maximal behavioural changes only at the time when the theta activity is at a maximum. On the other hand, peripheral effects will have appeared earlier. Again, we see behavioural changes at doses as low as 0·1 mg./kg. of physostigmine and at these doses there are no appreciable peripheral effects. It would, of course, be possible to do control experiments using drugs which have peripheral actions but no central effects.

NEUROPHYSIOLOGICAL AND BIOCHEMICAL CORRELATES OF EFFECTS OF DRUGS ON BEHAVIOUR: THE ACETYLCHOLINE SYSTEM

ROGER W. RUSSELL

Department of Psychology, Indiana University, Bloomington, Indiana

RECENT news releases in the United States have suggested that within a decade or two it will no longer be necessary to herd cattle on the range: developments in microbiology will give rise to a technology of biological engineering which will grow our steaks and chops on more sedentary vegetable stalks. Some of my colleagues believe this view is over-optimistic. However this may be, the cause for optimism has arisen during the past decade from one of the most striking discoveries in the history of biology, the discovery that nucleic acids play the central rôle in the transmission of molecular information. Presumably it is from this knowledge that the principles of biological engineering will come.

In a sense clinical psychopharmacology is a form of biological engineering. It assumes that relationships exist between biochemical events and behaviour and that drugs may be used to alter these relationships. Despite the basic nature of this assumption, research in psychopharmacology has, so far, been concerned much more with tests of hypotheses which relate drugs directly to behaviour than with consideration of the biochemical properties of the organism through which effects of drugs are transduced into patterns of behaviour. The concept of the "empty organism" does not lead to the development of models for relating biochemical events and behaviour, models which could be used to predict drug-behaviour interactions and from which systematic programmes for synthesizing new agents could be projected. I sense an analogy between the rôles which such models could play and the rôles served by the kind of model-building in microbiology to which I referred earlier. The central structures of the models in psychopharmacology will be fabricated from interrelations between two primary classes of variables: biochemical events and behaviour. That such interrelations can be studied empirically has already been amply demonstrated. As in the case of microbiology, much of the research necessary to establish a systematic chemistry of behaviour can most profitably be done using infrahuman biological systems. I shall concern myself with a few selected issues which I believe to be important to the methodology of such research, and illustrations will be drawn primarily from studies of relations between the acetylcholine system and behaviour.

CONCOMITANT VARIATION

Establishment of the fact that certain dimensions of behaviour are indeed related to certain biochemical events within the organism is dependent upon demonstration that the two vary concomitantly. In the experimental search for such concomitant variations, biochemical events usually constitute the independent variables. Drugs serve as "tools" to vary biochemical events systematically. Strictly speaking, in order to use them as tools in this sense, the experimenter needs drugs whose mode of action is specific and well known. That there are relatively few such drugs, particularly drugs which act upon the central nervous system, places immediate limitations on present research aspirations. What can be done while the knowledge required to minimize or remove these limitations is being sought? Since interactions occur between biochemical events and behaviour, the latter may be useful in analysing the actions of drugs in the former. Dr. Steinberg (1962) has referred to a "process of successive approximation" where ". . . one can take for granted neither the validity of one's methods for measuring behaviour nor the validity of available accounts of the action of drugs, and in the course of the same series of experiments one may find confirmatory evidence for aspects of both of these, or one may come to conclude that views on either or both need modifying". As I review research on drug-behaviour interactions, much of it falls at some stage within this process of successive approximation. The more exciting prospects of relating biochemical events to behaviour often overshadow the useful contributions which this kind of study can make to the essential preliminary stage of studying a drug's mode of action.

TEMPORAL CHARACTERISTICS

It is becoming clear from recent research that the study of interrelations between biochemical events and behaviour by way of concomitant variations of the two requires careful consideration of their relative distributions in time. When a drug upsets the normal steady state of a biochemical system, behaviour patterns related to the system would be expected to reflect the change. If the change is reversible, recovery of the system should be accompanied by a return of behaviour to its pre-drug levels. This is the simplest statement of the principle of concomitant variation, the implications of which I wish to consider further. But first let me illustrate a kind of dilemma which may arise when the principle is applied in research.

We (Russell, Levine and Lockhart, 1963) have recently analysed the results of an experiment on behavioural modes of action of reserpine, and their relation to biochemical events presumed to be affected by this drug. Fifteen *Macaca mulatta* monkeys served as subjects in a randomized groups design. Drug dosage constituted the independent variable; the dependent variables measured were: body weight, food intake, water intake, general activity, performance of a previously learned stereometric object discrimination, and acquisition of a planometric object discrimination.

Our results clearly show that behaviour was differentially sensitive to the doses of reserpine used, some measures being affected and others not. Analysis of the patterning of effects suggests two aspects of behaviour as targets for the action of

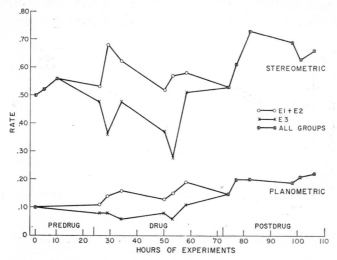

FIG. 1. The effects of reserpine on rates of responding in discrimination between planometric objects and between stereometric objects.
E_1 and E_2: groups receiving low doses; results not significantly different.
E_3: group receiving highest dose.

reserpine: motor output and the utilization of sensory information. Effects on the former were observable as decreases in amount and rate of responding; in the latter, as decreases in accuracy of responding. We interpret these results as being consistent with similar conclusions reached by other investigators using different measures of behaviour (Gross and Weiskrantz, 1961; John et al., 1958).

Let us now look more closely at the time characteristics of the events involved. Fig. 1 shows time characteristics for effects

ANL. BEH.—6

of the drug on two of the more sensitive variables: rates of responding in situations requiring discrimination among two-dimensional, planometric objects, and among three-dimensional, stereometric, objects. Animals receiving the highest dose, 3 mg./kg. orally, began to show a decrement in response rates for the stereometric discrimination at the first test session, two hours after administration of the drug. The decrement increased sharply and then reversed its trend during the following eight-hour

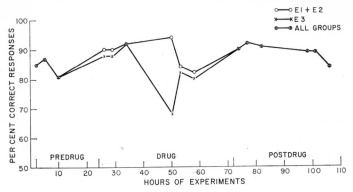

FIG. 2. Stereometric discrimination: learning set curves—trial 2 responses.

E_1, E_2 and E_3: as in Fig. 1.

period. A second dose of the drug, given 24 hours after the first, was also followed within two hours by a decrement in the rate of responding; this time the decrement was greater, suggesting the presence of carry-over effects from the previous drug administration. As with behaviour changes following the first dose, this second period was characterized by a decrement which reversed itself at or about the time of the five-hour test session. Fig. 2 summarizes the effects of the drug upon another behaviour pattern, learning sets, which is shown in the progressive improvement of an animal's ability to solve problems in an extended serial problem-solving situation; it is a process which Harlow (1949) has called: "learning how to learn"; significant effects appeared two hours after administration of the second dose. In the experiment all measures of behaviour which were affected significantly after administration of the drug had peak effect times within the range of 2 to 10 hours; recovery was complete within 10 hours, except for two measures where it was complete within 24 hours.

How do these time characteristics compare with the time characteristics for the absorption and metabolism or elimination of reserpine? Brodie and Shore (1957) have shown that reserpine reaches its peak concentration about 25 minutes after administration; this level then drops rapidly, approaching zero within one or two hours. Even the most sensitive of our behavioural measures were not affected significantly within this time. Since the changes in behaviour were not dependent upon the presence of the drug in the body, the most reasonable alternative place to look for concomitant variation would seem to be among biochemical systems modified by the action of the drug. Two systems, serotonin and noradrenaline, have received particular attention with respect to reserpine. Shore and Brodie (1957) have pointed out that: "The rate of release, the duration of the effect and the dose-response curves of both substances in rabbit brain are identical, indicating that the amines are bound by similar reserpine-sensitive mechanisms." Their data show that administration of reserpine in the range used in our experiment is followed within 15 minutes by a definite drop in the brain content of both substances (Brodie and Shore, 1957), 90 per cent or more disappearing within four hours. At this time the curve reaches an asymptote, which is maintained for 36 to 48 hours. It is clear that impairments in behaviour in our experiments developed to their maxima and recovered during a period corresponding to little or no change in brain serotonin and noradrenaline levels; there was no evidence for concomitant variation between these events.

The literature suggests further directions in which a search for biochemical correlates of our behaviour changes may be extended. In 1954, Erspamer presented evidence that serotonin inhibits the activity of brain cholinesterase in rats and guinea pigs. Recently Aprison (1962) has suggested a mechanism of action of serotonin in brain which postulates that "Through its action on acetylcholinesterase and the acetylcholine receptor protein, serotonin modulates the action of acetylcholine by direct competition with it for the active sites on these important proteins." Our changes in behaviour might be related to changes in the acetylcholine system; as I will report later, we have found significant effects upon certain behaviour patterns of experimentally induced changes in brain cholinesterase activity. Unfortunately, we do not yet have the time-response data necessary for this comparison.

One of my purposes in describing this experiment has been to illustrate the basic importance of data on temporal characteristics in establishing relations between biochemical events and behaviour. It also provides an opportunity to raise what I consider to be certain methodological weaknesses in much of the current research from which conclusions are drawn about the nature of such relations.

MEASUREMENT OF CHANGES IN BIOCHEMICAL EVENTS

The search for concomitant variations of this kind requires measurement of changes in *both* biochemical events and behaviour. This is not the approach most frequently used today. The popular experimental design is one in which a drug, selected for its action on a particular biochemical system, is varied in dose, preferably over a wide range of values, and effects on selected behaviour patterns are measured. Inferences are then made about relations between the intervening biochemical events and behaviour. The inferences may be inaccurate because the drug has multiple effects biochemically and there is no empirical check upon the fit between curves for the time characteristics of the particular biochemical and behavioural variables presumed to be related. Had we assumed, in the experiment I have just described, that, since reserpine affects the serotonin and noradrenaline systems, the selective changes in behaviour observed were directly related in some simple way to changes in these two systems, we should have been wrong. It usually takes considerable time to purge the literature of such inaccuracies!

There is another reason why measurement of biochemical events is essential in studies of the kind I have been considering. Recently Krech and his co-workers (1960; Rosenzweig *et al.*, 1962) have reported increases in cortical cholinesterase activity and in cortical weight of rats raised under conditions of environmental complexity and training when compared with litter mates kept in isolation. Steinberg and her co-workers (1961) have described the modification of drug effects by past experience. There is other evidence that persisting changes in steady state levels may occur as a result of behavioural interactions between an organism and its environment. It is important to consider this possibility in studying interrelations between behaviour and both drug actions and biochemical events. When groups of animals are exposed to different experiences before or during tests for relations between biochemical events and behaviour, this kind of control is essential. When behavioural tests and biochemical assays are run on parallel groups rather than on the same group of animals, all should be subjected to the same behavioural regimen. An investigator usually applies controls for genetic, nutritional, and experiential factors which might affect biochemical and behavioural variables; he assigns his subjects randomly to the various treatments required by the research design in order to control for individual differences in these variables. But his observations may still be affected by behaviourally induced changes in biochemical events occurring during the course of the experiment, effects which confound the interpretation of his results.

CORRELATIONAL APPROACHES

This last point, which has practical as well as theoretical implications for the research worker, emphasizes the reciprocal relationship which exists between biochemical events and behaviour. The term "biochemical correlates of behaviour" may refer:

(1) To circumstances in which behavioural variables are related to biochemical variables in such a way that changes in behaviour *follow* in time—are the consequents of—changes in biochemical events; or

(2) To those in which behavioural variables *precede*—are the antecedents of—changes in biochemical events.

Under experimental conditions an investigator may determine in advance which of the two variables is to constitute the antecedent, in this case, the independent variable. In non-experimental situations it may be very difficult to determine which is the consequent of the other. This serious methodological problem is illustrated in the most extensive programme so far undertaken to discover the relations between the acetylcholine system and behaviour (Rosenzweig *et al.*, 1960). Krech and his co-workers at the University of California have made wide use of an individual differences approach by which measures of behaviour are correlated, for example, with measures of brain cholinesterase activity without experimental manipulation of the latter. The programme has produced consistently positive correlations between individual differences in cortical cholinesterase activity and behaviour patterns involving "hypothesis formation" and between cortical cholinesterase activity and learning performance. Despite the consistencies the investigators recognized that "... these behavioural-biochemical correlations were not completely satisfactory supports ..." (Rosenzweig *et al.*, 1960) for their hypothesis that differences in behaviour are consequents of biochemical differences. This type of "cause and effect" hypothesis can only be verified experimentally.

INTERACTIONS WITH OTHER PROPERTIES OF THE ORGANISM

So far, I have been concerned with methodological problems which arise during the search for interrelations between biochemical events and behaviour. There are other properties of biological systems which must be taken into account in any final view of the effects of drugs on behaviour. Methodologically important issues arise from the fact that all these properties—anatomical, behavioural, biochemical, electrophysiological—are interrelated.

The differential distributions of biochemical systems in the body suggest that relations between biochemical events and behaviour are dependent upon the dynamics of actions *within particular structural sites*. A number of years ago reports began to indicate the complexity of the multiple interactions between biochemical events, anatomical sites and behaviour. For example, differential effects upon behaviour of the injection of drugs directly into the ventricular system of the brains of unanaesthetized animals through a permanently implanted cannula led Feldberg and Sherwood (1954a) to urge ". . . that consideration must be given to the pharmacological sensitivity and specificity of central synapses . . ." An example of their findings was that administration of acetylcholine and of anticholinesterases produced behaviour patterns analogous to catatonia in human patients. The view was advanced that the effects of anticholinesterases resulted ". . . from inhibition of cholinesterase and accumulation of acetylcholine in the region of the periventricular grey matter" (Feldberg and Sherwood, 1954b). In contrast, atropine, which has an anticholinergic action (Carlton, 1963), produced ". . . a condition of increased liveliness and restlessness . . ." (Feldberg and Sherwood, 1954a). More recently this kind of interrelation between the acetylcholine system, anatomical sites and behaviour has been demonstrated in another dramatic series of experiments (Grossman, 1962; Stein and Seifter, 1962). A micro-cannula system implanted unilaterally into the brains of albino rats was used to stimulate small areas with crystalline chemical substances. Results of the studies demonstrated ". . . that the placement of adrenergic substances into a circumscribed region of the diencephalon elicits specific changes in one type of motivated behaviour (food intake) while the placement of cholinergic agents into the same area of the hypothalamus evokes pronounced changes in a different type of motivated activity (water intake) . . ." (Grossman, 1962).

Another technique for restricting the anatomical site of drug action has involved injection of the drug into an afferent blood vessel irrigating a limited area of tissue. The technique is well illustrated in a series of experiments (Aprison *et al.*, 1954; Essig *et al.*, 1950; Freedman and Himwich, 1949) in which injection of an anticholinesterase drug into the right common carotid artery of several species of animals produced asymmetric biochemical lesions clearly discernible when cholinesterase activity levels of the frontal cortex and caudate nucleus on both sides of the brain were compared. The lesions were reversible and were observed to induce temporary circling movements analogous to behaviour previously obtained by extirpation or by electrical stimulation of the specific cerebral areas involved.

These examples are sufficient to reinforce the point that our knowledge concerning the effects of drugs on a biological system must eventually involve information about the multiple interrelations between all major properties of the system. To plan research with this in mind involves many administrative and methodological problems. In the latter category fall questions about which particular biological system to study; we know much about the behaviour of pigeons and rats, but more highly differentiated brains are desirable when sites of drug action constitute an experimental variable; new microchemical techniques are needed to study simultaneously certain characteristics of more than one biochemical system; the full list would be a long one.

CHRONIC DRUG ADMINISTRATION

My final illustration of the search for biochemical correlates of behaviour involves the chronic administration of drugs, a state of affairs that characterizes the use of drugs in clinical psychopharmacology.

During the past few years we have been particularly interested in the effects upon behaviour of varying the level of "true" brain cholinesterase activity. One of the organophosphorus anticholinesterases, Systox (O,O-diethyl S-ethylmercaptoethanolthiophosphate), has been used as the tool for changing this independent variable systematically. Preliminary studies with the chronic administration of Systox, involving a wide variety of behaviour patterns (Russell, 1954 and 1958) and using white rats as subjects suggested that, as cholinesterase activity was reduced, differential effects upon behaviour appeared before the pathological signs characteristic of extreme cholinesterase inactivation were evident: some aspects of behaviour were affected significantly and others were not. Further research (Russell *et al.*, 1961) provided evidence that the speed of acquisition of a conditioned avoidance response was not altered by reductions in brain cholinesterase activity within a range of 0 to 76·5 per cent, whereas extinction of the response was significantly slower. Results not yet published (Banks and Russell, 1963) show that errors during serial problemsolving increase significantly with reduction in brain cholinesterase activity. In these studies effects of variations in the enzyme activity level appeared differentially in situations requiring extinction of old responses in order to establish new behaviour patterns.

This relation between enzyme activity and behaviour was not a simple linear one: there appeared to be a "critical level" at about 60 per cent reduction, below which behaviour was significantly affected. We suggested that " . . . this critical level may represent a point at which the large margin of safety, characteristic of ChE in the nervous system, is no longer adequate to service the nerve impulse transmission required for the behaviour involved". More recently Aprison (1962) has reported on the relation between cholinesterase activity and acetylcholine content in the cortex and caudate nucleus of rabbit brain, showing that no change appears in free acetylcholine content until the cholinesterase inhibition falls below a critical value of about 60 per cent. Below this level acetylcholine content increases to over 200 per cent of normal as cholinesterase activity approaches zero, " . . . indicating the loss of physiological control of the enzyme for its substrate" (Aprison, 1962).

Data of this kind suggest that a dimension of behaviour may be related to biochemical events of the acetylcholine system. This would be more credible if other possible effects of the drug used to vary cholinesterase activity could be eliminated. Organophosphorus anticholinesterases affect peripheral, as well as central, nervous tissue. Clinical symptoms of organophosphorus poisoning are due to cholinergic hyperactivity from both sources. The question arises as to whether our results could be accounted for in terms of reduced cholinesterase activity in peripheral sensory or motor pathways, thus affecting information input or motor output. At least a partial answer to this question could be obtained by using a wide variety of behaviour measures in testing for drug effects, a generally useful plan in studying drug-behaviour interactions. In our preliminary studies of the Systox series we sampled widely among different behaviour patterns, finding no significant effects of the drug on consummatory responses, locomotion, simple learning, operant conditioning, and visual discrimination. We observed no gross signs of peripheral sensory or motor involvement, confirming similar reports by Barnes and Denz (1954) that rats of the same strain as ours " . . . behaved apparently normally even though their brain cholinesterase activity had been 85 per cent inhibited". This evidence does not entirely eliminate the possibility that peripheral effects were involved in our results, although it certainly provides it no support.

All animals were sacrificed on completion of their behaviour tests and levels of brain cholinesterase activity were determined. In a series of check experiments we found that, under our regimen of daily administration of Systox, consistent levels of reduction of brain cholinesterase activity were maintained for as long as 55 weeks, which was longer than the period involved in our studies. Other checks showed no significant differences in brain cholinesterase activity under conditions of *ad libitum* as compared with one-hour daily feeding nor when caloric control animals were paired with animals in the highest drug group. The relation between behaviour and cholinesterase activity occurred under conditions in which reductions in the latter were being maintained at consistent levels, rather than varying, as in the case of acute drug administration.

MODELS OF DRUG–BEHAVIOUR INTERACTIONS

This last example also sets the stage for a point on which I have strong feelings. In my opinion, perhaps the greatest present need in neuropsychopharmacology is for some insightful model-building. The disciplines involved with each of the properties of biological systems have, of course, been concerned with models which help to clarify their own areas of special interest. Spectacular progress in biochemistry and in physiology has made it possible to conceive of dynamic functions within the body in terms of intracellular processes and, now, molecular configurations; psychology has become much more sophisticated in measuring behaviour and in its use of both functional and mathematical models. But what seem to need more attention now are models which integrate the knowledge we have about the several properties of a biological system which are affected whenever it comes under drug control. Some moves have already been made in this direction (e.g., Rosenzweig *et al.*, 1960; Carlton, 1963) and the models proposed are being put to test. But there are many exciting possibilities which do not appear to have received attention yet. For example, the effects of drugs on distributions of individual differences around "critical levels" or "thresholds" suggest that populations of stimulus and response elements may be involved in the control drugs exert over behaviour; this is the kind of situation to which statistical models have been usefully applied in other contexts. In my opinion, model-building can be of great value at this time by helping to integrate the literature on drug-behaviour interactions, which is being amassed at such a frightening rate, by indicating new lines for research, and by suggesting where developments in clinical psychopharmacology through the synthesis of new chemical compounds are likely to occur.

Acknowledgment

The author wishes to acknowledge the support provided by Public Health Service Research Grant MH 06997–01 SRC 1 R10 from the National Institute of Mental Health.

REFERENCES

APRISON, M. H. (1962). *Recent Adv. biol. Psychiat.*, **4**, 133.

APRISON, M. H., NATHAN, P., and HIMWICH, H. E. (1954). *Science*, **119**, 158.

BANKS, A., and RUSSELL, R. W. (1963). To be published.

BARNES, J. M., and DENZ, F. A. (1954). *Brit. J. indust. Med.*, **11**, 11.

BRODIE, B. B., and SHORE, P. A. (1957). *In* Hormones, Brain Function and Behavior, p. 167, ed. Hoagland, H. New York: Academic Press.

CARLTON, P. L. (1963). *Psychol. Rev.*, **70**, 19.

ERSPAMER, V. (1954). *Pharmacol. Rev.*, **6**, 425.

ESSIG, C. F., HAMPSON, J. L., McCAULEY, A., and HIMWICH, H. E. (1950). *J. Neurophysiol.*, **13**, 269.

FELDBERG, W., and SHERWOOD, S. L. (1954a). *J. Physiol. (Lond.)*, **123**, 148.

FELDBERG, W., and SHERWOOD, S. L. (1954b). *J. Physiol. (Lond.)*, **125**, 488.

FREEDMAN, A. M., and HIMWICH, H. E. (1949). *Amer. J. Physiol.*, **156**, 125.

GROSS, C. G., and WEISKRANTZ, L. (1961). *Quart. J. exp. Psychol.*, **13**, 34.

GROSSMAN, S. P. (1962). *Amer. J. Physiol.*, **202**, 872.

HARLOW, H. F. (1949). *Psychol. Rev.*, **56**, 51.

JOHN, E. R., WENGEL, B. M., and TSCHIRGI, R. D. (1958). *Science*, **127**, 25.

KRECH, D., ROSENZWEIG, M. R., and BENNETT, E. L. (1960). *J. comp. physiol. Psychol.*, **53**, 509.

ROSENZWEIG, M. R., KRECH, D., and BENNETT, E. L. (1960). *Psychol. Bull.*, **57**, 476.

ROSENZWEIG, M. R., KRECH, D., BENNETT, E. L., and DIAMOND, M. C. (1962). *J. comp. physiol. Psychol.*, **55**, 429.

RUSSELL, R. W. (1954). *Bull. Brit. Psychol. Soc.*, No. 23, 6.

RUSSELL, R. W. (1958). *Acta. Psychol.*, **14**, 281.

RUSSELL, R. W., LEVINE, M. E., and LOCKHART, J. M. (1963). To be published.

RUSSELL, R. W., WATSON, R. H. J., and FRANKENHAEUSER, M. (1961). *Scand. J. Psychol.*, **2**, 21.

SHORE, P. A., and BRODIE, B. B. (1957). *In* Psychotropic Drugs, p. 426, ed. Garattini, S. and Ghetti, V. Amsterdam: Elsevier.

STEIN, L., and SEIFTER, J. (1962). *Amer. J. Physiol.*, **202**, 751.

STEINBERG, H., RUSHTON, R., and TINSON, C. (1961). *Nature (Lond.)*, **192**, 533.

STEINBERG, H. (1962). *Proc. Sixteenth Int. Congr. Psychol.*, p. 771. Amsterdam: North-Holland Publ. Co.

DISCUSSION

Abrahams: Professor Russell, you have used the term "acetylcholine system", by which you appear to mean the system by which acetylcholine is synthesized and then hydrolysed during the process of cholinergic transmission; but what you have been measuring are changes in the cholinesterase content of whole brain. Such changes may not actually tell you very much about the "acetylcholine system" nor about cholinergic transmission, for in the brain a substantial proportion of cholinesterases do not appear to be associated with neuronal structures. In our histochemical work on cat brain (Abrahams, V. C. [1963]. *J. Physiol. [Lond.]*, **165**, 55P; Abrahams, V. C., and Edery, H. [1963]. *In* Progress in Brain Research, Vol. 6. Amsterdam: Elsevier) we find, for example, that substantial quantities of true cholinesterase are in association with glial cells and glial fibre systems and are also present in other non-neuronal structures such as the subependymal cell plate. Pseudocholinesterase also has a substantial non-neuronal distribution, being present, for example, on the medial aspect of ependymal cells lining the third ventricle.

In work in which changes in brain cholinesterase are being examined it is not enough to know that the total level of enzyme activity has changed; one should also know at what site the changes have occurred.

Russell: This is an important point; had there been an opportunity to go into some of these issues in greater detail, I should have raised several additional questions. In the final analysis it will be essential to know which esterase is "critical" in a study such as the one I described and also where in body tissue the esterase is distributed. The data I presented were for acetylcholinesterase. A considerable number of investigations have provided evidence that this enzyme exists in nerve and muscle fibres and in red blood cells. It has properties different from those of other esterases, one of which is a relatively high affinity for acetylcholine. The relations I described were between variations in the activity level of this enzyme and certain changes in behaviour. There were some features of these relations, such as the "critical" level at about 60 per cent reduction in cholinesterase activity when significant changes in behaviour appeared and the free acetylcholine content began to rise rapidly, which suggest that there may be some "cause and effect" interaction between these two quite different classes of variables. But other possible interpretations must be considered as well.

The point you have raised concerns one of these: which cholinesterase was inhibited under the conditions of the studies I reported? Presumably you are referring to the possible action of the organophosphorus compound we used upon butyrocholinesterase, which, in addition to acetylcholinesterase, is found in significant amounts in the central nervous system (Holmstedt, B. [1959]. *Pharmacol. Rev.*, **11**, 567). We did in fact obtain data on changes in the activity level of this other enzyme and found it to vary in a similar manner to the acetylcholinesterase activity level under the experimental conditions. In our opinion, differences in distribution of the two enzymes and in their substrate specificities tend to favour the view that acetylcholinesterase is the one involved in the behaviour changes we observed. Nachmansohn has presented the full argument for this position (Nachmansohn, D.

[1959]. Chemical and Molecular Basis of Nerve Activity. New York: Academic Press).

Generally speaking, we are looking for concomitant variation in several properties of the organism that eventually have to be integrated in our thinking. I like to conceptualize the living organism as a system which is affected by the introduction of a drug and which may be described in terms of the system's behavioural, biochemical, electrophysiological and structural properties. The aim is eventually to describe a drug's effects in terms of interrelations among all these properties.

Some particularly useful steps have been taken in this direction during the past few years. I have always been very impressed by Professor Feldberg's work on intraventricular injection as one approach to delimiting the anatomical properties affected by particular drugs (Feldberg, W., and Sherwood, S. L. [1954]. *J. Physiol.* [*Lond.*], **123**, 148; **125**, 488). Recently, in Professor Miller's laboratory, work has indicated how really impossible it is, in the final analysis, to talk about interrelations between any two properties of a biological system without considering the others. I am thinking of experiments by Grossman (Grossman, S. P. [1962]. *Amer. J. Physiol.*, **202**, 872), who inserted microcannulae into the lateral hypothalamus and was able to produce, in the *same* animal and in the *same* location, eating with adrenergic stimulation and drinking with cholinergic stimulation!

Bein: You mentioned the rapid disappearance of reserpine from the brain, but as early investigators used a rather insensitive method for the determination of reserpine in the brain these figures might be misleading. A. J. Plummer, H. Sheppard and A. R. Schulert ([1957]. *In* Psychotropic Drugs, p. 350, ed. Garattini, S. and Ghetti, V. Amsterdam: Elsevier), using labelled reserpine, have since shown that it is still present 24 hours after injection.

Russell: Yes, I am acquainted with those studies using tritium-labelled reserpine in which peak-effect time was reached in the brain about 25 minutes after subcutaneous injection, followed by a rapid drop in the level of the drug, which approached an asymptote between one and two hours and was maintained for a period of at least 48 hours. The question has been raised as to whether the reserpine that does remain over this longer period of time is likely to be active. In any event, it seems to me that the results of these determinations tend to make my point a little stronger: the changes in behaviour we observed occurred and recovery was complete during a period in which the level of reserpine in the brain does *not* change. Similarly, work by Shore and Brodie (Shore, P. A., and Brodie, B. B. [1957]. *In* Psychotropic Drugs, p. 423, ed. Garattini, S. and Ghetti, V. Amsterdam: Elsevier) suggests that the changes we observed in behaviour developed to their maxima and recovered during a period corresponding to little or no change in brain serotonin and noradrenaline, both of which reach a low asymptote level within four hours after the administration of reserpine.

EFFECTS OF SOME POISONOUS SUBSTANCES ON THE CENTRAL NERVOUS SYSTEM

J. M. BARNES

M.R.C. Toxicology Research Unit, Carshalton

I propose to consider briefly the effects of a few of the many poisons capable of affecting the central nervous system in the context of possible correlations of biochemical effects and changes in behaviour. Any attempt to correlate two such very general fields of biological activity is unlikely to be easy; it therefore may be permissible to include chemicals other than those normally used as drugs if the information appears likely to be relevant.

Some poisonous materials may enter the general environment; others are confined to factories and similar places of work. While it may not be difficult to decide what level of exposure can be dangerous or can produce obvious signs of poisoning, it is much more difficult to assemble the evidence needed to pronounce a particular level of exposure quite safe.

The problem resolves itself into a search for the most sensitive systems in the whole animal within which minor deviations from normality may be detected. This subject comes into the framework of this symposium only because in some other countries, particularly the USSR, repeated claims have been made that the most sensitive index for detecting any harmful influence of a poisonous material is the reaction of the nervous system; especially the so-called higher nervous activity. At the same time there has, in recent years, been a more intensive attempt to recognize the nature of any biochemical lesion that may stem from the introduction of a poison into a biological system, including the whole animal.

It is only possible to make a rather superficial survey of the claims and achievements of behaviour studies as indices of toxic effects. Lyublina (1961) has outlined the type of investigations to be made in studying a toxic material likely to contaminate a factory atmosphere. The atmospheric concentration which in single or in repeated doses will disturb the establishment or course of a conditioned reflex must be determined, and the investigation should be done during or immediately after the period of exposure. Despite the claims made at the start of her short paper, that effects on nervous activity are the most sensitive reactions to poisons, it is also stated that conditioned reflexes are unaffected when up to 40 per cent of brain cholinesterase has been inactivated, while with other poisons an animal may display gross ataxia from a neurological lesion produced by the poison although its conditioned reflexes remain unimpaired. Perhaps it is not surprising that other reactions involving the nervous system, such as an unconditioned flexor reflex or swimming and studies of the effect of posture on the circulation and respiration of experimental animals, are included in the investigations on nervous activity. Man appears to be more sensitive than the conditioned rat to some poisons; formaldehyde, for example, will affect conditioned reflexes in rats only in concentrations twice as great as those needed to slow respiration in man.

Ryazanov (1962) has reported some studies on man to determine acceptable levels of atmospheric contaminants. Thus an odour at levels on the threshold of perception may effect the chronaxie of the response of the eye to electric stimulation. Dark adaptation can be affected for up to $1\frac{1}{4}$ hours after a twenty-minute exposure to a sulphuric acid aerosol at a concentration of 4 mg./m.[3] If cortical EEG current changes are studied, a conditioned reflex change in their pattern may be established by the use of a light together with exposure to a substance with an odour. Once established, the EEG changes may then be elicited without the light by the chemical at levels below the level of conscious perception. Ryazanov considers that the maximum concentration of a substance permitted in the air should be one which is too low to excite such a reflex. With this type of test it is not surprising that the maximum concentrations of industrial poisons allowed in Russia are often far below those permitted in Western Europe and North America. At the same time there seems little point in even beginning to search for a biochemical effect evoked by substances present in the small quantities needed to elicit this type of response, and this perhaps accounts for the apparent lack of interest in biochemical research as a basis for understanding industrial toxicology.

However, the Russians are not the only investigators who have been interested in studies on behaviour as possible indices of toxic reactions. Our own interest was aroused some years ago when we had some groups of rats receiving an organophosphorus insecticide in their diet at levels which produced over 90 per cent inhibition of the cholinesterase in their heart and brain as well as in the circulating blood. We were able to distinguish the treated group from the control group not by any obvious clinical signs of poisoning but simply by some ill-defined qualitative difference in their demeanour in the cages. This led us to ask Professor R. W. Russell whether differences in behaviour could be put on some quantitative basis. The work that developed from this has been published (Russell, Watson and Frankenhaeuser, 1961). The acetylcholine-cholinesterase system has been well discussed and will not be considered further here.

Trichloroethylene has been used as an anaesthetic but much larger quantities are used in industry and there has been much debate as to what concentration should be permitted in working atmospheres. Although it is a relatively safe solvent compared, for example, with carbon tetrachloride, in that it does not produce liver necrosis, there have been claims that exposure to concentrations of trichloroethylene which do not lead to gross physical injury may be the cause of a multitude of subjective complaints (Grandjean *et al.*, 1955). The metabolism of tri-chloroethylene in man has been studied in some detail and an estimate of the daily intake of factory workers can be gained by determining the amount of trichloroacetic acid in their urine. Ahlmark and Forssmann (1951) stated that there was an increasing number of subjective complaints in workers excreting urine containing more than 40 mg. trichloroacetic acid per litre. It has been reported that "rats exposed to 75 p.p.m. trichloroethylene showed a reduction in the time of latency of food-motivated reaction, an increased motor excitation between signals and dis-crimination disorders" (quoted by Grandjean, 1960). The currently accepted atmospheric level in the United States for man is 100 p.p.m. Grandjean (1960), who trained a small number of rats to climb a rope to get food at a signal, found that exposure to 200 p.p.m. of trichloroethylene for three hours led to an increased number of spontaneous climbs without the signal. This change in behaviour could be due to one of several things—excitability, loss of memory for signals, reduction in fear or increased hunger. If subjective complaints in man can be considered to be compar-able to changes in behaviour in rats, it appears that both species will respond to similar concentrations of trichloroethylene. How-ever, when an attempt is made to find a biochemical correlate other than the level of metabolite excreted, the search is dis-appointing. Trichloroethylene itself is believed not to be very active biologically but is oxidized first to chloral hydrate and then to the alcohol trichlorethanol, which is the active narcotic.

The biochemical reactions in brain under the influence of anaesthetics have been studied for many years. Quastel and Wheatley (1932) first studied the effects of barbiturates on the respiration of isolated brain preparations. Twenty-five years later Quastel (1958), discussing the enzymic mechanisms of the brain and the effects of some neurotropic agents, concluded that drugs, including a wide variety of narcotics, "affect the energetics of the nerve cell by interference with oxidative phosphorylation mechanisms or by effects on stimulated respiratory processes". Three years later the same author states that alcohol behaves similarly to other narcotics like barbiturates and goes on to suggest that all narcotics must owe their common action to some common physicochemical property, such as an affinity for lipids (Quastel and Quastel, 1961). Thus after over thirty years of quite intensive study of the action of narcotics on biochemical processes in the brain we do not seem to be much closer to understanding nerve cell function and its derangements in precise biochemical terms. If it is not yet possible to be more exact in determining the biochemical differences between a brain showing full behavioural activity and one incapable of any behavioural activity at all (narcosis), there seems to be a need for caution in any attempt to establish such correlates between lesser differences.

Another alcohol—2-methoxyethanol (Methyl Cellosolve)— which is widely used as a solvent in industry, has led to a number of cases of poisoning characterized by transient changes in behaviour and personality. Its effect was studied on rats conditioned to climb a pole by an electric shock and a sound stimulus. Repeated exposure for 14 days to vapour concentrations of 125, 250 and 500 p.p.m. interfered with the development of the conditioned reflex but only at 500 p.p.m. was the established reflex itself disturbed. Ethanol, on the other hand, affected the conditioned reflex only at 32,000 p.p.m., at which level co-ordination was beginning to be impaired. Even at this level the rats rapidly developed a tolerance to ethanol although they did not do so to the much lower concentration of Methyl Cellosolve (Goldberg, Haun and Smyth, 1962).

Whatever the biochemical mechanism which these alcohols may disturb in the neurones themselves, differences in the responses of the rats may also be due to biochemical mechanisms outside the central nervous system which modify the rates and routes of metabolism of the toxic substance and so influence the amounts reaching the brain.

For some years we have been interested in the toxicity and biochemical action of alkyl tin and alkyl lead compounds. Triethyl tin given to rats as a single dose at about the LD_{50} has a transient mild narcotic action, after which the animal at first recovers, but over the next 2–3 days it becomes quieter and progressively weaker and dies. The pathological lesion is oedema of the white matter of the central nervous system. The lesion in man is similar (Barnes and Stoner, 1959).

Tetraethyl lead is poisonous to animals because it is converted to the biochemically active triethyl lead ion. A single lethal dose to rats produces a condition of general excitability within 24 hours with the development of generalized tremors increasing in intensity and terminating in convulsions and death 2–3 days later (Cremer, 1959). Men poisoned with tetraethyl lead show a similar picture of agitation and tremors and sometimes wild excitement (Cassells and Dodds, 1946). No pathological lesions are seen and there is no oedema. In non-fatal poisoning by triethyl tin and triethyl lead in man and animals, recovery can be complete.

Both triethyl tin and triethyl lead are extremely active inhibitors of oxidative phosphorylation in isolated liver or brain mitochondria (Aldridge, Cremer and Threlfall, 1962). No distinction can be made between their actions in these systems. Similarly, brain slices from normal animals show a pronounced depression of glucose oxidation when the alkyl metals are added *in vitro* and the same metabolic disturbance is found in brain slices prepared from animals poisoned by the two compounds (Cremer, 1957; 1959).

However, when the transport of sodium–24 from blood to brain and cerebrospinal fluid was studied *in vivo* it was found that although triethyl tin immediately reduced this, triethyl lead had no such effect (B. J. Parsons, to be published). This is consistent with the fact that alkyl tin produces oedema but poisoning with alkyl lead does not. However, the similar effects of these two compounds on the oxidation of glucose indicated that depression of glucose oxidation alone could not be the biochemical lesion causing the different effects in the animal. A more extensive search for differences in the action of the two compounds on brain metabolism was therefore undertaken. The amounts of amino acids, and their specific activity after injections of $[^{14}C]$ glucose into rats, were studied in brain slices to which the alkyl lead and tin salts were added and in brain slices from animals poisoned with the alkyl metals and injected with $[^{14}C]$ glucose. Some differences were observed although on the whole they were small in relation to the interference in glucose oxidation which the alkyl metals produced. There was some diminution in both γ-aminobutyric acid and glutamic acid after triethyl tin and the specific activity of glutamine was lower. After triethyl lead there was no change in the specific activity of glutamine although there was some increase in the amounts present (J. E. Cremer, to be published). While the changes seen after triethyl tin were not dissimilar to those produced by barbiturates, the increased glutamine levels found after triethyl lead are also found in the brain after hyperactivity produced by other drugs. Despite a great deal of detailed analysis it has not proved possible to distinguish the biochemical lesions produced by these two poisons whose effects on behaviour are so different. Indeed, some of the changes seen may be the result rather than the cause of the differences in bodily activity. One has perhaps to consider the physical chemistry and note that while the relative distribution of triethyl tin between chloroform and buffer is 3·17 in favour of chloroform, for triethyl lead it is only 0·215 (Aldridge, Cremer and Threlfall, 1962).

A study of the effect of a poison on behaviour may begin without any preconceived idea of what sort of correlation will be suggested by the study. It was known that DDT produced persistent tremors which sometimes led to minor convulsive movements and death from respiratory failure in poisoned mammals. Very little was known about its physiological action though it had been stated to have a veratrine-like action in peripheral nerve elements (Eyzaguirre and Lilienthal, 1949). Larger doses were said to disturb central function in the cord and brain stem (Bromiley and Bard, 1949). Biochemically, virtually nothing was known except that in relatively high concentration DDT inhibits oxidative phosphorylation in liver mitochondria *in vitro* (Johnston, 1951; Parker, 1960), but no one has ever suggested that this is how DDT exerts its toxic action on mammals. When the behaviour of rats receiving diets containing different levels of DDT was investigated, Khairy (1959) noted changes in their gait which became more marked as the dose of DDT increased, but at the lowest level studied she found that the gait was hypernormal. These observations are consistent with the idea that DDT exerts its effects at the periphery and the apparent hypernormal response in the rat is similar to one seen in the fly. Under the influence of a sublethal dose of DDT, a fly will respond to a concentration of sucrose lower than that needed to attract a normal fly (Weiant, 1955). It seems more probable that more will be learnt about the mode of action of DDT by using conventional physiological techniques than by the use of biochemical ones, since no real clue as to the effect of the latter disturbances *in vivo* has been obtained so far.

Relatively little is being done, it seems, to try to correlate neurochemical changes with conventional neurophysiological reactions except in the acetylcholine–cholinesterase field and the mechanism of the ionic pump. It is easy to be critical of apparent lack of progress in correlating biochemistry with physiology, but attempts over a number of years to find the proper correlation between the effects of a poison on biological systems studied *in vitro* and the action of the poison on the whole animal have implanted a considerable degree of humility into our thinking. While nothing is likely to be lost if the possible relations of physiological responses to biochemical processes in cells and tissues are kept in mind, for a planned attack it may be desirable to have a very limited objective. Behaviour is such a broad field and its physiological roots are so ill-defined that it is likely that correlates will be difficult to discover or even to recognize. It might be better to consider a study of a specific nervous lesion and here the use of poisons has advantages which have been exploited throughout the history of experimental physiology and bio-chemistry.

We have found that rats given 6–8 doses of methyl mercury salts by mouth on successive days will develop a well marked ataxia after a further week or ten days. This may progress and the animals may die, or the animals may live and the ataxia persist. Rats which die with the well-developed syndrome show a very localized cell injury at death affecting only the granular layer of the cerebellar cortex. These observations confirm an older one on rats and monkeys (Hunter, Bomford and Russell, 1940). Rather more diffuse lesions occur in man poisoned by these salts.

The possible chemical reactions of a methyl mercury salt are somewhat limited but at the same time likely to be very general, such as reaction with sulphydryl groups. It seems probable that all the cells of the central nervous system will be equally exposed to the methyl mercury salt during its administration, yet in only a few does a reaction sufficiently serious to injure the cell take place. There is a considerable delay between the administration of the poison and the onset of an ataxia obvious to a toxicologist. It seems very probable that any chemical reaction between the mercury salt and cell constituents takes place long before the impairment in function becomes obvious. Where the develop-ment of a circumscribed lesion runs a well-defined course between the initial insult and the obvious manifestations of deranged function, it would seem to offer something which might be worth concerted study by physiological, biochemical, pathological and behavioural techniques. As a start, Tewari and Bourne (1962) have recently reported marked differences in the distribution of enzymes in the three cellular layers and in the white matter of the cerebellum of the rat.

Another less well-defined pathological lesion, but one which is said to be located in the hippocampus of the mouse, is produced by 3-acetyl pyridine (Coggeshall and Maclean, 1958). The poisoned animal shows progressive weakness and retention of urine. Mice and rats develop a similar syndrome but it is only in the mouse that brain cell changes have been described. 3-acetyl pyridine is believed to exert its effects by replacing nicotinamide and so leading to the formation of an analogue of nicotinamide-adenine dinucleotide. There is evidence of the synthesis of the false co-factor in the brain but not in the liver (Kaplan *et al.*, 1954; Kaplan and Ciotti, 1956). A study of the effects of 3-acetyl pyridine brings one immediately into a field of biochemistry likely to be familiar to many, but at the present time the location and nature of the pathological lesion is much less well defined than in the case of the methyl mercury compounds. On the other hand, the biochemical lesion produced by mercury com-pounds even in the kidney, where mercury has been intensively studied, remains remarkably ill-understood.

Many drugs that affect behaviour can have the most rapid and dramatic effects which are nevertheless completely and often equally rapidly reversible. A number of centrally acting poisons, on the other hand, act much more slowly but in many cases irreversibly. Nevertheless, the neurones ultimately affected seem to be able to function reasonably well until such time as the cell can be seen to be dead in the pathologists' preparations. Although studies of the latter type of lesion may well throw some light on the biochemical processes essential to a well functioning neurone, it seems more than probable that the processes disturbed by this kind of injury will be rather different from those transiently upset by the usual kind of drugs affecting behaviour. However, the ease with which these may be reversed in the whole animal makes the likelihood of observing them in isolated preparations seem somewhat remote. It is not inconceivable that drugs with completely reversible, even if dramatic, effects on the function of the central nervous system act mainly on the glial tissue with secondary effects on the passage of ions and nutrients to the otherwise uninjured neurone, while the irreversible poisons are those that attack the neurone itself. Neurophysiology is almost certainly a study of the responses of the neurones but it is not yet possible to be certain how far neurobiochemistry is a study of the neurones and what proportion is really the reaction in the supporting elements. In the central cortex the glial cells are said to outnumber the neurones by ten to one and the elegant experiments of Hydén on Deiters' nucleus of the rabbit indicate the existence of big differences in the metabolic activity of the neurone and glial cell (Hydén and Pigon, 1960).

While studies of deviations in behaviour seem to offer promising methods of recognizing the earliest effects of the lowest doses of drugs and poisons, it seems premature to feel very optimistic about linking any changes in function thus revealed with biochemical lesions that may result from the presence of the drug or poison in the nervous system.

REFERENCES

AHLMARK, A., and FORSSMANN, S. (1951). *Arch. industr. Hyg.*, **3**, 386.

ALDRIDGE, W. N., CREMER, JILL E., and THRELFALL, C. J. (1962). *Biochem. Pharmacol.*, **11**, 835.

BARNES, J. M., and STONER, H. B. (1959). *Pharmacol. Rev.*, **11**, 211.

BROMILEY, R. B., and BARD, P. (1949). *Bull. Johns Hopk. Hosp.*, **84**, 414.

CASSELLS, D. A. K., and DODDS, E. C. (1946). *Brit. med. J.*, **2**, 681.

COGGESHALL, R. E., and MACLEAN, P. D. (1958). *Proc. Soc. exp. Biol. (N.Y.)*, **98**, 687.

CREMER, JILL E. (1957). *Biochem. J.*, **67**, 87.

CREMER, JILL E. (1959). *Brit. J. industr. Med.*, **16**, 191.

EYZAGUIRRE, C., and LILIENTHAL, J. L., Jr. (1949). *Proc. Soc. exp. Biol. (N.Y.)*, **70**, 272.

GOLDBERG, M. E., HAUN, C., and SMYTH, H. F., Jr. (1962). *Toxicol. appl. Pharmacol.*, **4**, 148.

GRANDJEAN, E., MÜNCHINGER, R., TURRIAN, V., HAAS, P. A., KNOEPFEL, H. K., and ROSENMUND, H. (1955). *Brit. J. industr. Med.*, **12**, 131.

GRANDJEAN, E. (1960). *Arch. environm. Hlth*, **1**, 106.

HUNTER, D., BOMFORD, R. R., and RUSSELL, DOROTHY S. (1940). *Quart. J. Med.*, **9** 193.

HYDÉN, H., and PIGON, A. (1960). *J. Neurochem.*, **6**, 57.

JOHNSTON, C. T. (1951). *Arch. Biochem.*, **31**, 375.

KAPLAN, N. O., GOLDIN, A., HUMPHREYS, S. R., CIOTTI, MARGARET M., and GENDITTI, J. M. (1954). *Science*, **120**, 437.

KAPLAN, N. O., and CIOTTI, MARGARET M. (1956). *J. biol. Chem.*, **221**, 823.

KHAIRY, M. (1959). *Quart. J. exp. Psychol.*, **11**, 84.

LYUBLINA, E. I. (1961). *In* Proc. Int. Symp. on Maximum Allowable Concentrations of Toxic Substances in Industry, Prague, p. 109, ed. Truhaut, R. London: Butterworth.

PARKER, V. H. (1960). *Biochem. J.*, **77**, 74.

QUASTEL, J. H., and WHEATLEY, A. H. M. (1932). *Proc. roy. Soc. B*, **112**, 60.

QUASTEL, J. H. (1958). *Proc. IV Int. Congr. Biochem.*, **3**, 90. London: Pergamon.

QUASTEL, J. H., and QUASTEL, D. M. J. (1961). The Chemistry of Brain Metabolism in Health and Disease. Springfield: Thomas.

RUSSELL, R. W., WATSON, R. H. J., and FRANKENHAEUSER, M. (1961). *Scand. J. Psychol.*, **2**, 21.

RYAZANOV, V. A. (1962). *Arch. environm. Hlth*, **5**, 480.

TEWARI, H. B., and BOURNE, G. H. (1962). Int. Symp. on Enzymic Activity in the Central Nervous System, Göteborg. Abstract.

WEIANT, E. A. (1955). *Ann. ent. Soc. Amer.*, **48**, 489.

DIFFERENTIAL EFFECT OF SYMPATHOMIMETIC AMINES ON THE CENTRAL NERVOUS SYSTEM

W. G. Dewhurst and E. Marley

Institute of Psychiatry, Maudsley Hospital, London

The effects of sympathomimetic amines on the central nervous system depend largely on the following factors:

(a) MOLECULAR STRUCTURE

A methyl (CH_3) group on the α-carbon atom of the side-chain favours central excitatory activity, whereas a hydroxyl (OH) group on the β-carbon atom of the side-chain or –OH groups in the 3,4 positions on the phenyl ring diminish central excitatory activity (Goodman and Gilman, 1955).

(b) ROUTE OF ADMINISTRATION

The alerting effect of sympathomimetic amines varied only in magnitude when the drugs were given intravenously, intraperitoneally or orally to adult intact animals and to adult cat and monkey *encéphale isolé* preparations (Bonvallet, Dell and Hugelin, 1954; Bradley and Elkes, 1957; Key, 1958; Rothballer, 1956). However, on intracisternal injection in the dog, the amines differed in effect, for the amphetamine-like amines were excitant whereas the catechol amines evoked drowsiness (Leimdorfer, 1950). Adrenaline or noradrenaline given intraventricularly to adult cats (Feldberg and Sherwood, 1954) produced stupor although this was not accompanied by electrocortical sleep (Rothballer, 1959). After intraventricular injection the catechol amines may penetrate to regions of the brain normally protected by the blood-brain barrier.

(c) AGE OF ANIMAL TESTED

Qualitative studies of sympathomimetic amines in young animals

In the immature brain the blood-brain barrier is absent or not fully effective (Bakay, 1956; Lajtha, 1957). Thus, by comparing the effects of the amines in the immature with those in the mature animal, the influence of the blood-brain barrier on the central effects could be determined. A technique for recording cerebral electrical activity in conscious unrestrained young animals (Key and Marley, 1961*a*) allowed the effects of the sympathomimetic amines to be tested in both the young and adult animals of three species. The procedure was later modified so that drugs could be injected without handling the animals. A polyethylene cannula containing heparin-saline was tied into the jugular vein and the tube brought out from the scalp wound and fixed with the electrode wires to the skull by acrylic autopolymerizing resin. The electrode wires were wound round the polyethylene tube, which was long enough for the animal to move freely. Electrodes for recording the electromyogram were placed in the dorsal muscles of the neck. Methods for anaesthetizing newborn animals were developed for use in implanting the cannulae and electrodes (Marley and Payne, 1962).

Classification of amines

In 1 day–4-week-old chickens the individual sympathomimetic amines given intravenously had different effects on behaviour and electrocortical activity from those found in the adult (Key and Marley, 1961*b*; 1962). Some of the amines tested are shown in Table I. Those with –OH groups in the 3,4 positions on the benzene ring or with one –OH group in the 3 position and one on the β-carbon atom (Group 1) produced behavioural and electrocortical sleep; amines with methoxy substituents on the benzene ring had similar properties. The birds stood or squatted as in normal sleep and behavioural and electrocortical arousal could be obtained with sensory stimuli. Phenylethylamines without –OH groups (Group 3) produced behavioural and electrocortical arousal. The benzene ring was not essential for alerting as central excitation was produced by the aliphatic amine, tuaminoheptane,

Table I

FUNCTIONAL AND STRUCTURAL GROUPINGS OF SOME
SYMPATHOMIMETIC AMINES TESTED

Molecules with benzene ring drawn to emphasize phenylethylamine skeleton.

COMPOUND	FUNCTIONAL GROUPING	STRUCTURE							CHEMICAL GROUPING OF RING
(−)-ADRENALINE	1	H	OH	OH	H	OH	H	CH$_3$	CATECHOL
(−)-NORADRENALINE		H	OH	OH	H	OH	H	H	
(±)-ISOPRENALINE		H	OH	OH	H	OH	H	CH(CH$_3$)$_2$	
(±)-COBEFRINE		H	OH	OH	H	OH	CH$_3$	H	
DOPAMINE		H	OH	OH	H	H	H	H	
(−)-PHENYLEPHRINE		H	H	OH	H	OH	H	CH$_3$	PHENOL
(±)-HYDROXY METHYL AMPHETAMINE	2	H	OH	H	H	H	CH$_3$	CH$_3$	
TYRAMINE		H	OH	H	H	H	H	H	
(±)-HYDROXY AMPHETAMINE		H	OH	H	H	H	CH$_3$	H	
(−)-EPHEDRINE		H	H	H	H	OH	CH$_3$	CH$_3$	
(±)-PHENYLPROPANOLAMINE		H	H	H	H	OH	CH$_3$	H	
(+)-AMPHETAMINE	3	H	H	H	H	H	CH$_3$	H	BENZENE
(±)-METHYL PHENIDATE		H	H	H	H	COOCH$_3$ CH$_2$ CH$_2$—CH$_2$			
(±)-PHENMETRAZINE		H	H	H	H	O CH$_3$ CH$_2$—CH$_2$			
(±)-α-METHYL TRYPTAMINE		CH$_2$—CH·CH$_3$—NH$_2$ (indole)							INDOLE
(±)-CYCLOPENTAMINE		CH$_2$—CH·CH$_3$—NHCH$_3$ (cyclopentane)							CYCLOPENTANE
(±)-TUAMINOHEPTANE		CH$_3$—CH$_2$—CH$_2$—CH$_2$·CH$_2$—CH·CH$_3$—NH$_2$							ALIPHATIC

and by amines with indole or 5-carbon rings (Table I). The wave amplitude in the electromyogram was increased in birds alerted by amphetamine-like amines and reduced or abolished during sleep produced by Group 1 amines (Fig. 1). Group 2 amines, with one –OH group in the 4 position on the benzene ring or on the β-carbon atom, had equivocal effects.

These three groupings conform generally with the suggestion of Belleau (1960) that sympathomimetic amines with an unsubstituted benzene ring and small cationic head were excitatory, whereas the catechol ring conferred inhibitory properties. The division of the amines into three groups is also similar to structure-activity findings with denervated mammalian smooth muscle *in*

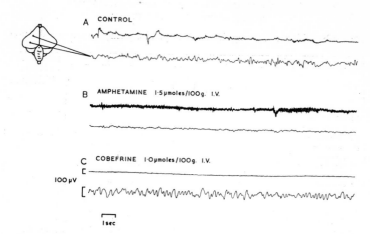

FIG. 1. Effect of amines on electromyogram (upper trace) and electrocorticogram (lower trace) in unrestrained, intact 5-day-old chicken, 50 g. weight. A, control, drowsy animal. B, increased activity in the electromyogram and alert electrocorticogram 5 min. after amphetamine. C, antagonistic effect of cobefrine to amphetamine. Slow wave electrocorticogram and reduced activity in the electromyogram 5 min. after cobefrine.

vivo (Fleckenstein and Burn, 1953; Marley, 1962) and mammalian smooth muscle *in vitro* (Vane, 1960). The activity on central receptors of an amine relative to others within the same group paralleled, with certain exceptions, its relative potency on peripheral receptors, and structure-activity findings for peripheral and central receptors could be inter-correlated.

In adult birds all amines, irrespective of group, elicited behavioural and electrocortical arousal, as has been found in the adults of other species. This difference in response was attributed to maturation of the blood-brain barrier which could have several possible consequences. For instance, catechol amines may be selectively excluded from the mature brain because of their low lipid solubility. If this is so, it would suggest that the actions of catechol amines in adult animals are produced through a primary peripheral mechanism, leading to central excitation. In this connexion, it is interesting that in the newborn guinea pig, which is more mature than most species at birth (Windle, 1940), electrocortical activity (Jasper, Bridgman and Carmichael, 1937) and the blood-brain barrier are both mature (Waelsch, 1955). Furthermore, newborn guinea pigs respond with behavioural and electrocortical alerting to all the amines in just the same way as the mature animal (Marley and Key, 1963).

Brain-stem receptors

The central site of action of the sympathomimetic amines in the chicken was investigated by testing the effect of the amines on cerebral electrical activity and "behaviour" after acute brain-stem transection (Marley, 1963). Under halothane and oxygen anaesthesia, the transection was made between the upper midbrain and the junction of the medullary bulb with the spinal cord: the anaesthetic was withdrawn and the bird artificially respired. After the transection the chicken lay immobile and asleep (Fig. 2A, B). Electrocortical arousal on sensory stimulation was poorly sustained and occurred only with visual stimuli.

In 1 day—4-week-old birds the amphetamine-like amines produced behavioural and electrocortical alerting (Fig. 2, E, F, I, J). Whereas there was an increase in amplitude of the slow electrocortical potentials after the catechol amines and a reduction of the electrocortical response to eye-opening (Fig. 2, C, D), the central depressant action was better seen in the restoration of "behavioural" and electrocortical sleep in birds first roused by amphetamine (Fig. 2, G, H). The effect of both groups of amines

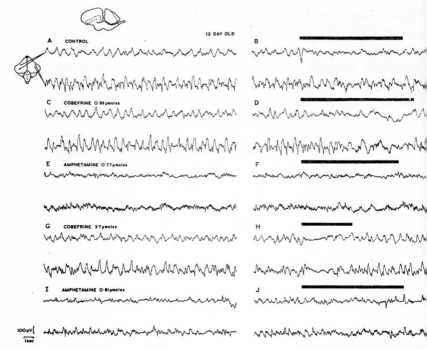

Fig. 2. Effect of transection of medullary bulb in 12-day-old bird. Transection indicated by dotted line. Left column, spontaneous and drug-modified electrocortical activity; right column, effect of eye-opening on electrocortical activity. Solid line; duration of eye-opening. A, B, controls. C, D, increase in amplitude of slow wave potentials 80 sec. after cobefrine (i.v.) with diminished electrocortical alerting on eye-opening. E, F, I, J, electrocortical alerting 7 min. after amphetamine (i.v.). G, H, antagonistic effect of cobefrine to amphetamine. Restoration of electrocortical slow potentials after divided doses of cobefrine (i.v.).

on electrocortical activity was abolished by transections above the mid-brain.

In adult birds after brain-stem transection, the amphetamine-like amines readily elicited arousal (Fig. 3, C). The catechol amines no longer had central depressant actions as in the young bird, nor did they cause prolonged arousal as in adult intact birds. There was a transient alerting effect which appeared to depend

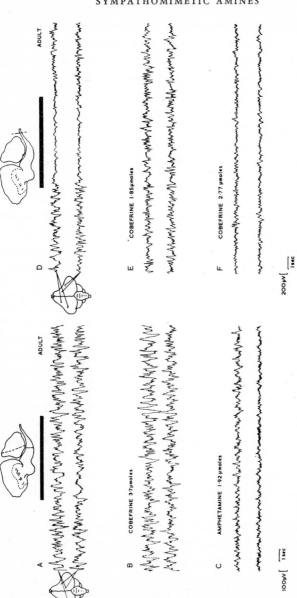

FIG. 3. Effect of brain-stem transection in adult birds. Transection indicated by dotted line. Left column, transection at level of trigeminal nerves. A, control, with minimal change in electrocortical activity on eye-opening (solid line). B, C, electrocortical arousal 6 min. after amphetamine (i.v.) but not cobefrine (i.v.). Right column, chicken *encéphale isolé* preparation. D, electrocortical arousal on eye-opening. F, electrocortical arousal after divided doses of cobefrine (i.v.).

on the integrity of sensory input to the brain stem, for electro-cortical arousal occurred only with transections below the level of the trigeminal nerves (Fig. 3, F). Thus, in 1 day—4-week-old birds the amines produced their antipodal effects on behaviour and electrocortical activity through receptors or systems in the brain stem; in the adult bird the amphetamine-like amines acted on brain-stem receptors or systems, but the alerting produced by catechol amines was due either to their action on peripheral receptors or it was mediated through the lower brain stem.

Quantitative studies

Methods for quantifying electrocortical activity, the electro-myogram, cheeping and movement were developed (Dewhurst and Marley, 1963). The bird was placed in a partially sound-proof box with controlled light, temperature, humidity and atmosphere and a one-way mirror in the front wall for observation. The polyethylene tube of the cannula and the electrodes were led to the exterior through a groove in the lid of the box. The bird could move freely and injections could be made into the cannula without introducing extraneous stimuli. An adjacent control box (a mirror-image of the experimental box) was placed so that the transparent side-walls of the boxes abutted. Social stimuli could be introduced from the control box without interfering with the test animal.

In early experiments electrocortical patterns were arbitrarily graded. Later, electrocortical activity was quantified by feeding the balanced output from the power-stage of the electroencephalo-graph into an impedance-matching transformer instead of the pen-coil. The transformer response was substantially linear down to 2 c./s. Output from the secondary of the transformer was rectified by a semiconductor bridge and fed into a d.c. integrating motor and counter (Fig. 4). The motor measured the summed integrals of the amplified voltages with respect to time. Large potential differences of long duration, as in electrocortical sleep activity, had large integrals, whereas small potential differences of short duration, as in the alert electrocorticogram, had small integrals. Thus the effects of sympathomimetic amines on cerebral electrical activity were expressed as a continuous integral of the wave form. The electromyogram was similarly integrated.

The methods for quantifying movement and cheeping were derived from a method of Parkes and Lessin (1960). Cheeping was recorded by crystal microphones in the roof of the box and the signals amplified and filtered to remove low-frequency noise

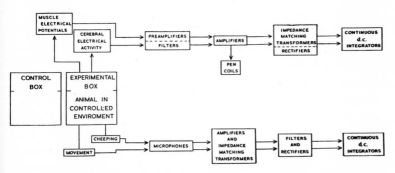

Fig. 4. Block-diagram of apparatus for recording and integrating cerebral and muscle electrical activity, cheeping and movement.

made by the bird's movements. The filtered signals were then rectified by a semiconductor bridge and fed into a d.c. integrating motor (Fig. 4). The noise produced by movement, which was taken as an index of activity, was also integrated. Signals of cheeping frequency were removed by filtering. Loud long sounds were represented by large integrals and increased amounts of movement and cheeping appeared as larger totals on the counter.

Postural changes of the bird were observed and given co-ordinates by reference to a graticule on the one-way mirror.

The techniques were used for measuring normal or drug-modified behaviour and cerebral electrical activity in small animals under controlled conditions. The following is a summary of the quantitative results obtained.

(a) *The normal.* Under specified conditions the cumulative integrals bore a substantially linear relation to time. Saline injections produced transient changes.

(b) *Response to the single dose.* Cumulative integrals were plotted over successive minutes; these produced sigmoid or exponential curves. The total count measured the response to a drug, whereas the curve showed the onset and duration of action.

(c) *Dose-response curves.* Cumulative integrals were obtained for several doses in the same animal. Linear relations were obtained between log dose and behavioural or electrocortical responses. Cheeping, movement, and brain and muscle electrical activity had different thresholds and duration of response to the amines. This had not been apparent in qualitative studies. For example, cheeping was abolished by a dose of cobefrine that did not alter the electrocorticogram or electromyogram. With amphetamine, the maximum increase in cheeping was produced by a dose just effective in eliciting electrocortical arousal. Thereafter, logarithmic increments in dose produced linear decrements in cheeping integrals but increased electrocortical alerting, postural and ataxic effects.

(d) *Physiological antagonism.* The antagonistic action of cobefrine to the changes produced in cheeping, movement and the electrocorticogram by $1 \cdot 0$ μmole amphetamine is shown in Fig. 5. The peak antagonistic effect did not differentiate between the different doses of cobefrine, whereas the integral of the antagonistic effects was linearly related to dose. The antagonistic effect of $1 \cdot 0$ μmole cobefrine lasted about 15 minutes.

(e) *Specific antagonism.* The suggestion that amphetamine acts on central tryptamine receptors (Vane, 1960) was supported by the similar response of the young chicken to amphetamine and to α-methyl tryptamine. A specific antagonist to tryptamines, methysergide (1-methyl-D-lysergic acid butanolamide, UML-

491), in a dose of 0·001 μmole, which did not affect normal behaviour nor electrocortical activity, prevented or abolished for

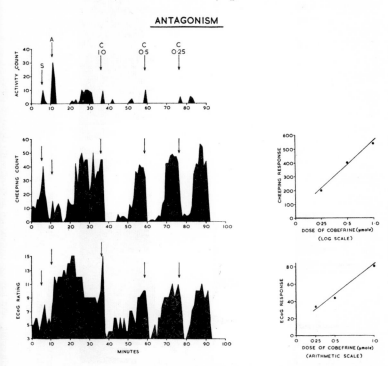

FIG. 5. Physiological antagonism: effect of amphetamine (A) on activity, cheeping and electrocortical activity abolished by cobefrine (C) in intact 8-day-old bird, weight 60 g. Ordinates, integrals/min. for activity and cheeping; ECG rating/min. (maximum alerting, 18; sustained sleep activity, 3). S, 0·1 ml. saline, i.v. Amphetamine, 1·0 μmole, i.v., produced increased amount of cheeping and electrocortical alerting but little change in activity. Prompt cessation of cheeping and appearance of slow wave electrocortical activity after cobefrine 1·0, 0·5 and 0·25 μmole, i.v. Right, dose-response curves for cobefrine plotted against decrement in cheeping response and ECG response. Linearity obtained respectively with logarithmic dose and with arithmetic dose.

more than 60 minutes the effect of 1·0 μmole amphetamine on cheeping, electrocortical activity, the electromyogram and posture. Phenoxybenzamine or "Hydergine" which block α receptors and

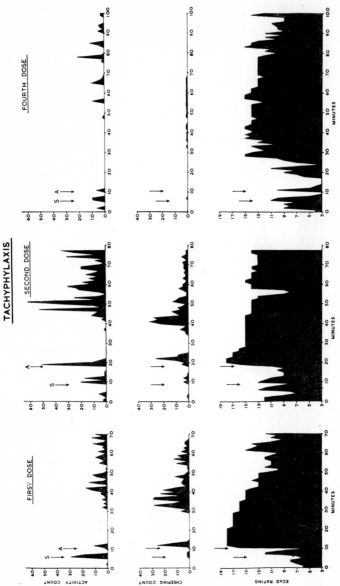

Fig. 6. Tachyphylaxis to amphetamine in 7-day-old bird. Responses plotted as in Fig. 5. S, 0·1 ml. saline, i.v. *First dose:* activity, cheeping and electrocortical alerting produced by amphetamine (A), 1·0 μmole, i.v. *Second dose:* amphetamine, 1·0 μmole, i.v., given 24 hours later. Increase in activity, but cheeping and electrocortical alerting slightly less than with first dose. (Third dose at 48 hr. not shown.) *Fourth dose:* 72 hr. after first. Amphetamine, 1·0 μmole, i.v., now produces little effect on cheeping, and less electrocortical alerting with delayed onset.

Nethalide (1-(2'-naphthyl)-2-isopropylaminoethanol hydrochloride) or dichloroisoprenaline which block β receptors were ineffective in equimolar doses or less. None of the substances so far tested specifically antagonized the depressant effects of the catechol amines (cobefrine, isoprenaline) on the normal cheeping, electrocortical activity and electromyograms of the chicken.

(f) *Tachyphylaxis*. Equal doses of amphetamine were given every 4 hours. After the fourth to fifth dose there was a diminution in the electrocortical, cheeping, motor and ataxic effects produced by amphetamine, with an increased delay in onset. Tachyphylaxis developed only occasionally with doses at 24-hour intervals (Fig. 6).

(a) MODIFICATION OF DRUG EFFECTS BY SOCIAL STIMULI

Whereas amphetamine (1·0 μmole/100 g., i.v.) produced electrocortical alerting, the "stereotyped" twittering (Selle, 1940) was only occasionally elicited in isolated birds. Twittering developed, however, when the bird was handled, or when another bird was introduced into the test or control box. In a cross-over experiment with 18 chickens there was a significantly greater incidence of twittering ($x^2 = 138$, $df = 1$, $P < 0\cdot001$) after amphetamine in *accompanied* (17/18) than in *isolated* birds (2/18). Thus electrocortical excitation produced by amphetamine was independent of social stimuli but the behavioural changes were not. In the isolated bird, with behaviour as the dependent variable, dose–response curves and the effects of antagonists upon them were altered by social stimuli.

Acknowledgments

Recent work has been supported by grants from the Bethlem Royal and Maudsley Hospitals Research Fund and the University of London Central Research Fund.

REFERENCES

BAKAY, L. (1956). The Blood–Brain Barrier, p. 86. Springfield: Thomas.
BELLEAU, B. (1960). *Ciba Found. Symp. Adrenergic Mechanisms*, p. 223. London: Churchill.

BONVALLET, M., DELL, P., and HUGELIN, A. (1954). *Electroenceph. clin. Neurophysiol.*, **6**, 119.

BRADLEY, P. B., and ELKES, J. (1957). *Brain*, **80**, 77.

DEWHURST, W. G., and MARLEY, E. (1963). *J. Physiol. (Lond.)*, **168**, 1P.

FELDBERG, W., and SHERWOOD, S. L. (1954). *J. Physiol. (Lond.)*, **123**, 148.

FLECKENSTEIN, A., and BURN, J. H. (1953). *Brit. J. Pharmacol.*, **8**, 69.

GOODMAN, L. S., and GILMAN, A. (1955). The Pharmacological Basis of Therapeutics (2nd ed.), p. 479. New York: Macmillan.

JASPER, H. H., BRIDGMAN, C. S., and CARMICHAEL, L. (1937). *J. exp. Psychol.*, **21**, 63.

KEY, B. J. (1958). Ph.D. Thesis, University of Birmingham, p. 84.

KEY, B. J., and MARLEY, E. (1961a). *J. Physiol. (Lond.)*, **155**, 29P.

KEY, B. J., and MARLEY, E. (1961b). *J. Physiol. (Lond.)*, **155**, 39P.

KEY, B. J., and MARLEY, E. (1962). *Electroenceph. clin. Neurophysiol.*, **14**, 90.

LAJTHA, A. (1957). *J. Neurochem.*, **1**, 216.

LEIMDORFER, A. (1950). *J. Pharmacol.*, **98**, 62.

MARLEY, E. (1962). *J. Physiol. (Lond.)*, **162**, 193.

MARLEY, E. (1963). *J. Physiol. (Lond.)*, **165**, 24P.

MARLEY, E., and KEY, B. J. (1963). *Electroenceph. clin. Neurophysiol.*, **15**, 620.

MARLEY, E., and PAYNE, J. P. (1962). *Brit. J. Anaesth.*, **34**, 776.

PARKES, M. W., and LESSIN, A. W. (1960). *Acta Int. Meeting on Techniques for the Study of Psychotropic Drugs*, p. 57, ed. Tonini, G. Modena: Societa Tipografica Modenese.

ROTHBALLER, A. B. (1956). *Electroenceph. clin. Neurophysiol.*, **8**, 603.

ROTHBALLER, A. B. (1959). *Pharmacol. Rev.*, **11**, 494.

SELLE, R. M. (1940). *Science*, **91**, 95.

VANE, J. R. (1960). *Ciba Found. Symp. Adrenergic Mechanisms*, p. 356. London: Churchill.

WAELSCH, H. (1955). *In* Biochemistry of the Developing Nervous System, p. 187, ed. Waelsch, H. New York: Academic Press.

WINDLE, W. F. (1940). Physiology of the Fetus, p. 163. Philadelphia: Saunders.

DISCUSSION

Bureš: I was very impressed by your findings, Dr. Marley, but I want to ask whether one should speak about corticograms in your experiments, since the cortex in birds is very primitive. I think it is probably the activity of the striatum which is concerned in this case.

Marley: This is an important question. The avian cerebral hemisphere is covered by a thin layer of cortex except for the anteromedial non-cortical nuclei diffusus dorsalis and diffusus dorsolateralis which are the avian homologues of the mammalian neocortex (Kuhlenbeck, H. [1938]. *J. comp. Neurol.*, **69**, 273). The recording electrodes therefore lay over cortex or cortical equivalents.

A point that exercised Dr. Key and me (Key, B. J., and Marley, E. [1962]. *Electroenceph. clin. Neurophysiol.*, **14**, 90) was that part of the avian dorsal cortex corresponds to the mammalian hippocampus; in mammals, there is an *inverse* relation between neocortical and hippocampal electrical activity (Green, J. D., and Arduini, A. [1954]. *J. Neurophysiol.*, **17**, 533). Adrenaline produced slow wave electrical activity in the mammalian hippocampus but neocortical electrical and behavioural alerting (Bradley, P. B., and Nicholson, A. N. [1962]. *Electroenceph. clin. Neurophysiol.*, **14**, 824). Did the electrical pattern of sleep produced in the 1–28-day chick by the catechol amines merely correspond to that elicited by adrenaline in the mammalian hippocampus?

Fortunately, it did not. With recording electrodes placed over many areas of the avian cerebral hemisphere, the behavioural and electrocortical changes occurring either spontaneously or after the sympathomimetic amines were invariably *directly* related. In the young chicken, slow wave electrocortical activity and behavioural sleep were produced by the catechol amines, and behavioural and electrocortical alerting were produced in the adult. The correspondence of the electrocortical changes in the adult chicken with those in adult mammals and the fact that the recordings were taken from the cortex justify the term *corticogram*.

Feldberg: Dr. Marley, do you think from your experiments on chickens that the alerting you obtained on intravenous injection, in contrast to the depression on intraventricular injection, is due to a peripheral action of the drug? Are sensory impulses perhaps responsible for the alerting reaction not only in hens, but in mammals, too, where we encounter the same difference and have the same problem?

Marley: We think that is so. Our evidence is of two kinds, the first of which is based on preliminary data.

After brain-stem transection, the chicken remains behaviourally and electrocortically asleep, and will only rouse with visual stimuli. In the 1–28-day bird amphetamine-like substances produced electrocortical alerting, antagonized by the catechol amines, with transection below but not above the mesencephalon. In the adult chicken the catechol amines elicited behavioural and electrocortical alerting; with transection in the lower part of the medullary bulb, the long-acting catechol amines such as cobefrine still produced transient electrocortical alerting. The arousal threshold was raised compared with the intact adult chicken, suggesting that spinal cord sensory input was important for the arousal elicited by the catechol substances. If transection was at or above the trigeminal nerves, abolishing sensory inflow from the face, arousal could not be obtained with cobefrine but was elicited with the amphetamine-like amines (Marley, E. [1963]. *J. Physiol. [Lond.]*, **165**, 24P). This suggested that arousal with the catechol amines was secondary to their peripheral action.

The other evidence is based on the difference in effect of the catecho amines in the newborn of various species (Marley, E., and Key, B. J. [1963]. *Electroenceph. clin. Neurophysiol.*, in press). In the young chick which has an immature blood–brain barrier (Waelsch, H. [1955]. *In* Biochemistry of the Developing Nervous System, p. 187, ed. Waelsch, H. New York: Academic Press) the catechol amines acted as central depressants. The guinea pig has a mature blood–brain barrier at birth (Waelsch, H. [1955]. *Ibid.*) and the catechol amines would have difficulty in reaching the brain because of their low lipid solubility. In contrast to the chicken, the catechol amines in the guinea pig produced behavioural and electrocortical alerting from the first day of life.

Session 3: Factors Modifying Behavioural Effects of Drugs

CHAIRMAN: Professor A. Summerfield

SCHEDULES OF REINFORCEMENT

P. B. DEWS

Department of Psychiatry, Harvard Medical School

THIS part of the symposium is concerned particularly with the experiential attributes of an animal that at present defy physiological recognition, but that nevertheless profoundly modify the effects of drugs on its behaviour. The schedule of reinforcement of the specific behaviour under study is one such factor. Schedule-dependent influences are important both because the effects are large and because they operate quite generally.

The schedule of reinforcement of some behaviour (called a response) is a specification of the relations between the occurrences of responses and the occurrences of environmental stimuli, particularly those stimuli that affect the future frequency of occurrence of the response (called reinforcing stimuli). The schedule is a formal statement that should specify the consequences of all possible relations between responses and stimuli. Occurrences of environmental stimuli can be made contingent on some numerical measure of responding (for example, number of respo.1ses made) or on the passage of time, or on some combination of responses and time. In all the examples to be discussed here, responses have been defined in terms of the operation of all-or-none devices in the apparatus, so they are all indistinguishable unitary events; but this is not a limitation inherent in the concept of a schedule. When the schedule has been formulated, it can be imposed on the animal by logical mechanical and electrical apparatus. The power of schedules, then, emphasizes the importance of the precise arrangements according to which experiments are conducted as determinants of the resulting behaviour. Pre-eminent are relations in time and it is these that have been most frequently overlooked or ignored in experimental psychology.

Three illustrations will be given of the power of schedules to modify the effects of drugs. The first illustration is of modification of the effects of pentobarbitone in pigeons. Pigeons were subjected to a fixed-ratio (FR 50) schedule; this schedule specifies that reinforcing stimuli (in this case presentation of food to the pigeon partially deprived of food) will follow every 50th response (in this case a peck of a plastic disc). The number of responses occurring in a 900-sec. period after various doses of pentobarbitone in each of four pigeons was determined. A dose-effect curve was plotted using as dependent variable the ratio of the number of responses made after pentobarbitone to the number made in a similar period before pentobarbitone. Before or after this series of experiments the same four pigeons were subjected to a 900-sec. fixed-interval (FI) schedule; this schedule specifies that reinforcing stimuli will follow the first response made when 900 seconds have elapsed. The effects of pentobarbitone were determined and a dose–effect curve plotted as when the animals were under FR 50. In comparing the dose–effect curve for FR 50 and 900-sec. FI it is important to remember that the animals, the response, the stimuli—the whole apparatus surrounding the pigeons—and the level of deprivation were identical during the operation of both schedules. Yet the dose–effect curves were quite different (Dews, 1955). Over a twofold range of doses the very direction of the effect was different, depending on the schedule; 2 mg. and 4 mg. produced increases of responding when the animals were under FR 50 but decreases to less than 20 per cent of the control levels when the animals were under 900-sec. FI.

The second illustration also concerns the differential sensitivity of responding under fixed-ratio and under fixed-interval contingencies, but is taken from work on rats, and involved the serial imposition of fixed-ratio and fixed-interval contingencies (correlated with stimuli) during a single session. The drug was

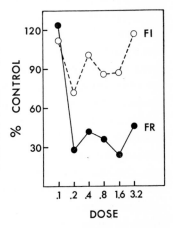

Fig. 1. Differential effects of hyoscine on behaviour of rats, depending on the schedule of reinforcement.

Ordinate: mean rate of responding after drug as percentage of mean rate in six sessions without drug. Abscissa: dose in mg./kg. FI: performance on 240-sec. FI. FR: performance on FR 24. The points show the averages for two rats, except at 0·2 mg./kg. and 0·4 mg./kg., at which doses only one rat was studied. Drawn from Table 1 of paper of Boren and Navarro (1959).

hyoscine. Again a difference in the effects, depending on which schedule was in operation, was found; but in this case it was responding under fixed-ratio contingencies that was reduced much more than responding under fixed-interval contingencies (Fig. 1) (Boren and Navarro, 1959). These experiments also illustrate the very low slope of the dose–effect curve often seen with hyoscine.

Finally, a large difference in the susceptibility of responding to reduction by chlordiazepoxide, according to schedule, has been shown by Cook (1964) in squirrel monkeys. Here again, the schedules were fixed-interval and fixed-ratio; the fixed-ratio responding declined at doses at which the fixed-interval responding was still above control levels. Remember that the animals, the response, and the level of deprivation were identical for both schedules; the effects on responding under the two schedules were actually observed during the same sessions. It follows that the observation that behaviour modified by punishment is affected differently by chlordiazepoxide from behaviour under another schedule not involving punishment does not serve to establish a specific effect by the drug on punishment (Geller *et al.*, 1962). The observed difference might be due to the difference in schedule.

To these three illustrations of schedule of reinforcement as a factor modifying the behavioural effects of drugs could be added many others from the work of other people involving additional drugs and species. Not many of these could be taken from the literature, because people actively working in the field have long accepted the importance of schedule factors, and have been concerned with the next step: identifying the specific attributes of particular schedules and particular drugs that determine the nature and direction of the behavioural effects.

If schedule effects are so important, it may be asked why they have only recently been recognized. This is partly because there has been so little systematic laboratory work on the behavioural effects of drugs. Conventionally trained pharmacologists have tended to avoid the field. The attitude, not usually explicit, has been that a drug must have a consistent effect on the brain, and that when this is known, the variable effects of the drug on behaviour depending on circumstances will be easily understood. The neurophysiological analysis of drug effects on the brain is, of course, an entirely praiseworthy pursuit, but as an exclusive approach it suffers from two limitations. It is gratuitous to suppose, for example, that a consistent effect of a drug on the electrical activity or on the 5-hydroxytryptamine content of a hypothalamic nucleus can yield an immediate understanding of the variable effects of the drug on behaviour. Secondly, studies on effects of drugs on the brain have contributed almost nothing so far to knowledge of *what* drugs do to behaviour, although they are, of course, indispensable in studying *how* effects are caused.

Even today, some people refuse to be impressed by the evidence of schedule dependence of behavioural effects of drugs because they are so convinced of the vagaries of behaviour that they are only too ready to believe it to be affected by anything under the sun. Schedules to them are merely one of innumerable factors that they believe to render a scientific analysis of behaviour hopeless.

Schedule-controlled behaviour, however, can be consistent and reproducible. Attempts have been made to dismiss this as a contrived finding arising out of the carefully restricted and confined conditions under which the experiments have been done. This is unfair. Reproducibility of results in behavioural pharmacology does, of course, depend on careful reproduction of conditions; but this is not a situation peculiar to behavioural pharmacology. Restricted and controlled conditions are the outstanding characteristics of laboratory science. Nevertheless, the case for the *importance* of schedule effects does require that it be shown that not everything that is changed in the experimental situation causes changes in the behavioural effects of drugs of comparable size to those resulting from change in schedule. Accordingly, examples of invariances will be given.

Change in parameter of a fixed-interval schedule leads to change in average rate of responding. Pigeons were subjected to a schedule with four different fixed intervals following one another repeatedly in each session (Dews, 1962) (Fig.2). Each fixed-interval length was uniquely correlated with a discriminative stimulus. The lengths were 180 sec., 360 sec., 540 sec. and 600 sec. The average rate of responding during the 180-sec. FI component (0·936 responses/sec.) was about twice that during the 600-sec. FI component (0·459 responses/sec.), with the rates for the 360-sec. FI and 540-sec. FI components falling between these extremes. The dose–effect curves for chlorpromazine for all four fixed-interval lengths were, however, quite similar when the rates after different doses of chlorpromazine were expressed as ratios of the respective control rates. Here the differences in control rates of responding did not determine much difference in sensitivity to drug effect. In this case, of course, the different rates resulted from a change only in parameter value rather than a change in nature of schedule.

Even grossly dissimilar patterns of responding, occasioned by different schedules, do not necessarily lead to different dose–

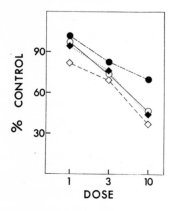

Fig. 2. Effects of chlorpromazine on behaviour of pigeons under FI schedules of different FI durations.

Ordinate: mean rate of responding after drug as percentage of mean rate in 10 sessions without drug. Abscissa: dose in mg.

●— – —● under 600-sec. FI
○————○ under 540-sec. FI
◆· · · ·◆ under 360-sec. FI
◇– – – –◇ under 180-sec. FI

The points show the averages for the five presentations of each FI duration in each session, during at least two sessions for 3 birds.

effect curves based on average rates of responding. Chlorpromazine, for example, does not differentially affect the average rates of responding of squirrel monkeys on the FI and FR components of the schedule already mentioned in the chlordiazepoxide studies (Cook, personal communication). An even more dramatic example for present purposes comes from work of the Wallers on dogs (Waller and Waller, 1962). In the presence of one stimulus the dogs responded to postpone an electric shock; in the presence of another stimulus, the dogs occasionally received food, the occasions being determined by a prearranged sequence of times (VI schedule). Control of the responding in the presence of the two stimuli thus differed both in schedule and also in the nature of the reinforcing stimuli. The latter difference belongs to the class of motivational differences that have been assumed to play a major rôle in determining differential drug effects (Dews and Morse, 1961). Yet the dose–effect curves for chlorpromazine were quite similar for responding under both conditions (Waller and Waller, 1962).

Systematic study of the change in the dose–effect curve of a drug with change in amount of "motivation" (for example, resulting from change in the level of food and water deprivation) would involve a large amount of work. No one seems to have considered it worth while. The best that can be offered is a composite of fragmentary data on several phenothiazines from experiments performed on two schedules for a different purpose. The experiments were made on pigeons, The schedules are shown diagrammatically in Fig. 3. Under 10 $(\overline{T10''N1})$, the 10th response concluding an inter-response time of greater than 10 sec. was followed by the reinforcing stimuli. Responses occurring less than 10 sec. after the preceding one simply started a new inter-response time. The specifications of 9 $(\overline{T10''N1})$ $\overline{T10''}$ were identical except that the requirement of the 10th response concluding an inter-response time of greater than 10 sec. was removed. In other words, under 10 $(\overline{T10''N1})$, all the requirements of 9 $(\overline{T10''N1})$ $\overline{T10''}$ had to be met, and then a single additional response made before the reinforcing stimuli supervened.

Performance under 10 $(\overline{T10''N1})$ was studied at two levels of food deprivation: when the animals were maintained at around 90 per cent of their *ad libitum* feeding weights and when they were around 70 per cent. Sporadic observations were made on the effects of promazine, chlorpromazine, triflupromazine, prochlorperazine, perphenazine, thiopropazate and trifluoperazine. To obtain sufficient information to compare the effects at the different levels of food deprivation, information on all these drugs was pooled, with the restriction that every dose of every drug under one condition was balanced by a similar dose under the other condition. The shape and positions of the curves are distorted by the large differences in potency between the drugs,

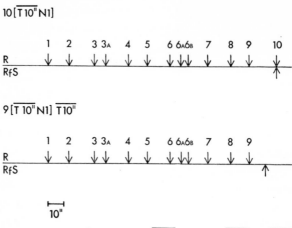

FIG. 3. Diagram of schedules 10 $\overline{(\text{T}10''\text{N}1)}$ and 9 $\overline{(\text{T}10''\text{N}1)}$ $\overline{\text{T}10''}$. Above the horizontal line is shown a hypothetical sequence of responses; below the line is shown the time of occurrence of the reinforcing stimuli, given that temporal sequence of responses. Responses occurring less than 10 sec. after a preceding one are labelled A, B; these have no effect except to start a new inter-response time. The only difference between the schedules is that 10 $\overline{(\text{T}10''\text{N}1)}$ requires an additional response (No. 10) after all the requirements for presentation of the reinforcing stimuli of 9$\overline{(\text{T}10''\text{N}1)}$ $\overline{\text{T}10''}$ have been met.

but the comparison between the curves permits an unbiased assessment of the consequence of change in level of deprivation. The level of deprivation does not seem to change the effects of the drugs in any large or systematic way (Fig. 4). Observations on the same series of drugs were made on birds working under 9 $\overline{(\text{T}10''\text{N}1)}$ $\overline{\text{T}10''}$. When the results for these experiments were pooled according to the same rules and compared with those of birds under 10 ($\overline{\text{T10''N1}}$), the resulting dose–effect curves were quite different (Fig. 5). At the 3 mg. level, in 11 out of 12 comparisons the birds responded more under 9 ($\overline{\text{T10''N1}}$) $\overline{\text{T10''}}$, relative to the control level, than under 10 ($\overline{\text{T10''N1}}$) ($P <$ 0·005). It seems a justifiable conclusion that a large change in deprivation level led to a smaller change in the effects of these phenothiazines than did a change in the schedule contingencies.

Why should schedule factors have such a large effect in determining the behavioural effect of a drug? Before speculating on

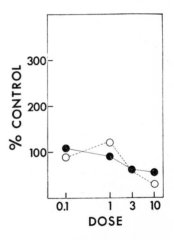

FIG. 4. Composite dose–effect curves of a number of phenothiazines in pigeons under 10 ($\overline{\text{T10''N1}}$). Ordinate: mean rate of responding after drug as percentage of mean rate on previous day without drug. Abscissa: dose in mg.

○－－－○ at the lower body-weight
●———● at the higher body-weight

Observations were made on 6 pigeons. The numbers of observations were 7, 11, 5 and 7 at 0·1 mg., 1 mg., 3 mg., and 10 mg. respectively.

this slightly philosophical question, consider some of the characteristics of schedule-controlled behaviour. It is usually stable behaviour, in the sense that after a period of adjustment, often surprisingly short, the performance in session after session is highly similar. The schedule engenders a whole pattern of behaviour that culminates in the presentation of the reinforcing stimuli. As long as the schedule contingencies are maintained unchanged, the pattern of responding remains unchanged. When the reinforcement contingencies are changed, however, the pattern of responding changes, usually very quickly. The stability of the pattern of behaviour seen under conditions of consistent scheduling is the stability of a steady-state condition rather than of a definitively "learned" piece of behaviour. Is it surprising that behaviour that is in this sort of dynamic equilibrium with the environment should be peculiarly and specifically sensitive to change by drugs? Drugs change the temporal patterns of force development by the heart; they do not make the heart secrete urine. Drugs change the likelihood that particular

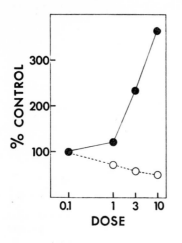

Fig. 5. Composite dose–effect curves as for Fig. 4.

o---o birds under 10 $(\overline{T10''N1})$

●——● birds under 9 $\overline{(T10''N1)}\ \overline{T10''}$

Observations were made on 8 pigeons. The numbers of observations were 11, 12, 12 and 9 at 0·1 mg., 1 mg., 3 mg., and 10 mg. respectively.

words and phrases will be used under particular circumstances; they do not much change a man's total vocabulary. Drugs affect patterns of behaviour under particular circumstances; they do not change what has been definitively learned. Schedule-controlled behaviour comprises behaviour that is in its nature typical of a large fraction of the behaviour that is susceptible to modification by drugs.

A schedule has been defined as a specification of the arrangements, including the timing arrangements, under which experiments will be made. Behaviour, of necessity, occurs in time; temporal sequencing of events in experiments is unavoidable.

The attributes of schedules that influence the resulting behaviour are not eliminated by ignoring them (Dews, 1963). There are many examples in the literature, where the importance of an independent variable in determining a drug effect has been purportedly established, in which the change in the independent variable was completely confounded with a change in schedule. Almost all experiments intended to show a difference between behaviour maintained by aversive stimuli and behaviour by positive reinforcement in sensitivity to a drug have involved concomitant change of motivation and *schedule*. Since schedule change alone can change sensitivity it is gratuitous to attribute the observed differences to differences in motivation. The importance of explicit scheduling of experiments cannot be ignored by anyone interested in behavioural pharmacology. Indeed, since schedule changes have been shown to influence a variety of other behavioural dependent variables, besides the effects of drugs, schedules cannot be ignored by anyone interested in behaviour.

Acknowledgments

Experiments from this laboratory reported in this paper have been supported by Grants MH02094 and MH02645 of the National Institutes of Health, USPHS. I wish to thank Dr. R. T. Kelleher for help in the preparation of this presentation.

REFERENCES

BOREN, J. J., and NAVARRO, A. P. (1959). *J. exp. Anal. Behav.*, **2**, 107.
COOK, L. (1964). This volume, p. 23.
DEWS, P. B. (1955). *J. Pharmacol. exp. Ther.*, **113**, 393.
DEWS, P. B. (1962). *Int. J. Neuropharmacol.*, **1**, 265.
DEWS, P. B. (1963). *In* Conflict and Creativity, p. 148, ed. Farber, S. M., and Wilson, R. H. L. New York: McGraw-Hill.
DEWS, P. B., and MORSE, W. H. (1961). *Ann. Rev. Pharmacol.*, **1**, 145.
GELLER, I., KULAK, J. T., and SEIFTER, J. (1962). *Psychopharmacologia*, **3**, 374.
WALLER, M. B., and WALLER, P. F. (1962). *J. exp. Anal. Behav.*, **5**, 259.

DISCUSSION

Miller: In his excellent paper Dr. Cook has shown not only that drugs have different effects on different schedules, but that these effects are consistent throughout a class of drugs, so that a certain class of drugs has a fingerprint, so to speak, in its interactions with schedules. Dr. Dews, have you been able to carry this any further? You hinted that the next step was not only to show how different schedules were affected differently by drugs but to discover general principles underlying these differences.

Dews: This is certainly our aim. We have been looking for the underlying attributes of the schedules and of the performance they engender, which together determine the drug effects, but we have not yet got very far. It is quite clear that there is no one single attribute which uniquely characterizes the schedule behaviour and which will determine the drug effects. A few years ago I tried to relate the effects of methamphetamine to the rate of responding only (Dews, P. B. [1958]. *J. Pharmacol. exp. Ther.*, **122**, 137). This seems to be useful as a first approximation. I have since looked for some comparable generalization for the barbiturates, and while in many circumstances it seems that the overall rate of responding is again an important determining factor, it is not a simple one. The specific question of the importance of the rate of responding, irrespective of schedule, as a determinant of drug effect, has turned out to be more difficult to answer than it seemed at first. This is because the comparability of rates of responding on two schedules depends on how closely you look at them. You can get an overall rate of responding on a fixed-interval schedule which is the same as that on a variable-interval schedule, for example, but the patterns may be quite different in detail; if you look at, say, inter-response time distributions you find entirely different distributions. Considerations of this kind have made it very difficult to pin down even this one factor, and I have little more to offer at the present time.

McIlwain: I should perhaps supplement Dr. Dews' remarks with some instances in which biochemical differences result from stimuli differently patterned in time. It is known that to demonstrate an effect of anti-convulsants on isolated cerebral tissue it is necessary to apply electrical stimuli to these isolated tissues at relatively high frequencies of 1,000 or 2,000 per second, and that little effect will be seen at frequencies of, say, ten per second (Greengard, O., and McIlwain, H. [1955]. *Biochem. J.*, **61**, 61).

Conversely, to display the maximum effect of protoveratrine on isolated cerebral tissue it is necessary to apply the stimulating impulses at two or three per second, and little effect will be seen if stimulation of the isolated cerebral cortex is carried out at higher frequencies of 50 or 100 per second (Wollenberger, A. [1955]. *Biochem. J.*, **61**, 77; McIlwain, H., and Joanny, P. [1963]. *J. Neurochem.*, **10**, 313).

Clearly, these phenomena are on a different level from those on which Dr. Dews comments, but the ultimate explanation of both types in terms of membrane phenomena is likely to be basic to the behaviour of the central nervous system, whether it is these relatively simple fashions of behaviour or the more complex phenomena he described.

Dews: I agree that the generalizations we are looking for should emerge as quantitative characteristics of behaviour that will correlate naturally with biochemical and physiological phenomena. Our generalizations will have to wait for a great deal more information on the temporal and other properties of behaviour.

Hurwitz: I should first like to ask Dr. Dews a question and then I should like to comment more generally on his paper.

Dr. Dews described how behaviour normally generated under a fixed-interval (FI) and a fixed-ratio (FR) schedule of reinforcement is differentially affected by the same dose of a drug. An interpretation of the results which immediately comes to mind runs as follows:

A fixed-interval reinforcement schedule represents a discriminatory task. The bird eventually learns not to peck at the disc for x seconds following each reinforcement. The drug supposedly interferes with the bird's discriminatory capacity and/or with the performance of a previously established discrimination. By contrast, a fixed-ratio schedule does not involve discriminations of this type and no change in response rate is predicted when the bird is drugged. But one could formulate an appealing alternative explanation: the drug affects a *response-cost* factor rather than the discriminatory capacity of the bird.

Perhaps Dr. Dews would like to comment on which of these interpretations is most likely to hold for the phenomenon he has described, for sooner or later a solution to this query will be demanded.

This brings me to my general comment: psychologists are interested in discovering the determinants of behaviour (its independent variables) and in analysing the structure and function of specific behavioural forms. Often the psychologist's traditional methods for studying behaviour do not help him in obtaining answers to his problems at an experimental level. The recent rapid development of the operant conditioning methodology holds out new hope: many of our intractable functional relations are becoming the subject of experimental study, new independent variables are being discovered and we are extending our ability to programme both simple and intricate patterns of behaviour. There has been a danger that operant methodology may become too closely identified with the study of a very restricted behavioural repertoire (response topographies), like the pecking of birds or lever pressing by rats. Wider publicity should be given at this stage to the variety of behaviours which are currently being studied in operant behaviour laboratories. For example, we have heard a great deal about the difficulty of deciding whether the change in an animal's behaviour following the administration of a drug is due to a disturbance of its discriminatory capacity or whether it is related to the manipulation of motivational factors. But this need not be a problem since already adequate screening techniques are available which will provide answers to such questions. For example, if it is suspected that a drug affects the discriminatory capacity of the animal, one could use a matching-to-sample programme, as described by Blough (Blough, D. S. [1959]. *J. exp. Anal. Behav.*, **2**, 151).

Other examples could be given but I think enough has been said in support of the claim that there exists an impressive armoury for analysing a wide variety of behaviours, many of them relevant to the clinical situation, which is of special interest to the present audience.

Dews: Your comment that one should keep in mind the possibility that drugs might affect discriminative behaviour is timely. We have suggested that many of the effects of drugs such as chlorpromazine that have been interpreted as effects on anxiety could rather be effects on discriminative behaviour (Dews, P. B., and Morse, W. H. [1961].

Ann. Rev. Pharmacol., **1**, 145). The effect of pentobarbitone on FI responding under a multiple FI/FR schedule is unlikely to be due to a potentiation of discriminative behaviour, since discriminative behaviour under other multiple schedules is impaired rather than enhanced by pentobarbitone (Dews, P. B. [1955]. *J. Pharmacol. exp. Ther.*, **115**, 380).

There is, of course, no dispute about the usefulness of scheduling techniques in the study of a great many categories of behaviour. We have tried to limit our work to schedules themselves because one cannot solve all problems simultaneously and schedules seem important for two reasons.

First, whether you make the schedule explicit or not, something comparable to a schedule is involved in all kinds of behavioural experiments. A range of contingencies is inevitably established, and whether you specify them or not, they will be operating in the determination of drug effects and of a wide variety of other dependent variables as well. It therefore seems important to work with the relatively simple, discrete sorts of situations which I illustrated, in order to discover how these schedule influences operate, before going on to the more complex situations where schedule and other influences are operating simultaneously, such as in matching-to-sample, which you mentioned, and in still more complex combinations of schedule contingencies.

Secondly, we believe that schedule-controlled behaviour is something more than a convenient dependent variable for assessing traditional psychological factors; that, in fact, the dynamics of schedule control are very directly dependent on fundamental behavioural processes.

Hollyhock: Dr. Dews, in your fixed-interval and fixed-ratio reinforcement schedules it appears to someone like myself, perhaps rather brainwashed by Pavlovian conditioning, that the reinforcement loading is very much less for a fixed-interval schedule, and I take it this would accord with Skinnerian philosophy in these matters too. Is it not possible that rather than being a different schedule on the *same* mode of behaviour, the fixed-interval observations are, in fact, to a greater or lesser degree influenced by a different behavioural modality, namely that of spontaneous activity?

Dews: At the parameter values of the schedules shown in the illustrations, the frequency in time of reinforcement and the proportion of responses reinforced were both greater under FR than under FI. Both these consequences of the schedules no doubt played their part in determining the pattern of responding engendered by the schedules.

The only definition of spontaneous activity I know is that it is activity whose prime determinants are unknown. There is evidence that schedules can greatly influence "spontaneous" activity (see for example, Skinner, B. F., and Morse, W. H. [1957]. *J. comp. physiol. Psychol.*, **50**, 279), but I know of no evidence that spontaneous activity can influence, to any great extent, schedule-controlled behaviour.

MODIFICATION OF BEHAVIOURAL EFFECTS OF DRUGS BY PAST EXPERIENCE

RUTH RUSHTON AND HANNAH STEINBERG

Department of Pharmacology, University College, London

ALL that psychoactive drugs can do is to act upon and modify ongoing behaviour, and ongoing behaviour is partly the result of the personality of the subject. It is therefore not surprising that past experience which contributes to the shaping of personality should be important in determining the subject's reactions to drugs. Clinically this has probably long been recognized, but experimentally the effects of factors of this kind have begun to be analysed only fairly recently.

The kinds of past experience that have been studied in animal experiments have been various. For example, the effects of isolating animals before testing them with drugs have been studied by Brown (1960) and Dr. Chance also has referred to them in his paper. Differential effects of a drug according to how far animals had learnt to perform a lever-pressing response have been reported by Bindra and Mendelson (1962). Work by Ross and Schnitzer (1963) has recently shown that rats which were under the influence of amphetamine sulphate during 45 minutes in activity cages were more active in these cages when retested without the drug a week later than control rats that had had their first exposure to the activity cage without any drug. In all this work fairly complicated interactions can be shown, and sometimes much seems to depend on the details of the experimental situation and the kind of behaviour tested. There is no doubt, however, that in the action of drugs on behaviour past experience can have an important and systematic rôle.

The work to be described was done chiefly with one kind of behaviour only, exploratory activity in a simple symmetrical Y-maze. The apparatus was 13 in. high, and each arm was 15 in. long and 5 in. wide. A trial consisted of placing a rat in the centre of the Y and leaving it in the apparatus for 3 minutes; the number of times it entered the arms was the measure of exploration (Steinberg, Rushton and Tinson, 1961).

Past experience in these experiments always took the form of previous exposure to the same Y-maze, and sometimes the animals were under the influence of drugs during the exposure and sometimes they were not. The animals were adult Lister hooded females which had been reared under standard conditions and had not left their home cages since weaning. Being put into the Y-maze could, therefore, be regarded as experience of a radically new environment and was presumably fairly disturbing to the animals (cf. Steinberg and Watson, 1960, who found that changes of environment produced marked and persisting arrests of gain in body weight in rats).

Initially we hoped to develop a group of rats which would give a stable level of activity in the Y-maze in repeated trials so that this level could be used as a baseline from which differences due to small doses of drugs could be measured. Fig. 1 shows that rats did indeed develop such a stable level of activity. We gave each rat a 3-minute trial twice weekly and after about 12 trials the mean activity stabilized at about 10 entries in 3 minutes. Defecation, which has often been shown to be negatively correlated with activity (Broadhurst, 1957), stabilized at zero at about the same time. The activity curve has been plotted so that each point represents the mean of four successive trials and the first point actually conceals a drop from the first to the second trial and a gradual recovery from this. This drop we have found repeatedly and it will be referred to again later.

Next we tested the rats with drugs. The drugs were amylobarbitone sodium 15 mg./kg., amphetamine sulphate 0·75 mg./

kg., a mixture of these two doses, and saline as control. The lower diagram in Fig. 2 shows the results. The "experienced" rats, that is the rats whose performance in successive trials is plotted in Fig. 1, showed practically no response, the separate drugs produced a slight drop in activity and the mixture was not effectively distinguishable from saline. So our original idea that

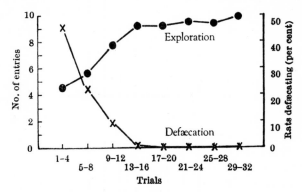

FIG. 1. Pre-drug trials of "experienced" rats. The figure shows the mean number of entries into the arms of a Y-shaped runway made in 3 min. by 24 rats in 32 successive trials, and the percentage of rats which defecated during these trials. The results have been grouped for four successive trials at a time, so that each point on the graph represents the mean results for four trials. Reproduced from Steinberg, Rushton and Tinson (1961) by permission of the Editor of Nature.

rats which had a stable level of activity in the Y-maze would be suitable subjects for testing the effects of small doses of these drugs did not succeed. Clearly, these animals were not very sensitive. However, we also tested a group of "inexperienced" rats, that is, rats which had had the same amount of handling as the experienced ones, but which had not been put in the runway. With these we obtained the effect shown in the top half of Fig. 2. Saline produced activity which was similar to activity at the first trial of the "experienced" rats in Fig. 1. Amylobarbitone and amphetamine produced a slight increase in activity but the mixture produced a very large increase in activity, something like

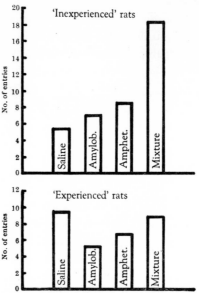

FIG. 2. Effects of drugs on exploratory activity. The figure shows the mean number of entries into the arms of a Y-shaped runway made in 3 min. by four sub-groups of "inexperienced" and of "experienced" rats ($n = 6$). Three of each of the four sub-groups received a drug, respectively amylobarbitone sodium 15 mg./kg., amphetamine sulphate 0·75 mg./kg., and these two doses combined in a mixture; the fourth sub-group were saline controls. Reproduced from Steinberg, Rushton and Tinson (1961) by permission of the Editor of *Nature*.

3 times as much as with saline. This effect seems to have genuinely depended on whether or not the animals had had the past experience of having been exposed to the Y-maze. We have since looked at the effects of handling alone to see whether the effect

would have been different if instead of being handled the in-experienced rats had never been touched until being used for the experiments; we found that on the whole this sort of limited handling makes little difference; it seems that the previous ex-posure to the environment was mainly responsible for the big difference in the effect of the mixture in the two groups. Why this should be so is not certain. It seems to fit in with the often advanced view that, on the whole, well established and well trained responses are apt to be less easily disturbed by the effects of drugs than poorly established, poorly learned performances. Dr. Cook's example of performance in early trials being more affected by ribonucleic acid in his test than performance in later ones seems to fit in with this (p. 41) and so does Dr. Stein's suggestion (p. 98) that prolonged or "strongly engaged" be-haviour is less sensitive to amphetamine than the opposite kind.

Why the mixture rather than the separate drugs should produce such a big effect in our experiments is also not certain. We have since studied dose-response relations of these mixtures (Rushton and Steinberg, 1963), and there is no doubt that in the Y-maze situation there is true potentiation; that is, mixtures can produce maximal effects on exploratory activity which are far in excess of effects produced by any dose of the separate drugs and of effects which could be expected from simple addition of those of the constituent doses. In psychological terms, it is possible that the effects of the mixture are so big because amphetamine alone increases activity directly, while small doses of barbiturates increase activity indirectly by reducing fear (see Miller, this volume, p. 1), including perhaps fear of new environments. But for the time being one could content oneself with saying that we have shown that "experienced" animals are less sensitive to the effects of these doses of drugs than inexperienced animals.

We next studied the effects, not of repeated previous exposure to the environment, but of a single exposure to the environment, and the results are shown in Fig. 3 (Rushton, Steinberg and

Tinson, 1963). Four groups of 15 rats were tested twice in the runway, three days apart. At the first trial, groups 1 and 2 had saline and groups 3 and 4 had the drug mixture used in the previous

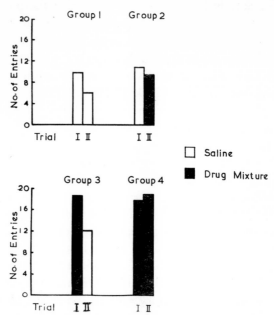

FIG. 3. Effect of a single experience on subsequent reactions to drugs. Rats were given two trials, 3 days apart, in a Y-shaped runway. The reactions tested were exploratory activities, scored as the number of entries into the arms of the Y in 3 min. Four groups of fifteen rats were tested, with the rats of a group under the influence of either an amphetamine–barbiturate mixture or of saline, at the first and/or the second trial. The number of entries are the means per group of fifteen rats. Reproduced from Rushton, Steinberg and Tinson (1963) by permission of the Editor of *The British Journal of Pharmacology*.

experiments. At the second trial, groups 1 and 3 had saline and groups 2 and 4 had the drug mixture. The results that are shown in Fig. 3 are somewhat complicated to interpret. Two things stand out. First, in group 1, the saline–saline group, there was a drop in activity at the second trial, and this was similar to what happened at the second trial of the experienced rats described in the previous experiment (Fig. 1); but in group 2, where the mixture was given at the second trial, there was no drop. The mixture, however, merely produced an effect similar to that of saline at the first trial. In other words, the mixture did counteract the drop

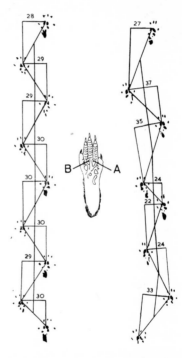

FIG. 4. Measurements used for studying gait, with prints of hind feet of rats given saline (left) and an amphetamine–barbiturate mixture (right). The numbers indicate the "splay" in mm. Irregularity of splay was used as a measure of ataxia. The diagram of the sole of the right hind foot (Greene, 1935) shows the second (A) and third (B) interdigital pads which determined the point from which measurements were made. Reproduced from Rushton, Steinberg and Tinson (1963) by permission of the Editor of *The British Journal of Pharmacology*.

that normally occurred at trial II, if trial I had also been under the influence of saline; but even a single previous experience in the runway under saline was sufficient to abolish the large increase of activity which the drug mixture normally produced. Secondly, if trial I occurred under the influence of the drug mixture, the results at trial II were different. In group 3, where the second trial took place under saline, activity was as great as, and even a little greater than, at the first saline trial in groups 1 and 2. In group 4, where both trials occurred under the influence of the drug mixture, activity was as great at trial II as at trial I. One might almost say that after a first trial with the drug mixture, the animals reacted at the second trial as though the first trial had not occurred at all.

A fuller explanation of these results must probably await a better understanding of the significance of exploratory behaviour (Barnett, 1958; Bindra, 1959; Berlyne, 1960) and especially of why there often is a drop in activity at the second trial (cf. Glanzer, 1961), and of the mode of action of amphetamine–barbiturate mixtures. At the very least, however, these results suggest that even a single, brief previous experience can markedly modify behavioural reactions to drugs; and if animals are to be used repeatedly in experiments such interactions should be taken into account.

In addition to exploratory activity we also wanted to assess motor inco-ordination or ataxia, since we had observed in our first experiment that animals given the drug mixture appeared unsteady when they walked. Although there are many reports in the literature of animals being made ataxic by drugs, we were unable to find a suitable objective and quantitative method for measuring it. Eventually we decided to try a modified version of a method for studying gait used by Shirley (1931) with children and by Khairy (1961) with rats. The method depends on analysing the spacing of the footprints along a standard path and we discovered that the best measure of ataxia was a measure of the irregularity of the "splay" (Fig. 4). We used the log variance of the splay measurements to express the degree of ataxia. The mixture produced about double the log variance of the saline controls ($P < 0.001$), and this effect was in no way altered by previous experience (Rushton, Steinberg and Tinson, 1963).

Next we did experiments in which animals were tested repeatedly, at 3-day intervals, in the runway and were given the same drug each time. This was similar to the very first experiment, the results of which are shown in Fig. 1, except that drugs were given. In order to determine how far any changes in exploratory activity during successive trials were due to the drugs themselves or to interactions between drugs and exposure to the environment, we also used animals which were merely injected

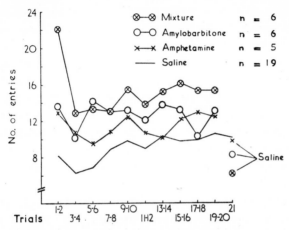

FIG. 5. Activity of four groups of rats tested under the influence of drugs at successive trials three days apart. The results have been grouped so that each point on the group represents the mean of two successive trials. At the 21st trial all groups were tested with saline.

with the same drugs at the same time as the animals which were tested in the runway but were then put back into the cage. These experiments are still in progress, and Fig. 5 shows preliminary results for the groups that were tested in the runway. At the first two trials the results of the mixture and saline groups roughly agree with the results for "inexperienced rats" shown in Fig. 2, though the curves have actually been plotted by combining the results for two trials at a time. In the saline group there was a drop in activity between the first and the second trial and then a gradual recovery and stabilization at about 10 entries in 3 minutes, similar to the results shown in Fig. 1. In the mixture group the scores at the first two trials were high and about the same at the two successive trials. This was similar to the results of group 4 in Fig. 3. From the third trial onwards, however, the mixture scores dropped and eventually stabilized at a much lower level than the initial one, though they were still higher than saline. The scores with the separate drugs were intermediate between scores with saline and with the mixture. After 20 trials we tested all rats in the runway with saline. It can be seen that there was no transfer of the level of activity from the mixture to the saline condition; on the contrary, rats previously given the mixture obtained the lowest scores under saline of all the groups tested. This is comparable with Miller's results (1961); in his experiments involving the experimental extinction of fear he found that the beneficial effects of amylobarbitone did not continue when the drug was withheld. Similarly Bloch and Silva (1959) found that what had been learned about a 4-unit T-maze while animals were under the influence of pentobarbitone was not retained when the animals were tested without the drug. In our own experiments the group of animals which had merely been injected and put back into the cage gave, when tested with drugs in the runway, no very conclusive results. The mixture group showed more activity than animals on saline, but both mixture and saline scores were intermediate between those shown at the first trial in Fig. 2; the number of animals was, however, small (between 3 and 5 per group), and this work needs repeating.

All of the work reported constitutes evidence for the fact that past experience can have a very marked effect and can actually abolish the increase in activity which normally results from a drug mixture. We do not know, however, what would happen if the interval between the first and second exposure had been longer than three days. It may be that after a week or a month the effect would have been different, and we are hoping to study this.

EXPERIMENTAL CONDITIONS

Finally we should like to stress that we have found it important that experiments of this kind should be carried out with rats which have been reared under uniform conditions and that the details of the experimental procedure should always be followed in a uniform way.

Our present method of husbandry for the rats is as follows: female Lister hooded rats are weaned when 21 days old and are transferred from the breeding room to the colony room. There they are numbered by ear punch and females from two or more litters* are housed in groups of fifteen in metal mesh cages ($25 \times 12 \times 8$ in.) fitted with external food containers and catch trays for excreta. These cages are suspended at the lowest level in the racks and the animals are not handled again until used for an experiment at about 120 days. The cages are not moved, opened or cleaned, routine attention only being given to food and water supplies and change of trays. The diet used is M.R.C. 41B cubes, and the thermostat in the animal house is set at 72° F.

For experiments the procedure is as follows: 10 minutes before an experiment begins the cage is taken out of the rack and placed on a board on the floor. The rats are allocated to their drug treatments by a predetermined random order and two rats are taken out of the cage at 8-minute intervals to be injected. The injections are subcutaneous in the flank and the animals are held very loosely during the injection; they are allowed to watch themselves being injected. They rarely squeak or show other signs of fear. After injection the animals are painted with patches of vegetable dyes according to a simple code in order to make identification at the time of testing easier. The rats are tested in the Y-maze 35 minutes after injection and 8-minute intervals allow enough time for injection and testing by two

* It is realized that it might be better to allocate members of the same litter to different cages at random instead of keeping litter mates together. The number of weanlings available to us is, however, too small for this.

observers using two mazes. The observers take care not to make movements or to cast shadows over the Y-maze during the tests. If ataxia is to be measured this is done immediately after exploratory activity has been measured, and then the interval allowed is 11 minutes. All handling is done as gently as possible and every effort is made to minimize noise and other disturbances during the experiment.

When we started this work we used animals which had been reared under ordinary animal house conditions and results were apt to be somewhat variable from experiment to experiment. Since we have kept to the husbandry described and have also through repetition become very uniform in our treatment of the animals during experiments, our results have usually been very consistent. For example, we tested two groups of rats in the Y-maze with saline, six months apart; the members of each group were tested only once but the work was spread over a period of several weeks. When we came to compute the means of these two groups, one group had a mean of 14·7 entries in 5 minutes, S.D. 5·8 $(n = 16)$ and the other group had a mean of 14·9 entries, S.D. 7·4 $(n = 15)$.

Acknowledgments

The preparation of this paper was supported by research grant MY-3313 from the National Institute of Mental Health, U.S. Public Health Service.

REFERENCES

BARNETT, S. A. (1958). *Brit. J. Psychol.*, **49**, 289.

BERLYNE, D. E. (1960). Conflict, Arousal and Curiosity. New York: McGraw-Hill.

BINDRA, D. (1959). Motivation: A Systematic Reinterpretation. New York: Ronald Press.

BINDRA, D., and MENDELSON, J. (1962). *J. comp. physiol. Psychol.*, **55**, 217.

BLOCH, S., and SILVA, A. (1959). *J. comp. physiol. Psychol.*, **52**, 550.

BROADHURST, P. L. (1957). *Brit. J. Psychol.*, **48**, 1.

BROWN, B. (1960). *Arch int. Pharmacodyn.*, **128**, 391.

GLANZER, M. (1961). *J. comp. physiol. Psychol.*, **54**, 433.

GREENE, E. C. (1935). *Trans. Amer. phil. Soc.*, **27**, 1. (Fig. 5.)

KHAIRY, M. (1961). *In* Neuro-Psychopharmacology, **2**, 159, ed. Rothlin, E. Amsterdam: Elsevier.

MILLER, N. E. (1961). *Amer. Psychologist*, **16**, 12.

ROSS, S., and SCHNITZER, S. B. (1963). *Psychol. Rep.* **13**, 461.

RUSHTON, R., and STEINBERG, H. (1963). *Brit. J. Pharmacol.*, **21**, 295.

RUSHTON, R., STEINBERG, H., and TINSON, C. (1963). *Brit. J. Pharmacol.*, **20**, 99.

SHIRLEY, M. M. (1931). The First Two Years, p. 61. University of Minnesota Press.

STEINBERG, H., RUSHTON, R., and TINSON, C. (1961). *Nature (Lond.)*, **192**, 533.

STEINBERG, H., and WATSON, R. H. J. (1960). *Nature (Lond.)*, **185**, 615.

DISCUSSION

Wilson: Dr. Steinberg, I wish to ask two questions about your experiments with the amylobarbitone–amphetamine mixture. First, have you considered whether the previous experience of the animals with regard to how they were housed affects your results? For example, do previously isolated animals react differently in the Y-maze from previously grouped animals?

Secondly, how can this result with the mixture be applied to clinical tests in man?

Steinberg: We have compared rats which have been housed in big cages holding about fifteen with rats housed in small cages in isolation and with rats housed at three per cage. We think that previous grouping does affect performance in the Y-maze but we have not yet done enough experiments to analyse these effects fully.

As regards applicability to man, we have tried to interpret the animal experiments illustrated in Figs. 1 and 2 along the following lines. Our rats are not moved or handled at all between being weaned and being used in the experiments, about 100 days later. Being put into the Y-maze is presumably therefore a big environmental change for them. There is a good deal of evidence that novel environments evoke in animals "curiosity" or a tendency to be active on the one hand, and "fear" on the other hand, which reduces activity. If fear is very great, for example if a sudden noise or an electric shock is introduced, activity is apt to stop altogether and the animal "freezes". Hence the actual amount of activity in the Y-maze can be regarded as a sort of compromise between curiosity and fear, and on the very first occasion both these can be expected to be maximal.

It is probable that amphetamine by itself increases the tendency to be active even further, while amylobarbitone by itself, as Professor Miller has shown, is apt to reduce fear, and this would allow the effects of curiosity to manifest themselves more fully. In this way one might account for the big increase in activity with the drug mixture on the very first occasion in the Y-maze. On the other hand, when animals have become familiar with the new environment, fear has probably been largely overcome and their tendency to be active in the apparatus has become stable at what is presumably a natural level for them under these conditions; the drug mixture therefore does not affect activity.

Clinically, amphetamine-barbiturate mixtures are much used to alleviate mild anxiety. We (Dickins, D., Lader, M. H., and Steinberg, H., to be published) have used amphetamine-barbiturate mixtures with human volunteers and have also found effects which were different from effects of the separate drugs. In particular, subjects given the mixture reported feelings suggesting a cheerful, sociable mood more often than subjects who were given either constituent separately (see discussion, p. 423).

Chance: I was glad to see that Dr. Steinberg put controlled conditions of keeping her animals as a first prerequisite. She has provided a model which other people might be able to follow for listing relevant information in subsequent reporting of tests of this kind. Denenberg and his colleagues have reported effects of early infantile stimulation by separation and handling (Denenberg, V. H., and Morton, J. R. C. [1963]. *Anim. Behav.*, in press). It showed that there is a great difference between such animals, and it is excellent to see that Dr. Steinberg's animals have been kept in uniform conditions with such rigour.

There is one point which is relevant to the question of the exploration of the physical environment. We did a piece of work showing that rats become familiar with their surroundings, particularly a cage, in five days, in the sense that the interference with the rate and latency before feeding reaches a stable level after five days, when rats are tested against various degrees of unfamiliarity of the cage used for the feeding experiment. It is therefore relevant whether or not one utilizes an interval within or outside five days (Chance, M. R. A., and Mead, A. P. [1955]. *Behaviour*, **8**, 174).

I do not want to occupy a hermit's position over this question of fear, and so I should like to define my objections to the use of this term.

You will see from my histograms (pp.72-5) that the possibilities of conflict arising between the various patterns of arousal of different drive systems must be very large when we have five different drive states; and the concomitant autonomic or emotional patterns are also likely to be very varied. Therefore the idea of emotionality or of "fear", which is one specific form of emotionality, is meaningless in this context until we have understood and analysed the patterns that are likely to be present.

I might add, in further criticism of the use of this term, that it is, after all, no more than a label. I cannot agree with Professor Miller that it is, in fact, a hypothetical explanation of his results. It is merely a label, derived from our own experience and not from the experience of the rats or from our observation of them. I suspect, too, that the studies we conduct on animals are likely to revise our own view of our *own* experiences, of what we mean by feeling hungry, for example.

Steinberg: I agree that the interval at which one successively tests rats is crucial, and if one tests them every day or several times on the same day one usually finds a sharp decline in activity. In our experiments, we tested the rats twice a week with either three- or four-day intervals (in preliminary tests we found that it made no difference whether it was three days or four days) and we found the eventual stabilization of activity shown in Fig. 1 (p. 209).

As regards the interpretation of the results in terms of fear, there are, of course, other possibilities. For example, the drug mixture might impair perception and/or memory in such a way that the "inexperienced" animals fail to recognize that they have been in a particular arm of the maze before and so keep going back. We hope one day to investigate this experimentally. Again, one might simply say that we have demonstrated that animals which have had previous experience of the environment are less sensitive to the stimulant effects of this drug mixture than animals which have not had previous experience. But one usually tries to go further and look for explanations, even if for the time being they are very tentative explanations.

Knight: Have you tried to interpret the differences between the habituated or experienced rats and the naive rats in your maze experiments as due to differences in levels of "arousal"? Have you, for example, made neurophysiological measurements to study this?

Steinberg: We have considered this, but have not so far been able to investigate neurophysiological differences.

Hollyhock: Dr. Steinberg, I should be grateful for some clarification concerning defecation. This slightly mundane point arises in connexion with your Y-maze and, of course, with Hall's open field. We are accustomed to hearing this referred to as emotional defecation caused by apprehension in the new environment. But may it not be allied to the defecation shown by rats in their natural conditions when establishing new runs? It has been suggested that they are here providing themselves with olfactory servo-clues to their exploratory behaviour. It would be relevant to know whether the defecation rate tends to fall more readily if the Y-maze, or the Hall's field, is cleaned out after the first run and then again on succeeding runs.

Steinberg: I agree that the interpretation of defecation is not straightforward. The defecation curve in Fig. 1 went down very markedly with increased familiarity with the maze, and settled down at zero at about the same time as the exploratory curve settled to its stable level. But whether this decline in defecation means that the animals were less afraid of the new environment, or that they had established their territorial claims and so did not need to defecate any more because this was now in some sense *their* runway, is impossible to say. We did clean the runway carefully after each trial.

Broadhurst: This problem of the validity of defecation as a measure of emotional responsiveness has exercised us greatly. In our experiments employing bi-directional selective breeding for this characteristic in the rat, we have assumed that it is related in some way to fear responsiveness, and my impression from a review of the literature is that this identification stands up fairly well. But the crucial test is how such selected strains behave in situations other than that used for the actual selection—Hall's open-field test of emotional elimination. We have tried these strains in many other behavioural situations thought to arouse fear. In general, the animals from the emotionally reactive, high defecating strain behave in the way you would expect more fearful animals to behave, and *vice versa* with the non-reactive strain. But it does seem that in a situation such as escape-avoidance conditioning, in which it is disadvantageous for rats to be emotionally reactive (because freezing and other emotional responses interfere with the response to be learned), the reactive strain learns less quickly than the non-reactive (Broadhurst, P. L., and Levine, S. [1963]. *Brit. J. Psychol.*, **54**, 121).

Barnett: From my observations of wild rats I doubt whether defecating rats in a Y-maze are indulging in territorial marking. If you have a male wild rat in a cage and you put in another male, the resident precedes his attack on the newcomer by approaching with raised hair; and as he does so he defecates and urinates. He is in an environment entirely familiar to himself, already well covered by his odour trails (which are attractive to other rats); and the whole performance looks, to put it anthropomorphically, as though he is extremely worked up about something (Barnett, S. A. [1958]. *Proc. zool. Soc. Lond.*, **130**, 107; Barnett, S. A. [1958]. *J. psychosom. Res.*, **3**, 11; Barnett, S. A., Eaton, J. C., and McCallum, H. M. [1960]. *J. psychosom. Res.*, **4**, 251). I am therefore very sympathetic to people who think that defecation in these conditions has some significance in terms of emotion, fear, and so on.

Payne: Alternatively, this might be an aggressive response, by which the animal proves it to be his territory.

THE HEREDITARY BASE FOR THE ACTION OF DRUGS ON ANIMAL BEHAVIOUR

P. L. Broadhurst

Institute of Psychiatry, University of London

Hereditary influences manifest themselves in many ways. They can so alter the whole character of an organism's development, as in various inborn errors of metabolism, that genetic determination of the phenotype observed is virtually complete. At the other extreme there are subtle effects, which may make themselves felt only in an appropriate environment. Moreover it is axiomatic that the expression of a particular genotype will vary according to the environmental setting. Behaviour is the outcome of the interaction of genetic and environmental forces, and the environmental contribution is subject to modification in many ways. One of these is by the action of drugs.The environmental effects detected in such interaction with hereditary determinants can relate to major changes in the life history and experience of an animal rather than to those usually associated with transient and often reversible drug action. But this need not be so; it is well known that apparently trivial experiences can profoundly influence later behaviour. The differences in drug response due to the environmental effects of previous psychological experience (Rushton and Steinberg, 1964) or diet (Watson, 1964) are cases in point, and may be regarded as environmental manipulations, which may or may not summate with drug action in determining the phenotypic expression of the behaviour we observe. Thus drug action can be thought of as a special way of manipulating the environment of an organism, in this case its intimate internal environment. Hence the nature of hereditary influences on drug action can be regarded as part of the larger question of the interaction of hereditary and environmental determinants, a question which is central to the study of behavioural inheritance. The attack on this problem has hardly been attempted yet, even for simple behavioural traits in animals.

However, there are signs of movement in this field, since psychogenetics, or, as our American colleagues call it, behaviour genetics, is fortunately undergoing something of a revival after many years of comparative neglect. In the last decade there has been a resurgence of interest, and at the same time as this revival, and perhaps as a contributory stimulus to it, there has been a recognition of the nature of the problem of the genetic analysis of behaviour. In general, behaviour shows quantitative variation rather than the discontinuous variation with discrete phenotypes which was first analysed by Mendel and is found in many characteristics of domestic animals. Such continuous variation yields poorly to classical Mendelian analysis based on the postulated action of two or three genes of major action, and it has been the absence of a suitable method of analysis for continuous variation which has, in the past, led to disappointing results from attempts to analyse behavioural inheritance. However, in the past forty years mathematical methods have been developed which are based on the assumption of the additive action of many genes of small individual effects, and these have greatly altered the situation. It has now been demonstrated that the application of these methods of biometrical genetics (Mather, 1949) has a place in the analysis of behavioural inheritance (Broadhurst, 1960; Broadhurst and Jinks, 1961), and these methods may eventually help us to unravel the interaction of hereditary and environmental, including pharmacological, determinants of behaviour in a way hitherto not attempted. But it must be confessed that so far little has been done in this connexion. Accordingly, what follows is more of a blueprint for future research than a record of work accomplished. However, some of it indicates possible lines of attack.

NATURE OF HERITABLE VARIATION IN DRUG RESPONSE

Pharmacologists have long been unpleasantly aware of individual differences in reactions to drugs both in man and animals (Irwin, Slabok and Thomas, 1958), and sometimes it has been possible to implicate constitutional variables. Such constitutional effects are usually classified as species differences, strain differences and sex differences. Of these the most important in the present context are strain differences, but it is worth while noticing a few examples of the interaction of drugs with the other two constitutional determinants of behaviour.

Species differences in behavioural responses to drugs can be quite striking. Differences in the action of some analgesics and anaesthetics depend on the nature of the biochemical process involved (Brodie, 1956) and especially upon differences in the rate of metabolism of the drug. Thus there are marked differences between the mouse, rat, rabbit and dog in the duration of action of hexobarbitone (Quinn, Axelrod and Brodie, 1958).

Sex differences have unfortunately been less studied in comparative psychology than they deserve, so that there are few examples of sex differences in behavioural responses to drugs. However, Wallgren (1959) has shown that male rats have a lower threshold than females for inco-ordination of motor responses in the tilting plane test after the same dose of ethanol. The female rat, on the other hand, displays a fourfold greater susceptibility to hexobarbitone than the male (Brodie, 1962).

Much more has been written about *strain differences* both in pharmacology and in psychology. Consider the action of hexobarbitone: different inbred strains of mice show as much as 500 per cent variation in sleeping time in response to the same dose (Jay, 1955). This contrasts with the more uniform response given by members of the same strain, as is usually the case. A difference in variability between such inbred strains and the F_1 hybrids derived by crossing them was pointed out some time ago by Mather (1946). Its importance for biological assay lies in the fact that the heterozygous F_1's are often less variable in response than their homozygous inbred parents (Biggers, McLaren and Michie, 1958; Becker and Chai, 1962). There is disagreement, however, as to whether this is also true for behavioural traits. While Caspari (1958) notes that behavioural phenotypes might differ characteristically from other phenotypes in the absence of an F_1 variance lower than that of the parental generations, Broadhurst and Jinks report in a recent review (1961) that some 40 per cent of the many cases they examine *do* show the effect. The conclusion seems to be emerging that there are no hard and fast rules regarding the superiority of pure-breds or hybrids for drug assay, and that each case must be judged on its merits. That is to say, the hereditary (strain) determinants interact with the environmental ones (such as the drug being used and the conditions of test) in different ways in different cases, much as one might expect.

Psychological differences between strains are also frequently reported: Fuller and Thompson (1960) and Broadhurst (1960) give reviews which are, however, already outdated by the rapidly growing volume of work in this area. The strain differences studied have been of two kinds: first, differences between different strains, usually inbred, derived by selection for some particular behavioural characteristic and secondly, differences between strains which have been selected for other, usually somatic, characteristics of little interest to the psychologist. Most of the studies using drugs have been done on the former, though it is to be anticipated that once psychopharmacological differences have been widely established between other inbred strains already in existence, greater use will be made of them. An example is the aggregation response in mice given amphetamine, which leads to a greater toxicity of this drug in crowded as opposed to isolated animals (Chance, 1946) and which has been shown to be partly dependent upon strain (Weaver and Kerley, 1962).

The creation of new strains by selection can take several forms. Animals can be selected directly for a given drug action, so that the phenotype is the differential sensitivity for the drug. This is the way in which strains of bacteria resistant to antibiotics of various kinds arise, though here natural, as opposed to artificial, selection is operating. Examples of deliberate selection of this kind are less common: one is a bi-directional selection for high and low thyroid response following the administration of thiouracil to chickens (Shaklee and Shaffner, 1955) and of radioactive iodine to rats (Sunder, 1960); another is the use for selection of the sedation threshold (Shagass, 1954) determined by the injection of pentobarbitone in mice (Cornetsky, personal communication). Chase (1950) selected for insulin tolerance among mice which were derived from a cross between insulin-susceptible and resistant strains, and found a marked increase in the proportion of individuals in successive generations which tolerated the initially maximum dose.

The more usual form of selection experiment has been to breed for a behavioural characteristic and then to study a correlated change in drug susceptibility. Two different sets of bi-directionally selected rat strains of this kind have been especially used in psychopharmacology: they are the descendants of the strains selected for "maze-brightness" and "maze-dullness", by Tryon (1942), and the Maudsley Reactive and Non-Reactive Strains (Broadhurst, 1960, 1962) selected for emotional elimination in Hall's open-field test (1934).

USE OF SELECTED STRAINS IN PSYCHOPHARMACOLOGY

The Maudsley strains

The Maudsley strains have been in existence since 1954, when selection for high and low defecation was started, and have reached what appears to be a stable level of response to the selection practised up to the fifteenth generation (S_{15}), as may be seen from Fig. I. The relaxation of selection for five generations in which the parents of each subsequent generation were selected at random has not led to a reversion towards the original, parental value. These strains have been used in many investigations, some

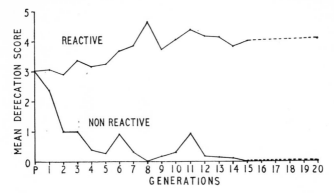

FIG. I. Progress of selection in the Maudsley Reactive and Non-Reactive Strains: ordinate, the mean number of faecal boluses deposited by each rat during four successive daily trials in the standardized open-field test; abscissa, the successive generations in the experiment. Solid lines indicate the response to the selection pressure exerted up to S_{15}; pecked lines, the response to the relaxation of both selection and measurement thereafter, until the latter was resumed at S_{20}.

involving drugs, which have often but not always (Sinha, Franks and Broadhurst, 1958) led to the identification of an interaction between the effect of the hereditary (strain) and environmental (drug) variables. Among early examples are the work of Watson (1960) and of Singh (1961; Singh and Eysenck, 1960). A recent finding involving such an interaction comes from studies of the effect of alcohol upon learning to escape from shock (J. A. Easterbrook, personal communication). The significant interaction of strain and drug effects may be seen in

Fig. 2. Ethanol appears to have facilitated, at least in the intermediate dose, the acquisition of the response among the reactive
rats. It is tempting to assume that the greater behavioural
responsiveness among the reactive rats to fear stimuli of many
sorts—an effect observed in many tests other than those involving

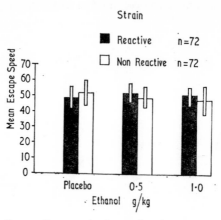

FIG. 2. Drug–strain interaction in response
to ethanol. The bar diagram shows the mean
and standard deviation of the speed scores
(expressed as $100\sqrt{[1/(t+1)]}$ where $t=$ time
in seconds) of escape from shock by pushing
a panel. Three groups of female rats of the
S_{14} and S_{15} generations of the Maudsley
strains were used and ethanol was given orally
in the doses indicated. Data supplied by
J. A. Easterbrook (personal communication).

drug responses (Eysenck and Broadhurst, 1963)—is depressed by
ethanol so that the escape response is learnt more efficiently in a
way usually characteristic of the non-reactive strain.

The difference between the strains in situations involving
escape from shock is more clearly seen in escape-avoidance
conditioning in the usual shuttle box arrangement. As has been
noted, the emotionally reactive rats are at a disadvantage here
and do not acquire the avoidance response with the same facility

as the non-reactive ones (Broadhurst and Levine, 1963). It is interesting to note that small doses of reserpine have been reported to facilitate the acquisition of this response, in contrast to the usual blocking action on the performance of the learned response

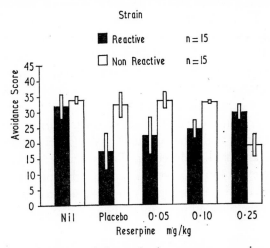

FIG. 3. Drug–strain interaction in response to reserpine. The bar diagram shows the mean and standard deviation of the number of avoidance responses made in 50 trials in learning a running response to a buzzer, the onset of which preceded that of the shock by 8 sec. Five groups of male and female rats of the S_{20} generation of the Maudsley strains were used, and reserpine was injected intraperitoneally two hours before the beginning of training, which lasted one hour.

of this and other types of tranquillizers (Walk, Owens and David-son, 1961). This effect of reserpine parallels the strain difference just referred to, and an attempt was made to manipulate the relative standing of the two strains by giving reserpine. The outcome was a significant interaction between strain and drug of the now familiar type shown in Fig. 3, but it cannot be claimed that its interpretation is entirely obvious. Most striking is the differ-ence between the two strains in the placebo reaction, which is not significant on its own account, but clearly contributes to the total effect. Two possible hypotheses merit further investigation. First, the intraperitoneal injection used might be more traumatic for the emotionally reactive strain and its effects, even two hours later, might interfere with the acquisition of the avoidance response. The suggestive increase in the avoidance score with successively increasing doses of reserpine might, if confirmed, bear out this view. Secondly, the fact that the blank vehicle used in the placebo contains a compound which may be psychopharmacologically active should not be overlooked. This compound is benzyl alcohol and the volume of the injections was such that each rat received 20 mg./kg. of it; this is a very small dose compared with the amounts given when other alcohol congeners are used. Moreover, Easterbrook's findings would lead one to expect an effect on this strain in the opposite direction, so that perhaps this explanation can be discounted and attention focused on the possibly more interesting psychological one.

The Tryon strains

The other psychogenetic selection experiment which has figured in psychopharmacological work, Tryon's study of rodent intelligence in mazes, has been especially fruitful. McGaugh and his associates have used the descendants of these strains in a study of the effects of drugs on the consolidation of learning. They had previously shown that rats injected with strychnine sulphate before testing gave an improved performance on a standard maze (McGaugh and Petrinovich, 1959), whereas injection, *after testing*, of the medullary stimulant picrotoxin, facilitated the learning and retention of the maze-dull strain more than of the maze-bright rats (Breen and McGaugh, 1961), as shown in Fig. 4. The absence of a significant superiority of the maze-bright strain in this case is attributable to testing conditions somewhat different from those used for the original selection (McGaugh, Jennings and Thomson, 1962) and reflects the lack of generality of the trait. McGaugh, Westbrook and Burt (1961) further showed that injection of the drug diphenyl-diazadamantan, which has a strychnine-like action, also gives a similar effect according to the strain used, and further that its effect upon the F_1 or hybrid cross from these two strains can also be differentiated, as may be seen in Fig. 5. This has made possible one of the few analyses of the

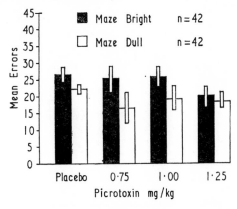

FIG. 4. Drug–strain interaction in response to picrotoxin. The bar diagram shows the mean and standard deviation of the number of errors made in six successive daily trials in a 14-unit T-maze for a food reward. Four groups of male and female rats, descendants of the Tryon strains, were used and picrotoxin was injected intraperitoneally in the doses indicated 30 sec. after each trial. After Breen and McGaugh (1961).

hereditary determinants of a drug action as such (Isaeva and Krasuskii, 1961). We can now analyse two phenotypes, first, the response of the strains and their first filial cross to the drug administered and secondly, the phenotype derived from the same strains and their cross under the placebo injection procedure. In this case, biometrical analysis suggests that the performance on placebo shows a strong heritable component with no significant dominance, whereas under the drug this heritable component disappears due, no doubt, to the levelling-up effect on the means as shown in Fig. 5: the environmental or drug effect is strong enough to swamp heritable differences. But this analysis is technically unsatisfactory for several reasons. More elaborate

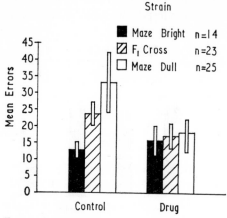

FIG. 5. Drug–strain interaction in response to diphenyl-diazadamantan. The bar diagram shows the mean and standard deviation of the number of errors made in 14 trials on four successive days in a four-unit maze for a food reward. Six groups of male and female rats, descendants of the Tryon strains and the F_1 cross between them, were used and 1·0 mg./kg. diphenyl-diazadamantan was injected intra-peritoneally 10 min. before the first of the daily trials. After McGaugh, Westbrook and Burt (1961).

analyses of data especially collected for the purpose are needed; an estimate could then also be made of the stability, as opposed to the extent, of the drug response, over which some genetical control is almost certain to be exerted.

The future

Sufficient may have been said to indicate that selection can be a powerful technique in the manipulation of hereditary determinants, when it is desired to vary in a controlled manner the constitutional background of environmental, and especially drug, action. Selection can be made for purely behavioural characteristics, and other such experiments will doubtless be undertaken. Appropriate selection techniques can be used to establish populations which differ reliably, not in one constitutional characteristic, but in two or more simultaneously. The psychopharmacologist will then be able to specify in advance the behavioural constitution of the animal population he requires for screening or other experimental work, just as the market research worker can specify a preference test of products on a sample stratified according to intelligence and social class. Populations may thus be chosen which differ in known ways in respect of the animal counterparts of characteristics of human personality such as emotionality, intelligence and introversion-extroversion. In this way a more secure basis for our understanding of drug action may be achieved, and our knowledge of the hereditary mechanisms contributing to such action may be increased.

REFERENCES

BECKER, W. A., and CHAI, C. K. (1962). *Nature (Lond.)*, **193**, 1264.

BIGGERS, J. D., McLAREN, A., and MICHIE, D. (1958). *Nature (Lond.)*, **182**, 77.

BREEN, R. A., and McGAUGH, J. L. (1961) *J. comp. physiol. Psychol.*, **54**, 498.

BROADHURST, P. L. (1960). *In* Experiments in Personality: Vol. I. Psychogenetics and Psychopharmacology, p. 1, ed. Eysenck, H. J. London: Routledge and Kegan Paul.

BROADHURST, P. L. (1962). *Psychol. Rep.*, **10**, 65.

BROADHURST, P. L., and JINKS, J. L. (1961). *Psychol. Bull.*, **58**, 337.

BROADHURST, P. L., and LEVINE, S. (1963). *Brit. J. Psychol.*, **56**, 423.

BRODIE, B. B. (1956). *J. Pharm. Pharmacol.*, **8**, 1.

BRODIE, B. B. (1962). *Ciba Found. Symp. Enzymes and Drug Action*, p. 317. London: Churchill.

CASPARI, E. (1958). *In* Behavior and Evolution, p. 103, ed. Roe, Anne, and Simpson, G. G. New Haven: Yale University Press.

CHANCE, M. R. A. (1946). *J. Pharmacol. exp. Ther.*, **87**, 214.

CHASE, H. B. (1950). *Genetics*, **35**, 101.

EYSENCK, H. J., and BROADHURST, P. L. (1963). *In* Experiments in Motivation, p. 285, ed. Eysenck, H. J. London: Pergamon.

FULLER, J. L., and THOMPSON, W. R. (1960). Behavior Genetics. New York: Wiley.

HALL, C. S. (1934). *J. comp. Psychol.*, **18**, 385.

IRWIN, S., SLABOK, M., and THOMAS, G. (1958). *J. Pharmacol. exp. Ther.*, **123**, 206.

ISAEVA, I. I., and KRASUSKII, V. K. (1961). *Dokl. Akad. Nauk SSSR.*, **141**, 248.

JAY, G. E., Jnr. (1955). *Proc. Soc. exp. Biol.* (*N.Y.*), **90**, 378.

MATHER, K. (1946). *Analyst*, **71**, 407.

MATHER, K. (1949). Biometrical Genetics. London: Methuen.

McGAUGH, J. L., JENNINGS, R. D., and THOMSON, C. W. (1962). *Psychol. Rep.*, **10**, 147.

McGAUGH, J. L., and PETRINOVICH, L. (1959). *Amer. J. Psychol.*, **72**, 99.

McGAUGH, J. L., WESTBROOK, W., and BURT, G. (1961). *J. comp. physiol. Psychol.*, **54**, 502.

QUINN, G. P., AXELROD, J., and BRODIE, B. B. (1958). *Biochem. Pharmacol.*, **1**, 152.

RUSHTON, R., and STEINBERG, H. (1964). This volume, p. 207.

SHAGASS, C. (1954). *Electroenceph. clin. Neurophysiol.*, **6**, 221.

SHAKLEE, W. E., and SHAFFNER, C. S. (1955). *Poultry Sci.*, **34**, 572.

SINGH, S. D. (1961). *J. psychol. Res.*, **5**, 1.

SINGH, S. D., and EYSENCK, H. J. (1960). *J. gen. Psychol.*, **63**, 275.

SINHA, S. N., FRANKS, C. M., and BROADHURST, P. L. (1958). *J. exp. Psychol.*, **56**, 349.

SUNDER, J. H. (1960). *Fed. Proc.*, **19**, 172. (Abstract.)

TRYON, R. C. (1942). *In* Comparative Psychology (2nd ed.), p. 330, ed. Moss, F. A. New York: Prentice Hall.

WALK, R. D., OWENS, J. W. M., and DAVIDSON, BETTY S. (1961). *Psychol. Rep.*, **8**, 251.

WALLGREN, H. (1959). *Nature* (*Lond.*), **184**, 726.

WATSON, R. H. J. (1960). Proc. IVth Europ. Conf. on Psychosomatic Research, p. 160, ed. Jores, A., and Freyberger, H. Basel: Karger.

WATSON, R. H. J. (1964). This volume, p. 249.

WEAVER, L. C., and KERLEY, T. L. (1962). *J. Pharmacol. exp. Ther.*, **135**, 240.

DISCUSSION

Chance: Dr. Broadhurst, was the variance of the two different emotionally reactive strains of rats changed by your selection procedure, which separated their mean performance quite considerably?

Broadhurst: The variances for the first fifteen generations show a small but significant decrease.

Hurwitz: In distinguishing between the reactive and non-reactive strains of animals you cite the results of an experiment employing a discriminative avoidance technique. One must be cautious in using the results of such an experiment for the purpose of identifying psychological process variables. Recent work by Smith and his co-workers (Smith, O. A., McFarland, W. L., and Taylor, E. [1961]. *J. comp. physiol. Psychol.*, **54**, 154) has shown that much of what has been classified under conditioned avoidance behaviour should more properly be subsumed under the heading of pseudo-conditioning. Their experiments showed that any stimulus change in an environment in which punishment is periodically given comes to trigger off responses which have served to terminate such punishment or which have a topographical affinity to such responses. Did the experiments you have cited include controls for pseudo-conditioning?

Broadhurst: The interpretation of the psychological processes is a difficult one and I share your desire to know what actually is happening. I do not, however, think that the explanation can be quite as simple as differential shock sensitivity. This we know from the active programme of research we have at the moment which shows that the strain differences are not only behavioural but also physiological, and relate especially to their endocrine status. This work has been in progress for some years in collaboration with Dr. Feuer (Feuer, G., and Broadhurst, P. L. [1962]. *J. Endocr.*, **24**, 127, 253, and 385). Moreover, I do not at the moment accept your evaluation of pseudo-conditioning as an important element in avoidance learning. We routinely allow habituation to the buzzer to take place before introducing the shock, so there should be no pseudo-conditioned avoidance responses from that source.

Hurwitz: I did some work on the use of defecation as a predictor in experiments on learning ten years ago, but this has only recently been reported. In these experiments we found that, some time in advance of the animal changing its behaviour to conform to a change in the experimental condition, it defecated. This is, of course, a different use of the defecation measure from that described in your experiments (Hurwitz, H. M. B., Bolas, D., and Haritos, M. [1961]. *Brit. J. Psychol.*, **52**, 377).

THE EFFECTS OF GROUP COMPOSITION ON DRUG ACTION

C. W. M. WILSON AND R. E. A. MAPES

*Department of Pharmacology and General Therapeutics,
University of Liverpool*

WHEN considering the relationship between the composition of experimental groups and the effects of drugs on the animals in the groups, it must be realized that the familiarity of the animal group with its environment always has an underlying effect on its behaviour. This environmental effect modifies group behaviour. Introduction or removal of animals influences group stability, which indicates the extent to which the individual animals are integrated together to form socially stable groups. When the effect of drugs on animal behaviour is being investigated, a further variable factor is introduced into an already complicated experimental situation.

The investigator should take these factors into account in relation to the experimental design and consider to what extent they may influence his experimental results. The factors, together or separately, may affect the actions of drugs on the animals to which they are administered. If the experimental animals see, or come into contact with, untreated animals, the latter may influence the behaviour of the former. It is rare for untreated animals to come into contact with treated animals during the course of an experiment; but if an animal which has been treated with a drug shortly before the experiment is placed in the experimental group, the behaviour of the treated animal will influence behaviour of the other animals in the group.

The influence of the physical environment

Chance and Mackintosh (1962) have described this as the Home Cage effect in their discussion on the effects of caging. It is clear that this effect does not extend only to the animals' normal environment, to their home cage, but also includes any physical environment on which a group establishes a claim through prior occupation or as a result of group dominance. Chance and Mackintosh (1962) suggested that this phenomenon varies between

Table I

MEAN ACTIVITY RATES OF SIX STABLE GROUPS OF NINE MICE EACH, BEFORE AND AFTER
TREATMENT WITH THALIDOMIDE. ACTIVITY EXPRESSED AS TOTAL
GROUP ACTIVITY PER 2½-MINUTE PERIOD

Experimental observations	Stable groups		Significance level
	Untreated	Thalidomide treated	
No. of mice per group	9	9	
No. of tests	36	36	
Initial activity	158·0± 33·4	150·7± 38·4	P=0·4
Minimum activity	50·3	13·5	
No. of tests in which zero activity was reached	None	6	
Period (mins.) required to attain activity rate of 50·3	30·0±6·5	16·5±5·8	P=0·001

animals in relation to their territoriality, but they indicate that under normal conditions there is a tendency for animals in their own cages to have the best of any encounters. Introduction of an animal group into a new environment stimulates exploratory activity, and Dews (1953) used this exploratory stimulus as the basis of his method for measuring activity. The exploratory phase of a stable group of nine mice becomes exhausted after 30 minutes in an activity box, and its activity becomes reduced to a minimal basic value (Table I). However, if the group is treated with thalidomide half an hour before being introduced into the box, the duration of this phase is significantly reduced and the activity of the mice is much less than when they are untreated. Exhaustion of the exploratory phase suggests that the group has established the bounds of its territory and that social stability has been effected in the new environment. The physical environment has profound effects on the behaviour of isolated and grouped animals. Heimstra (1962) has however shown that when a rat is introduced into a novel physical environment the effect of the latter is less important than the effect of simultaneous social stimulation, and Wilson (1962) has demonstrated that the introduction of a "rogue" mouse into a stable group of mice in their home cage causes significant alterations in their behaviour.

The size of animal groups

Wilson (1963) has pointed out that the size of the group in pharmacological experiments is of considerable importance, but that there is little information about what the optimum group size is. It has been shown that gastric ulcers induced by phenylbutazone are significantly more severe in rats housed singly than in rats which are grouped two or four to a cage (Fig. 1) (Martindale Somers and Wilson, 1960). Chance (1946) has shown that alteration of group size from 32 down to 2 animals per group causes significant changes in the toxicity of sympathomimetic amines in mice. This effect has been confirmed by Höhn and Lasagna (1960) and by Greenblatt and Osterberg (1961). These investigators made the assumption that the mouse groups which they used were homogeneous and stable, and that only the size of the groups affected the mean values in their experimental results. However, more recent work by Chance and Mackintosh (1962) has demonstrated that the variance of the experimental observations is affected by altering the size of the experimental groups. It is important, therefore, that effects should not be attributed to drugs which may be partly explained by alterations in behaviour.

Such alterations may be brought about by changes in group size with their consequent effects on group structure.

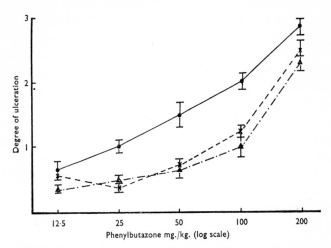

FIG. I. Ulcerative action of phenylbutazone in grouped and single rats. Each point is the mean, with the standard error, from four rats. I per cage (●—●); 2 per cage (×--×); 4 per cage (▲-.-▲).

The degree of social stability in animal groups

The development of stereotyped behaviour patterns and consequent social stability in groups of mice has been little investigated. Single mice are reported to build up aggression and stereotyped behaviour patterns quickly after isolation (Chance and Mackintosh, 1962). Grant and Chance (1958) have shown that rank order becomes established in groups of four rats within two weeks and remains stable thereafter. Our experiments with mice have demonstrated that territoriality, as assessed by exhaustion of exploratory activity, becomes established within a few hours. Other experiments suggest that social stability, as assessed by movements of individual mice, may become established within 1–2 days. It is therefore probable that intense social activity will be taking place during the first few days after previously isolated mice have been introduced to each other in a new home cage. It will be maximal at the time of introduction and will then gradually diminish. It is to be anticipated that it will be more intense in groups of previously isolated mice than in groups made up of strangers taken from previously stable groups. In our experiments we have assumed that group social stability is established after a minimum period of one week in the home cage.

Höhn and Lasagna (1960) and Greenblatt and Osterberg (1961) used previously isolated mice which were strangers to each other in order to maintain the constancy of variable factors in their aggregation experiments; however, since their experiments continued for four hours or longer it is clear that their groups were socially unstable at the beginning of the experiments, and that some degree of rank order and social stability was effected while the stimulant drugs were acting during the course of the experiments. In her experiments on aggregation, Askew (1962) maintained group size at the expense of group stability by replacing mice which had died (after the administration of amphetamine) by unknown strangers. There is evidence that social stability is an important factor in experiments in which the action of drugs is examined on animal groups. However the time required for, and the extent of, its development before and during the experiments have been little considered.

The effect of social stimuli in animal groups

Greenblatt and Osterberg (1961) realized the importance of social stimuli in their experiments. They took precautions to ensure that mice in one cage were not able to see mice in other cages. Heimstra (1962) measured the effect of social stimuli more fully. He examined the behaviour of single amphetamine-treated and control rats which were separated from unstable groups of three animals by a fine-mesh cloth barrier, and found that amphetamine increased barrier–directed activity.

Wilson (1963) has investigated the effect of a social stimulus on the production of audiogenic seizures. He introduced non-sensitive isolated "rogue" mice into stable groups of five seizure-sensitive mice in their home cages (Table II). The introduction of one rogue significantly increased the severity of the seizures in comparison with their severity in control groups. Two rogues did not however increase the seizure severity so much, and the effect of the social stimulus also appeared to be related to strain differences in the rogue mice. These experiments indicated that a social stimulus, isolated from any stimulation produced by

Table II

EFFECT OF CHANGES IN GROUP STRUCTURE ON
SEVERITY OF AUDIOGENIC SEIZURES

Group characters 5 CE/LAB	Rogues introduced	No. of tests	Severity of group seizures		Significance stable vs. others
			M	SE	
Stable	None	64	11·00	0·53	—
Unstable	1 Schofield	16	14·25	0·94	P < 0·005
Unstable	1 Balb/C	45	15·02	0·59	P < 0·001
Unstable	2 Schofield	29	13·66	0·99	P < 0·01
Unaffected	2 Balb/C	29	13·10	1·19	P < 0·07

M: Mean   SE: Standard error

change in the physical environment, produced a significant alteration in the behaviour of the stable groups. The stimulus was less marked when two rogues were used because their attention was directed towards each other as well as towards the group. Fighting occurred between the rogues and between group members; the stereotyped behaviour pattern of the groups was altered, and the extent of this alteration was related to the degree of disruption of social stability in the groups.

Mapes and Wilson (1963) have investigated disruption of social stability in relation to activity by introducing varying numbers of strangers into stable groups of nine mice. Social stimuli were produced by removing members of the stable groups and intro-ducing strangers, unknown to each other or to the groups, in their places. The experiments were performed in three phases: during phase 1, the stable groups became accustomed to the environment of the activity box, during phase 2, one to five group members

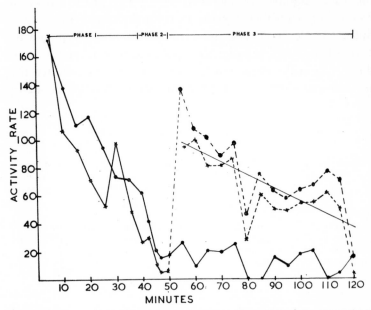

FIG. 2. Activity rates of a stable group of nine mice, 9G (●—●), which was undisturbed throughout the three phases of the experiment, and of a stable group, 9G(×—×), which was altered to a group containing four residual group members, 4G, during phase 2 (×--●). During phase 3, five strangers, 5S, were added to the latter group. The total activity of the newly formed group is shown by the upper line (●--●), and the activity of the residual group members alone is shown by the lower line, during phase 3 (×--×). The continuous straight line is the calculated regression line for residual group activity, 4G.

were removed, and during phase 3, group members were replaced by strangers. The experimental method is illustrated in Fig. 2.

Tests were carried out on six stable groups before and after treatment with a dose of thalidomide which reduced group activity but caused the mice to go to sleep only momentarily.

Stranger activity was counted independently of that of the group members. Examination of the results during the third phase involved the comparison of activities of residual groups varying in size from four to nine animals. It was essential to take this factor into account when analysing the results; accordingly, the activity of residual group members was weighted up to nine and

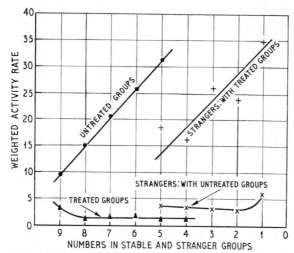

FIG. 3. Mean weighted activity rates of untreated and treated residual groups, and of untreated strangers introduced into the groups, during phase 3. Untreated groups (●—●); treated groups (▲—▲); strangers with treated groups (+ —+); strangers with untreated groups (× —×).

the activity of the strangers was weighted up to five. Comparisons were then made by the use of a nonparametric method for the analysis of variance.

Removal of group members caused an increase in activity which was proportional to the number of members removed. This did not occur after the groups had been treated with thalidomide. When strangers were introduced into the groups there was a much greater increase in residual group activity, which was proportional to the numbers of strangers introduced (Fig. 3).

Stranger activity, however, always remained low and was almost independent of the number of strangers introduced. When the groups were treated with thalidomide, the reverse situation occurred. The untreated strangers assumed the dominant active rôle previously played by the residual group members, and the treated group members became inactive and apparently socially disrupted. Some evidence was obtained which suggested that thalidomide positively inhibited social stability in the groups.

When investigating exploratory behaviour in individual rats Steinberg, Rushton and Tinson (1961) attributed alterations in behaviour to the net result of competition between the two opposing tendencies of curiosity and fear as elicited by a novel situation. Such reactions are affected by the physical environment of the animals and the extent to which they have become habituated to it. When animal groups are investigated, these two reactions play a part in determining behaviour, but the behaviour pattern will also be influenced by the social relationships which have been allowed to develop between individual animals before or during the course of the experiments.

The relationship between group behaviour and drug action has been little investigated in animals, but the experiments which have been done have demonstrated conclusively that drug action is affected by group interactions. In man it is generally acknowledged that the social environment does influence the action of centrally acting drugs. The effect of these drugs can generally be assessed in patients, but their effect on groups of patients has been little investigated, and the effects produced on the people with whom the patients come into contact is completely unknown. Study of these factors in animal experiments might provide a method of predicting the effects of drugs on man in his social environment.

REFERENCES

ASKEW, B. M. (1962). *Brit. J. Pharmacol.*, **19**, 245.
CHANCE, M. R. A. (1946). *J. Pharmacol. exp. Ther.*, **87**, 214.

CHANCE, M. R. A., and MACKINTOSH, J. H. (1962). *Coll. Pap. M.R.C. Lab. Anim. Centre*, **11**, 59.

DEWS, P. B. (1953). *Brit. J. Pharmacol.*, **8**, 46.

GRANT, E. C., and CHANCE, M. R. A. (1958). *Anim. Behav.*, **6**, 183.

GREENBLATT, E. N., and OSTERBERG, A. C. (1961). *J. Pharmacol. exp. Ther.*, **131**, 115.

HEIMSTRA, N. W. (1962). *J. Psychol.*, **53**, 233.

HÖHN, R., and LASAGNA, L. (1960). *Psychopharmacologia*, **1**, 210.

MAPES, R. E. A., and WILSON, C. W. M. (1963). *Psychopharmacologia*, in press.

MARTINDALE, K., SOMERS, G. F., and WILSON, C. W. M. (1960). *J. Pharm. Pharmacol.*, **12**, 153T.

STEINBERG, H., RUSHTON, R., and TINSON, C. (1961). *Nature (Lond.)*, **192**, 533.

WILSON, C. W. M. (1962). *J. Physiol. (Lond.)*, **163**, 44P.

WILSON, C. W. M. (1963). *In* C.N.R.S. Coll. The Psychophysiology, Neuropharmacology and Biochemistry of the Audiogenic Seizure, p. 51. Paris: Centre National de la Recherche Scientifique.

DISCUSSION

Irwin: Dr. Wilson, did you employ any selection in removing members from the in-group before bringing strangers in, perhaps with regard to positions in the dominance hierarchy which had been established within the group, or did you remove them on a more or less random basis?

Wilson: We carried out two experiments, using the same animals in each. In the second experiment we treated the animals with thalidomide. In both experiments we removed animals from the stable groups according to a Latin square, so that all the animals were removed at some time during the experiments. The strangers also were randomly selected from the groups from which they had been taken, by means of a Latin square. Consequently, we think that these experiments do not give us any direct information about group hierarchy, but they do give us information about the behaviour of animals in group situations during the development of social stability in a familiar environment. Social stability itself is dependent upon the development of group hierarchy, and we have evidence that activity in a familiar environment provides a measure of social stability.

Bonta: Dr. Wilson, you mentioned that the response to phenylbutazone in terms of ulcer formation was dependent on whether the drug was given to animals in a group or to isolated animals. In work on ulcers caused by restraint-stress, Bonfils found that the formation of ulcers was much enhanced when many animals were together in one room and was less when the animals were isolated (Bonfils, S., Liefooghe, G., Rossi, G., and Lambling, A. [1957]. *C.R. Soc. Biol.*, **151**, 1149). We found (Bonta, I. L., and de Vos, C. J. [1960]. Unpublished data) that the noise produced by other rats had an enhancing effect similar to that of grouping the animals.

MODIFICATION OF THE EFFECTS OF DRUGS ON BEHAVIOUR BY THE NUTRITIONAL STATE

R. H. J. WATSON

*Department of Nutrition, Queen Elizabeth College,
University of London*

IT will be readily understood that gross changes in the nutritional state of an animal may affect both its behaviour and its reactions to drugs; for example, hunger compared with satiety, or vitamin deficiencies. It is not always appreciated, however, that relatively small changes in the nutritional state of the animal can have crucial effects in an experiment on the effects of drugs on behaviour. Earlier work on the influence of diet in behaviour studies has been more concerned with its influence on the more customary factors of toxicity and tolerance. For example, Fitzhugh and Meiller (1941) showed that low-protein diets increased the toxicity of cadmium. Despite the more recent interest in behaviour studies, the effects of dietary changes have not received the attention they deserve. In many cases it would be difficult to ascertain the composition of the diet that has been used, and its caloric value is still less frequently mentioned.

The case for the importance of nutrition in experiments on the effects of drugs on behaviour will be presented here by giving as an example the results of a small-scale experiment which was carried out specifically for this symposium and which, it was hoped, illustrates some of the problems involved.

The two basic items which had to be decided were the kind of dietary change and the kind of drug to use. For the dietary change we decided to compare the effects of a synthetic diet which contained 60 per cent carbohydrate with a diet in which the carbohydrate had been replaced by protein. Both diets are fully adequate for the animal and are isocaloric, giving 4·55 Calories/g. in the present experiment. In the case of the protein diet, of course, energy must be obtained by metabolizing amino acids. This change of diet is one which is frequently recommended to obese patients, who are told to cut out carbohydrates and to eat a greater proportion of proteins. The choice of drug was therefore not very difficult to make. Such people are frequently given amphetamine or similar drugs to help them to reduce their food intake.

Twenty male hooded rats, approximately 80 days old, were assigned to the experiment. They had previously been maintained in the laboratory colony on a mixed fresh food diet. They were divided into two equal groups and the feeding of the synthetic diets was begun. One group, which will be referred to as the sucrose group, was fed on a diet composed of 60 per cent sucrose, 20 per cent casein, 15 per cent arachis oil and 5 per cent Dunn's salt mixture (Harris, 1938). Vitamin supplements were administered to ensure more than adequate amounts of vitamins A, B-complex, D, E and K. The other group received a similar diet, the only difference being that the 60 per cent sucrose was replaced by casein, making a total casein content of 80 per cent. This group will be referred to as the protein group.

The animals were housed individually, and food and water were available *ad libitum*. Body weight and food and water intake were recorded daily. The regime was continued throughout the experiment. After being on the diets for six weeks, by which time the body weights had stabilized to a mean weight of 272 g. in the protein group and a slightly higher mean weight of 291 g. in the sucrose group, the animals were ready to be put on the behaviour test. Their mean food intakes were 48 and 51 Calories per day respectively.

The behaviour investigated was exploratory behaviour, and this was done using a series of Y-shaped runways. The animal was placed in the apparatus for a period of four minutes during which two aspects of its behaviour were measured. These were:

Exploration, which was measured by counting the number of times the animal either entered the arms of the apparatus, or crossed the central portion (minute by minute totals were kept).

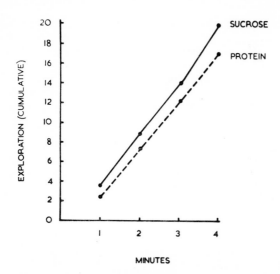

FIG. 1. Effect of diet on the exploration score of rats before the administration of dexamphetamine.

Exploration score: the number of times the rat entered the arms of the apparatus or crossed the central portion during the four-minute test period.

Rearing, which was measured by recording the time spent by the animal in the four-minute period in standing on its hind legs.

In order that the animals could be used as their own controls, they were placed in the apparatus on the first day without having been given either the drug or the saline control.

It will be seen from Fig. 1 that the rate of exploration of the protein group was lower than that of the sucrose group. This is in keeping with the findings of other workers, for example, Lat

(1959). We have therefore arrived at the first problem before any drugs have been administered, namely, that the nutritional state may affect the behaviour baseline from which behaviour changes are to be measured. In the case of rearing behaviour no such differences were observed and the overall mean rearing time was 51 seconds.

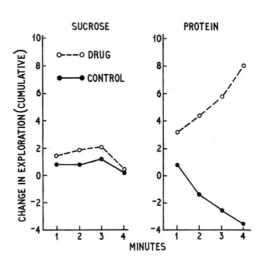

FIG. 2. Change in the exploration score after the administration of dexamphetamine. Control sub-group received saline solution.

On the second day each diet group was divided into two equal sub-groups, one of which received 3 mg./kg. dexamphetamine sulphate intraperitoneally one hour before the behaviour was measured. The other sub-group received an equivalent volume of physiological saline as control. Since the exploratory behaviour of the two groups before drugs had been different, it was thought more appropriate to express the effect of the drug as change in behaviour from the baseline of the animal's pre-drug score.

Fig. 2 shows the changes in exploration due to drug or control treatments with the two different diets. In the case of the sucrose group there is no difference in behaviour between the two sub-groups, both of which show a small increase in the early part of the four-minute period and a decline in the latter part. In the case of the protein group marked differences occur. While the

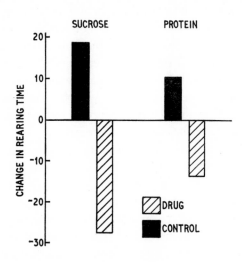

FIG. 3. Change in rearing time (in seconds) after the administration of dexamphetamine. Control sub-group received saline solution.

saline sub-group shows a decline in exploration after the initial first minute rise (again a reflection of their lower activity compared with animals with carbohydrate in the diet), the dex-amphetamine sub-group shows a marked increase in exploration.

Fig. 3 shows the changes in the time spent in rearing behaviour induced by the drug and control treatments. Both saline sub-groups show increases in the time spent rearing, while both sub-groups given amphetamine show decreases. In the case of the sucrose/amphetamine group the decrease was considerable, and rearing time was reduced to some 40 per cent of its value on the day before the drug was given.

It will be seen from the changes in both exploratory and rearing behaviour that two further problems are illustrated. First, the difference in diet may produce effects which depend on the repeated testing of the animal. Secondly, the difference in diet may interact with the effect of the drug and so produce differences in behaviour between similar drug treatments.

It will be recalled that one of the reasons for prescribing amphetamine is that it induces some degree of anorexia. Examination of the food intakes of the animals, which were continued after the drug had been given, showed that only the sucrose/amphetamine group showed any reduction in food intake. None of the other three groups showed decreases.

It will be seen that the variation in diet produced a number of changes in the effects of amphetamine on the aspects of behaviour studied. It would seem that this is not a simple relationship since the greatest effect on exploration was in the protein group, whereas the greatest effect on rearing was in the sucrose group. It must, however, be remembered that the experiment was on a small scale and that only a single dose was used. Clearly it would be premature to say whether the sucrose or the protein animals were more resistant to the effects of the drug until an experiment has been done using several doses and plotting adequate dose-response curves. What one would then most likely find would be a shift in the curve as a result of the different diet.

It is premature, too, to suggest why such differences occur, or whether they are a direct result of the change in the metabolism of amino acids for energy. But it must be remembered that these differences could well be due to indirect effects. For example, the increased nitrogen excretion of the protein group results in their drinking over twice as much water as the sucrose animals (mean daily intake of water 31 g. compared to 15 g. in the sucrose-fed animals). This increased water turnover could result in faster removal of the drug from the body.

The importance of our findings for studies on the interaction of drugs and behaviour need not be stressed further. It may well be that some of the differences that are found between experiments from different laboratories could be explained in terms of differences in diet, as well as differences like genetic endowment and past experience, which have been discussed earlier in this meeting.

SUMMARY

A small-scale experiment is described in which the effect of a carbohydrate-free diet on a test of the effect of dexamphetamine sulphate on behaviour is investigated.

Two groups of rats were maintained for six weeks on synthetic diets. The diet of one group contained 60 per cent sucrose; in the other group this was replaced by raising the casein content from 20 to 80 per cent.

Before administration of the drug the protein group showed less exploratory behaviour than did the sucrose group.

Changes in exploration after drug or saline had been given showed marked differences between those fed sucrose and those fed the high protein diet. Little effect was seen in the animals on the sucrose diet, whereas in the protein-fed group, control animals showed reduced exploration and the amphetamine-treated animals showed a marked increase in exploration.

In the case of rearing behaviour, both groups given amphetamine showed reduced rearing times, in contrast to both control groups which showed increases.

Reduction in food intake following amphetamine was found only in the sucrose group.

It is suggested that in future studies of the influence of drugs on behaviour the nutritional state of the animals must be considered as an important variable.

REFERENCES

FITZHUGH, O. G., and MEILLER, F. H. (1941). *J. Pharmacol. exp. Ther.*, **72**, 15.

HARRIS, L. J. (1938). Vitamins and Vitamin Deficiencies, vol. 1, p. 115. London: Churchill.

LAT, J. (1959). *Proc. Nutr. Soc.*, **18**, xxiv.

DISCUSSION

Irwin: Dr. Watson, you have excellent data, but I question your interpretation of them on the sucrose versus the protein-fed group. You seem to get very little effect in terms of increased exploratory activity in the sucrose group. May this not indicate a much greater sensitivity to amphetamine, inasmuch as the dose you used is one which produces disorganized, stereotyped behaviour? You may have produced a stereotyped, shifting, "head-searching" behaviour in which the animal is less likely to engage in rearing and exploration. Have you observed this type of activity, which would not permit as much exploratory activity and would, in fact, indicate a much greater drug effect?

Watson: What one must do, of course, is construct a dose–response curve, and then one usually finds an initial increase in exploratory behaviour which falls off with increased dose; activity eventually declines and the animal does very little at all. From consideration of factors such as the change in rearing performance, anorexia (which was present with the sucrose) and the fact that the high protein group has a larger water turnover, we concluded that at the particular dose we used, we were finding, in the case of the animals on high sucrose, a response representative of that associated with a *higher* dose of the drug than was shown by the animals on high protein. That was my impression. I would predict that the different diets result in shifts in the dose–response curve.

Irwin: You therefore obtained a *greater* effect with the sucrose?

Watson: I think so, although the activity is apparently lower.

Kosterlitz: I should like to add another possible explanation for the differences Dr. Watson has observed between the high-sucrose and the high-protein animals. It is well known that in protein deficiency the concentration of enzymes in the liver decreases, and therefore one would have a higher concentration of these enzymes in animals fed on protein-rich diets than on a low-protein diet. This difference might affect the metabolism of the drug and therefore influence activity in the two groups.

GENERAL DISCUSSION

STANDARDIZATION OF EXPERIMENTS

Janssen: Many of the communications here suggest that often we cannot reproduce results described in the literature because most of our experimental designs are inadequately standardized. Hereditary factors, group composition, nutritional state, past experience, schedules and designs and other factors may all contribute to this lack of standardization. We do need to standardize our techniques and to use these standard techniques consistently so that we are publishing data which are of more than historical significance.

Cole: I wonder if anybody has been able to produce what one might call a "standard rat"? Dr. Broadhurst referred to differences between rats according to species, strain and sex. D. P. Dearnaley and I have found that rats of the same strain, sex and litter showed different reactions to some of the amine oxidase inhibitors. The general pattern of the reaction may be the same, but the intensity varies very much with the individual. We found that certain of these inhibitors produced excitement, but in two cases the rats went into a state of hypermania and one died. When we added a single dose of reserpine, on the second day of a four-week period of daily iproniazid, we had two fatalities out of a group of about twenty. We have one very interesting rat at the moment which is showing gross impairment, whereas his litter mates are not nearly so impaired. We find this individual variation a very great problem in assessing results, but consider it of fundamental importance for the study of drugs before they are used clinically (Acheson, R. M., Cole, J., Dearnaley, D. P., and Dearnaley, E. J. [1961]. *Psychopharmacologia,* **2,** 277).

Dearnaley: Our rats also showed individual changes in the urine. When we examined the urine of animals which had been given iproniazid or niamid, we were able to find *iso*nicotinoyl glycine which appears to be the principal metabolite of the drugs. This appears in the urine as the end product of the principal means of detoxication of the drugs.

Mr. Cole referred to two animals which entered this so-called "hypermanic" state, one of which died. On examination of the urine of these two rats, we found that during the period preceding death or while the symptoms were greatly intensified the drug metabolite was not present in the urine, or only in very small quantities. This suggested that the biochemical variation between these rats and their litter mates, which followed a different pattern, was some kind of block in the detoxication of the drug.

Broadhurst: I am sure there is no such beast as a "standard rat". One can only look at all the factors concerned very carefully and consider whether any of them may be affecting one's results. It may be that some particular combination of the situation and the effects of the compound one is investigating is susceptible to some particular background variation, whether it is constitutional or environmental. Perhaps yours might be a case where the superiority of the F_1 hybrid for bio-assay might be employed to advantage?

Barnett: Certainly, much of the work referred to has been on inbred strains of rats and mice. These animals are very peculiar. They tend to be physiologically rather unstable: they often have a high phenotypic variance in their responses to various conditions (Michie, D. [1955]. *Coll. Pap. Lab. Anim. Bur.*, **3**, 37). The hybrids between two inbred strains may vary much less in some of their responses, though not in all; they are also much more like the wild type. An F_1 hybrid mouse between two of the standard inbred strains is probably much more like a wild mouse than either of the parent strains (for example, see Barnett, S. A., and Coleman, E. M. [1960]. *Genet. Res.*, **1**, 25; Barnett, S. A., and Scott, S. G. [1963]. *Proc. roy. phys. Soc. Edinb.*, in press). I suggest that attention should be paid to the differences between hybrids and inbreds in relation to the survival value of the behaviour and other responses being studied.

Stein: There is one way to get a "standard rat" and that is to use a rat as its own control. This is done frequently in behavioural experiments, when the conditions under study are reversible. It cannot be used, of course, if conditions are irreversible, and it must be kept in mind, too, that the response of an individual will vary somewhat from moment to moment. When the technique is applicable, however, it is a powerful means to eliminate what is usually the largest source of error in biological experiments, namely, variability between individuals.

Chance: On the question of the standardization of animals or of procedures, I think we should proceed cautiously. At this early stage we are opening up ideas and concepts which may reveal mechanisms of which we have not previously been aware. Until we know what the underlying mechanisms are, it is premature to restrict our attention by procedures which are unnecessarily limiting, although I am quite certain everyone is capable of standardizing experiments. I think this has happened before, especially over terminology. People have rushed into an attempt to standardize terminology which has ultimately become completely redundant because it does not describe the underlying pattern of events.

Steinberg: I think Dr. Janssen's point about the mere historical interest of experiments which do not agree with one another indicates a basic difference in aim. Dr. Janssen is looking for strict comparability of procedures in order that comparable experiments can be performed in different laboratories, and that is, of course, one very definite and admirable aim that can perhaps lead to the discovery of new drugs. But if one is trying to analyse how drugs act on different organisms under different conditions, one is apt to find interesting in their own right these variations in results which Dr. Janssen would like to suppress. We ourselves are rather pleased to be able to find these big differences depending on the previous experience of the rats.

Moreover, if one hopes eventually to use new drugs clinically, one will not only have to put up with these complicating factors in the clinical setting but perhaps even make use of them, so the more one can find out about them, the better.

Weiskrantz: I should like to speak against an obsessional concern with the search for sources of variance in animal experiments, because I think it is apt to lead us astray. It is relatively easy in science to produce variance and then become concerned with it. One could imagine that in investigating gravitational factors, Galileo, instead of examining the question in terms of invariant factors, might have developed a standard tree with standard leaves and noted how they fell under standard conditions and how groups of leaves fell differently from individual leaves, and how their falling varied with wind strength, temperature, age of leaf, time of day, season, and so on. In so doing I doubt very much if he would have discovered the facts about falling objects for which he is well known. I think there is a pragmatic value, at least, in ignoring certain sources of variance before one settles questions which relate to invariances.

Summerfield: It seems to me that we have been concerned with interactions which are interesting in themselves, and not solely with how to produce standardized experimental conditions.

Steinberg: In disagreement with Dr. Weiskrantz, I think that so far as giving drugs to a human patient is concerned, one cannot very easily ignore individual variation. For example, there is the question of whether to reinforce drug treatment with suggestion. S. Fisher and J. O. Cole (personal communication) have found with amphetamine that if one instructs subjects appropriately beforehand, one can get opposite effects on mood and performance to the usual ones. One can also observe differences in reactions to drugs in subjects with different kinds of personality (e.g. Felsinger, J. M. von, Lasagna, L., and Beecher, H. K. [1955]. *J. Amer. med. Ass.*, **157**, 1113) and so on. Eventually one might fit the right drug and the right conditions and the right instructions and the right social environment to the right patient.

Miller: Since drug effects do interact with so many variables it is quite possible, as has been pointed out, for people in different laboratories to get differences between their results which are not simply dependent on the other laboratory having an inferior technique! It is therefore important that we do not suppress negative results. We may not know what the difference is that produces the different results, but it may exist and we must investigate it. If the negative results are suppressed, we may never realize that there is a problem. Both the individual experimenter and the editors of the journals should be more tolerant of negative results, or of failures to confirm.

Dews: There is a reluctance by journals to accept simple confirmations of things which have been published once or twice already. If you take your information on reproducibility from a statistical analysis of material in the literature, this is therefore extremely biased. Many of the dose–effect curves and other precise relationships we have been hearing about have been seen in many laboratories, with quite wide variations in unimportant aspects of the procedure, but they have simply not been published. This would be extremely valuable information which might well be collected for use in other laboratories.

Steinberg: May I also add to Professor Miller's point? I remember once asking Dr. Marthe Vogt why it was that sometimes one could not repeat one's own results. She said, "This is what one must expect, because one tries to repeat the conditions exactly each time, but one tends with practice to streamline procedures and so imperceptibly one alters conditions the relevance of which one is not aware of." I think publication of more details of procedure might help one to become more aware of the conditions under which experiments are done.

Herxheimer: A further factor which may influence the effects of drugs on behaviour is the lighting regime in the animal colony; it has been shown to be very important in many kinds of physiological and pharmacological experiments. One striking example is that the lethality of various toxins and poisons is much greater at one hour of the day than at twelve hours out of phase with that time (Halberg, F., Johnson, E. A., Brown, B. W., and Bittner, J. J. [1960]. *Proc. Soc. exp. Biol. (N.Y.)*, **103**, 142). There may be a threefold difference or more in toxicity at these different times. I should like to ask the speakers who reported some of their work here which of them actually use reversed lighting and conditions standardized for circadian periodicity.

Broadhurst: We do not use reversed lighting but we do standardize the light cycle.

Watson: We do precisely the same. We have a twelve-hour light cycle, although it is light in the day and dark at night.

Steinberg: We also standardize the light cycle and our experiments are always done at the same time of day, between 2 and 5.30 p.m.

Chance: We have not done any major studies of recycling but since the animals are so much more active at night, not only in terms of activity measured in an activity cage but also in the variety and volume of their social activity, it is certainly essential for our work. You could not otherwise record 2,000 or 3,000 postures in less than an hour. There are a few scattered observations on the rate at which various physiological rhythms are reversed, such as the change in the level of the white blood cells.

Wilson: Like Dr. Steinberg we carried out experiments at the same time each day, for two hours during the morning, and two hours during the afternoon. I agree with Dr. Chance that one can get very much more information by reversing the lighting.

It is also of great importance to relate behavioural investigations to the time when biochemical changes in the animal are at their greatest; for example, in the rat we know that histamine excretion in the urine is greatest during the night. Rats drink much greater quantities of water during the night. Therefore in Skinnerian experiments, in which water is used as a reward, it may be important to consider whether the reward is given at night or during the day.

Dews: In the experiments we have been doing with pigeons and with monkeys, we find that any daily rhythm is utterly trivial in its effect compared with the kinds of scheduling factors which I described. We study the animals at different times of the day, but we cannot tell from which part of the twenty-four hours the records are taken.

Session 4: Relevance of Behavioural Effects of Drugs in Animals to Effects in Man

CHAIRMAN: Sir Aubrey Lewis

SCREENING TESTS AND PREDICTION FROM ANIMALS TO MAN

PAUL A. J. JANSSEN

Research Laboratory Dr. C. Janssen, Beerse, Belgium

I WAS invited to speak about "screening tests and prediction from animals to man", but I have not very much to say about screening tests that you are not all thoroughly aware of. The problem of how to predict from animals to man, on the other hand, should logically be discussed in terms of statistical probability. There does not seem to be enough reliable and relevant pharmacological and clinical experimental data of the type that would permit a more or less satisfactory scientific approach to that problem. In the present circumstances, therefore, I feel like the chess-player who is invited to explain logically how to predict from one move to the next, or how to play a perfect game. The basic rules of chess are simple enough, of course, but the real game of chess is much more than a matter of logical thinking. Although a very strong chess-player is obviously much better at predicting from one move to another than an average player, I am not sure that he could explain to his own satisfaction how he does it.

An ideal screening test should have all of the following characteristics:

(a) *High efficiency*, a minimum of effort being required to yield a maximum of reliable and relevant data. The achievement of such efficiency is a question of organization, automation, experimental design and selection among the theoretically equivalent methods of testing.

(b) *High speed*, the experimental data being collected within a short period of time. Because of the very nature of the problem, however, slowness is sometimes unavoidable.

(c) *Simplicity*, the experiment requiring little training, inexpensive equipment and readily available animals. In certain fields, of course, it is almost impossible to avoid complicated techniques.

(d) *Reproducibility*, the important factors determining the results of the experiment being known and adequately controlled. With standard drugs the same results are obtained over and over again. This is, of course, an absolute requirement, although surprisingly little information of this type is being published.

(e) *Specificity*, a given drug effect being characteristic for a well-defined class of chemicals and indicative of a specific mode of action. In the preliminary stages of screening, however, a few aspecific methods of testing may be useful. In order to examine the degree of specificity of a given test, one must have reliable data on the results obtained with a large number of unrelated standard drugs.

(f) *Adequate design*, the experimental design being, of course, the main factor in determining efficiency, reliability and reproducibility. In general it is desirable to randomize each experiment, to apply a sequential method of testing, to eliminate subjective bias by using coded solutions and more than one technician per test. One should keep in mind that in large-scale testing the stupid error is often the worst enemy.

(g) *Adequate data processing, statistical analysis and symbolization of the results*. Ideally the results should be expressed in a condensed form using a minimum of statistically meaningful symbols. All relevant conclusions should be symbolized. In large-scale screening the finding of optimal methods of data processing and data retrieval is among the most difficult problems to solve adequately.

(h) *Good correlation with other tests* is, of course, the chief criterion of whether or not a particular test is likely to be useful for predicting the outcome of other tests with the same species or with other species, including man. A correlation coefficient implies the existence of at least two sets of comparable data. This, as we all know only too well, is simply not the case in many areas of pharmacological research, particularly in clinical pharmacology. Without the necessary data one can merely speculate about possible correlations and predictions.

In brief, a satisfactory screening test is characterized by high efficiency, good reproducibility and adequacy of experimental design. No time or effort is wasted by it, the degree of its specificity is known, the data are efficiently processed and the results are summarized in statistically meaningful symbols. Millions of different chemical substances are known and probably even more different living structures exist. The study of the interactions of all these combinations is the fantastic task that theoretically faces the pharmacologist. Even the most ambitious pharmacologist is therefore forced to make up his mind to select somehow a few of these possible problems on which to work. Many, I am sure, are driven to make their selection by plain curiosity. Others are asked to solve a certain problem or feel the desire to compete with other laboratories in tackling a problem which happens to be in vogue. Quite a few of us, however, like to think of our work and endeavour as being specifically aimed at the discovery of new and clinically important drugs.

Here the problem of how to predict from animals to man has to be faced sooner or later. I have no clear idea of how this difficult problem is being solved elsewhere. One would assume that much time and effort must have been spent in finding reasonable scientific solutions. To the best of my knowledge, however, nothing much has been published on this subject so far. On the other hand I am sure many of us are relying to a large extent on what the Germans would call *Fingerspitzengefühl*, a special kind of flair for the problem, comparable to the kind of instinctive flair a chess-player uses when playing a brilliant fast game.

In our laboratory we use a battery of screening tests specifically designed to answer the question: "To what extent is the pharmacological profile of the new chemical different from the profiles of known chemicals, qualitatively and quantitatively?" (p. 392). If it is found that the profile of a new chemical is practically identical with the profile of a clinically known drug, then of course one can rather safely predict by analogy from animals to man. The greater the differences between these profiles, obviously the more difficult it is to make reasonable predictions of this kind. In behavioural pharmacology there are a number of adequate screening tests for predicting by analogy the most obvious clinical effects of morphine-like narcotics, of chlorpromazine-, haloperidol- or reserpine-like neuroleptics, of imipramine- or iproniazid-like antidepressants, of amphetamine-like stimulants, of meprobamate-like muscle relaxants, of barbiturate-like hypnotics, of diphenhydramine-like sedatives, or of general anaesthetics like chloroform.

We find it difficult, however, to make useful clinical predictions for compounds showing experimental anticonvulsant or convulsant activity, for compounds like LSD-25, mescaline, phencyclidine and similar drugs producing hallucinations in man, for the central effects of tertiary amines with anticholinergic activity, like hyoscine, benactyzine or benztropine, for aspirin- or butazolidine-like analgesics and in general for all compounds suspected of modifying subtle mental processes in man, such as learning ability.

The best we can do, in my opinion, when we find a new compound capable of modifying the behaviour of animals in ways that we cannot recognize as similar to anything we have seen or heard of before, is eventually to ask a good experimental psychologist or psychiatrist to run a series of clinical pilot studies in volunteers and in patients suffering from different forms of mental disease. In such a case we should try to proceed on a purely empirical basis without paying too much attention to hypothetical anthropocentric extrapolations and so-called predictions from animals to man.

I must confess I have often wondered whether this business of trying to predict from animals to man is really part of pharmacology. According to its etymological significance, pharmacology (φαρμακον λογος) is the language the scientist should use when talking about the interaction between dead and living matter. The only possible source of pharmacological knowledge is, of course, the pharmacological experiment. After having performed a sufficient number of such experiments one can try to describe them accurately, one can try to draw all the possible logical conclusions from these experiments, and it is also possible to study from two or more sets of experimental data the correlations between the physical or chemical properties of dead substances and their effects on living matter, and *vice versa*. What the pharmacologist basically needs in order to do all this is incentive, favourable circumstances, common sense and a working hypothesis. This matter of predicting from animals to man is, in my view, at best a working hypothesis, the reliability of which can only be tested experimentally. I wonder, therefore, whether the description of a pharmacological working hypothesis should be considered an intrinsic part of pharmacology, or whether it belongs merely to the realms of fancy, to be described by those who are interested in that particularly intriguing aspect of mankind which is called psychology.

[Discussion of this paper was postponed until after the following paper by Dr. S. Irwin.]

PREDICTION OF DRUG EFFECTS
FROM ANIMALS TO MAN

S. Irwin

*Department of Biology, Neuropharmacology Research, Schering Corporation,
New Jersey*

In predicting drug effects from animals to man, one assumes
that animals are organized in a manner sufficiently similar to man
so that their responses to drugs are also similar. Thus the problem
is not whether prediction from animals to man is possible, but
rather what are the limits within which such prediction can
reasonably be made. Attitudes on this vary widely. This is not
at all surprising, since there are enormous differences among
investigators in their approach and emphasis, and there appears
to be very little in the way of an organized body of knowledge,
structured approach or common experience in this area. The
purpose of this paper is to analyse some of the factors which
influence prediction and examine the possibilities for prediction
of drug effects across species. It represents an extension of the
content of two earlier papers, in which drug screening and
evaluative procedures and the factors that contribute to variability
in drug response were analysed and reviewed (Irwin, 1962, 1964a).

Basic research versus drug evaluation

One cannot embark on drug evaluation and prediction
intelligently without basic research. From basic research come the
structural foundations of understanding from which simpler
tools, models and concepts emerge for use in drug evaluation
and in the prediction of drug effects across species. However,
let us understand from the beginning that, while science uses a
method, the practice and pursuit of science is an art involving

the use of intuitive reasoning. This is even more true in the process of drug evaluation and prediction, where the important elements are not just techniques, but judgment and experience in the use of techniques; not just factual data, but relevant data; not just objectivity, but a sense of relatedness to the problems at hand. It should become clear, therefore, that drug evaluation requires the talents and resources of a diagnostician; a good measure of common sense also does little harm.

Although similar tools are used both in drug evaluation and in basic research, the nature of the questions asked and the kinds of information required in each of these disciplines are generally quite different. Failure to recognize this difference has been a major stumbling block in the prediction of drug effects to man, for it has resulted in the systematic application of the approaches and concepts of basic research to drug evaluation where often they seriously undermine possibilities for prediction.

A biological system is in a continuous state of flux; it is neither rigid nor static. Depending on the influences which impinge upon it, the responses of a system may be stable and predictable or unstable and unpredictable. In basic research, where it is important to uncover the mode of action of a drug or the relationship between certain measures in a system, a useful approach is to reduce the variables affecting a system by isolating it, as with curarization, anaesthesia, denervation, surgery or restriction of the environment.

The greater the isolation or restriction of the system, the greater is its "rigidity", and the more stable and reliable are the events that are recorded. Such procedures also make experimenting and the handling of subjects easier. However, it is a truism that the results of studies *in vitro* or on isolated organs often cannot be demonstrated *in vivo*, and the same applies when comparing the results of drug studies in anaesthetized or denervated preparations with those from intact, unanaesthetized animals. For the same reason, it is questionable to what extent information derived from the *in vitro* equivalent, for example the isolated conditions of operant conditioning bar-press techniques which demand great stability of performance, is directly applicable to the behaviour of an organism in an essentially free environment. The human behaviour of therapeutic concern is more often interactional, transitional in nature, and less likely to be under such vigorous stimulus control. Moreover, the more stable the behaviour investigated, the larger are the doses of drug required to modify it.

In general it can be said that a system made more "rigid" through isolating its parts or restricting the environment often serves the needs of basic research; but the converse is true in drug evaluation where the information derived under "rigid" conditions is proportionately of less value in predicting drug effects in man than are studies conducted with the intact, unrestricted organism.

In basic pharmacological research a method or preparation is used as a tool. The only requirement is that it be sufficiently sensitive to measure drug-induced changes, regardless of what the dose requirements might be and without concern for their clinical relevance. The latter, with respect to dose, also applies to the use of a drug as a tool. By contrast, in drug evaluation *no* behavioural procedure should be considered acceptable unless it is sufficiently sensitive to measure drug effects in animals comparable with those considered acceptable for man. It is far easier to predict the clinical efficacy and side effects of a drug from a realistic baseline than from the extreme, even toxic, baselines of activity from which comparisons are usually made. When this is done, except where unusual differences in species sensitivity exist, it is not surprising to find that the dose requirements of drugs in animals on a milligram per kilogram basis or, with some drugs, on the basis of the ratio of body-weight to body-surface area (for example, approximately 2·5, 5·0 and 10·5 times greater for the cat, rat and mouse respectively), are quite similar to those for man. For example, with one observational procedure, significant behavioural changes can be observed in the cat after 0·001 mg./kg. of LSD-25, 0·1 mg./kg. of methamphetamine, 0·3 mg./kg. of perphenazine, 1·0 mg./kg. of methaminediazepoxide, 2·0 mg./kg. of pentobarbitone, 3·0 mg./kg. of imipramine, and 8·0 mg./kg. of meprobamate administered orally, or after 0·01 mg./kg. of morphine administered subcutaneously—doses quite comparable with those used in man. For animals larger than man, smaller mg./kg. doses of drug are usually required. The recent death of an elephant with what was considered to be a "safe" dose of LSD-25 is an example of this.

While dose-response relations are always important in drug evaluation, the minimal dose of a drug producing an effect sufficient to be of clinical significance, therapeutic or otherwise, is particularly crucial. It is revealing that in pharmacology we have no term to describe the ratio between the probable therapeutic and the side effect dose of a drug in animals. The term "therapeutic index", which best describes this relation, is in fact applied to the ratio between the ED_{50} and LD_{50} of a drug—a ratio more appropriately labelled the "mortality index".

In basic research, if one wishes to study the effects of a drug on cardiac output, blood pressure, peripheral vascular resistance and heart rate, one can measure these indices separately in different animals, or separately in the same animal at different times. In this age of sophistication, however, we have learned that these are related events and that one can learn a great deal about the cardiovascular actions of a drug by measuring the events simultaneously in the same animal. Simultaneous measurement of the multiple effects of a drug is of critical importance in drug evaluation; it is also important in basic research, but it is a principle often ignored until its necessity becomes apparent.

Because of this habit of unitary recording in basic research, as opposed to a pluralistic approach, and because of the need for objectivity and quantitative precision in measurement, the investigator increasingly indulges in instrumental recording of unitary components of behaviour. In much drug evaluation this is a blind alley, for the doses of a drug required to modify behaviour vary widely from procedure to procedure and from animal to animal as a function of factors which are not related to the drug, such as previous experience, incentive, stimulus parameters, scheduling, and the arousal-provoking quality of the experimental situation. For example, Edwards (1961) has shown the ED_{50} of morphine on several behavioural measures in the rat to vary from 0·37 to 5·9 mg./kg. as a function of the degree of discomfort resulting from failure of the animals to perform. From such variability it is almost impossible to make quantitative predictions to man. It is necessary to adjust the characteristics of the procedures in such a way that they become more sensitive to drug effects in the rat and also sufficiently sensitive to measure the effects of doses of drug similar to those used in man. Only then can one have some assurance of a relation between the drug effects observed in the laboratory and the effects produced by therapeutic doses in man.

In basic research, precise measurement and quantification is very important; in drug evaluation it is less so, for variability of individual animals in response to drugs is great and far outweighs the factor of experimental precision. In drug evaluation one merely requires a degree of precision commensurate with the reproducibility and the overall reliability of the data; beyond this, precision is of little practical use. There are far too many factors, unrelated to the drug, which affect response and variability and which are beyond the investigator's control. This may sound like heresy; it is nonetheless true. One should always attempt to develop reliable quantitative information. However, one should also be prepared to sacrifice some precision of measurement in order to obtain more general information about a drug. This is far more valuable for making predictions. Much valuable information is often lost in the pursuit of complete objectivity and instrumental precision.

In short, the conditions necessary for basic research are often contrary to those required for drug evaluation. A totally different framework of approach is needed.

Development and use of a method

In our laboratory, we have emphasized the development and use of systematic observational techniques in screening and evaluating drugs, and as an aid in predicting drug effects from animals to man. We consider an observational approach to be a vital element in drug evaluation, since it is more directly analogous to the conditions under which a drug is used and evaluated clinically, and many attributes of drug action cannot be measured otherwise. This is not to imply that we do not also use and attach great importance to the use of instrumental techniques. However, we almost always augment instrumental measurement with observation aimed at detecting and quantifying the multiple components of behaviour which are present in every experimental situation.

A good deal of effort is required in "shaping up" a procedure for use in drug evaluation. For example, in the measurement of "fighting behaviour" of paired mice with a procedure first described by O'Kelly and Steckle (1939), where an electroshock stimulus is used as an excitant and where one ordinarily records only the frequency and duration of fighting bouts, we also record the latency for fighting, the motor reactivity of the animals to the shock stimulus, the intensity of vocalization, the "viciousness" of the fighting, the presence of muscle weakness or inco-ordination before stimulation, and the duration of the inhibition of movement that follows cessation of the shock stimulus. However, before using the procedure, considerable time was devoted to determining the conditions of shock intensity, duration, and the strain and sex of animals optimal for studying drug effects. From such studies it was learned that CFW mice had a lower shock threshold for fighting behaviour and motor reactivity than CF#1 mice, and that the effectiveness of drugs in suppressing the behaviour was the inverse of the shock intensity. Thus, CFW mice were more sensitive to drug effects than CF#1 mice and, therefore, more suitable for the procedure; no sex differences in response were noted. However, it was also observed that drugs like methaminediazepoxide or perphenazine, which reduced the fighting behaviour, also reduced the motor reactivity of the animals to the shock stimulus. This suggested that one was measuring drug effects on a mechanism other than fighting behaviour with the procedure, namely, an increased threshold for evoked motor responsiveness—fighting or otherwise. This measure may be even more important than the one for which the procedure was initially designed. Due attention should therefore be given to the "shaping up" of a procedure. When it is suitably carried out, one can determine the optimal conditions for evaluating drug effects and have a far better understanding of what is really being measured.

Bar-press operant conditioning

One can make judgments on the behavioural effects of drugs on the basis of data derived entirely from operant conditioning techniques, or from the use of observational techniques alone. There is no single methodological panacea for drug prediction. Both instrumental and non-instrumental techniques are required. However, certain approaches in drug evaluation provide data of greater or lesser value for the prediction of drug effects in man. Also, it seems logical that one should seek to employ the simplest, most rapid and efficient approaches for obtaining the information required, for example, on the level of wakefulness, discrimination, locomotion, affect, social behaviour, endurance, co-ordination, muscle tone or autonomic function. Operant bar-press techniques are poorly equipped to provide such general information.

From the standpoint of research, where one wishes to isolate and analyse certain elemental components of drug action or of schedule effects on behaviour, or where it is important to exercise complete control over environmental variables, bar-press operant conditioning is a technique that can provide information with great quantitative precision. From the standpoint of drug evaluation, however, it has many limitations: (1) the initial training of animals takes an exceedingly long time and later considerable effort and time are needed to maintain a stable baseline of performance; (2) the response required is not the one most natural for the species; (3) the anatomical topography of the response often varies; (4) the range of information provided about behaviour is usually much too narrow, and is derived under highly restricted experimental conditions; (5) the direction and magnitude of response to drugs is very much dependent on the schedule; (6) except with enormous facilities, the number of animals available for daily testing is small, so that generalizations are often made from studies with only one or two animals, despite wide variability among animals in baseline behaviour and responsiveness to drugs; (7) the information provided, for example, response rates, inter-response times, or the temporal distribution of responses, is costly and is often no more revealing than that produced by other, simpler techniques. It is almost entirely of an empirical, inferential nature, more suited for the classification of a drug than for its evaluation, since in most instances the data cannot be directly translated to man in terms of its therapeutic or overall behavioural consequences; (8) finally, no drug has yet been developed by operant bar-press techniques that could not have been developed by other, simpler techniques. Bar-press operant conditioning remains a superb quantitative tool for research, where cost is less important. However, some of the features that make it useful for research, for example, its isolation of experimental variables and the inflexibility of the behaviour it produces, also make it very much less useful for evaluating drugs.

Prediction of drug effects in man

In evaluating a drug one necessarily studies its effects in a variety of species, and it is the collective information from which predictions are made. However, if one had to select the single, most valuable animal for the prediction of drug effects in man, I would favour the cat. Its sensitivity to the behavioural, neurological and autonomic effects of drugs is more nearly like that of man than any other laboratory animal. Also, the ratio between the behavioural and side effect doses in the cat most closely approximates that in man. A rule of thumb for most behaviour drugs in the cat has been an oral dose approximately three times greater than the average mg./kg. dose in man. However, a major disadvantage is that the cat is stimulated by certain classes of drugs which are depressant in man, such as narcotic analgesics, antihistamines, meprobamate or imipramine-like drugs. In such cases, one must predict the probable responses in man from the pattern of stimulant or depressant activity observed in other species. However, one can take advantage of this "aberrant" response in the cat in identifying different classes of compounds.

In a similar vein, our most useful tool in drug evaluation and prediction to man has been the use of standardized, multidimensional observational procedures for the measurement and quantification of drug effects in animals. The virtue of this approach is that a large amount of information on the behavioural, neurological and autonomic actions of a drug can be obtained from a single procedure, and that the information so obtained is completely integrated on a time-dose-response basis. This is shown in Figs. 1 and 2, which summarize the results obtained with perphenazine in the mouse and the cat; the methods are described elsewhere (Irwin, 1964*b*). An additional virtue of an observational approach is that behaviour that can be observed is more likely to be observed in animals and man alike and, as such, is more directly relevant to man.

TEST: CNS ACTIVITY AND ACUTE TOXICITY SCREEN	PERPHENAZINE	TEST NO. P - 3	CHEMIST
SPECIES: MOUSE	SEX: MALE	ROUTE: oral	WEIGHT (GM): 18-24
0.2% ☒ SOL. ☐ INSOL.	2.0% ☒ SOL. ☐ INSOL.	pH = 5 / pH = 3	VEHICLE: H_2O

B.F. = 1.18	Awareness				Mood					Motor Activity				CNS Excitation					
mg/kg Dose (3 anim./dose)	Alertness	Visual Placing	Passivity	Stereotypy	Grooming	Vocalization	Restlessness	Irritability (Aggression)	Fearfulness	Reactivity (Envir.)	Spontaneous Activity	Touch Response	Pain Response	Startle Response	Straub Tail	Tremors	Twitches	Convulsions	
Normal Score	4	4	0	0	4	0	0	0	0	4	4	4	4	0	0	0	0	0	
.01																			
.03																			
.10		3								3	3								
.30		2								2	2	3							
1		2			5					2	1	1	1			1			
3	1	1				1				1	1	1	1						
10	0	1	5			1				0	1	0	1						
30	0	0	8							0	0	0	1			2			
100	0	0	8							0	0	0	0						
300	0	0	8							0	0	0	0				1		
1000																			

B.F. = 1.18	Posture		Motor Incoord.			Muscle Tone					Reflexes		
mg/kg Dose (3 anim./dose)	Body Posture	Limb Position	Staggering Gait	Abnormal Gait	Righting Reflex	Limb Tone	Grip Strength	Body Sag	Body Tone	Abdominal Tone	Pinna	Corneal	IFR
Normal Score	4	4	0	0	0	4	4	0	4	4	4	4	4
.01													
.03													
.10		3					3						
.30		3			2	3	2		3	3			
1		2	1		3	3	1		2	2	2	3	2
3		1			4	1	1	2	1	1	0	2	1
10		0	1		7	1	1	3	0	0	1	1	1
30	P	0 S			8	0	1	8	0	0	0	0	1
100	P	0 S			8	0	0	8	0	0	0	0	0
300	P	0 S			8	0	0	8	0	0	0	0	0
1000													

B.F. = 1.18	Autonomic											Misc.			Dead	
mg/kg Dose (3 anim./dose)	Writhing	Pupil Size	Palpebral Opening	Exopthalmos	Urination	Salivation	Piloerection	Hypothermia	Skin Color	Heart Rate	Respir. Rate	Lacrimation			No. Acute	No. Delayed
Normal Score	0	4	4	0	0	0	0	0	4	4	4	0			0	0
.01																
.03																
.10																
.30																
1			3		1											
3			2		1											
10			2		1						3T	1				
30			1		2						3T					
100			1		2			1	3		2T	1				
300			1		2						1T					
1000																

FIG. 1. Dose-response profile of perphenazine in the mouse.

The data represent peak drug effects, with 3 animals used at each dose level. Normal scores are indicated above, and deviations from normal score below. A rating scale of 0–8 intensity was employed. For signs *normally present*, the normal score was set at 4, an increase or decrease from this value respectively representing the degree of stimulation or depression produced. For signs *normally absent*, the normal score was set at 0, an increase of this value toward 8 indicating the degree of change produced. *Code:* P = prostrate; S = straddled; T = thoracic. B.F. = 1·18 indicates the base factor, i.e., the ratio of the molecular weight of the salt to that of the free base. All doses were calculated as the free base.

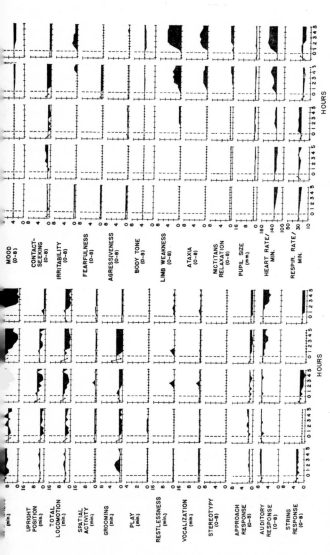

FIG. 2. Time-dose-response profile of perphenazine in the cat. A horizontal line was drawn through the mean of the two values obtained 30 and 60 minutes pre-treatment; the darkened areas, as an aid to visualization, indicate the deviations from this pre-treatment mean during the course of observation. The vertical interrupted lines indicate the time of drug administration. The procedure was carried out on a completely "blind" basis, with randomization of treatments. Significant behavioural changes may be noted after 0·3 mg./kg. of perphenazine, and significant neurological and autonomic changes after 1·0 mg./kg.

Conclusions

This paper has dealt with some of the difficulties that arise in predicting drug effects from animals to man, and the means by which some of them can be overcome. The difficulties stem largely from the application of the approaches of basic research to drug evaluation where they are probably inappropriate. However, not all the problems of prediction arise from the laboratory and from animal studies; one aspect not touched upon is the extent to which new drugs fail because they are inadequately evaluated in man. The present state of the art is not quite so bleak as it may seem, for one can make certain predictions for man within reasonable probabilities, such as predictions as to the nature, dose, side effects and therapeutic ratio of a compound. With time, better methods and greater understanding, one is likely to do better in these matters than one does at present. The human animal, however, like other animals, is capricious. Despite all advances in the art of prediction, he will continue to respond to drugs as he "damn well pleases".

REFERENCES

EDWARDS, R. E. (1961). *Fed. Proc.*, **20**, 397.
IRWIN, S. (1962). *Science*, **136**, 123.
IRWIN, S. (1964*a*). *In* Clinical Pharmacology: Animal and Human Techniques, Chapter 2, ed. Nodine, J. H., and Siegler, P. E. Chicago: Year Book Medical Publ. In press.
IRWIN, S. (1964*b*). *Ibid*, Chapter 4. In press.
O'KELLY, L. I., and STECKLE, L. C. (1939). *J. Psychol.*, **8**, 125.

DISCUSSION

Hume: Dr. Janssen listed eight requirements for a good screening test. I hope he will consent to add a ninth, which I am sure he looks for in practice although he did not include it in his list. This is the moral obligation to choose techniques which entail a minimum of discomfort or distress for the rats and other animals to which medicine is so greatly indebted.

McIlwain: Dr. Janssen has rightly emphasized the extremely large number of conceivable chemical compounds and the large number of tests which could be run for their proper evaluation, but in both his account and Dr. Irwin's there is a certain lack of reality because the authors give no information on the initial selection of compounds, or on how the results of testing are fed back to the process which produces the compounds. The immediate result of screening in animals is the selection of types of compounds for further synthesis and I should like to ask at what stage decisions are made regarding synthesis. Do you wait for results from a very large number of compounds before deciding how to guide your programme of synthesis, or do you test perhaps half a dozen structural variants before deciding that a given class of compound is not of immediate use, and continue with some completely different group of substances?

Janssen: I can only answer this very general question by telling you how we work in our laboratory; I am quite sure that this kind of game can be played in many ways!

Psychologically it is very important to get a rapid answer back to the chemist, within a few days, even a preliminary answer, as long as the screening methods are reliable, and correspond to all the criteria which I have enumerated.

Irwin: I might add that it is important to make no assumptions about what a drug is likely to do, no matter what the chemist predicts for it. What we are basically trying to do is to develop very simple, rapid, and efficient techniques for picking up drug activity in the autonomic area, neurological area, and the behavioural area. Our approach is simply to adopt those techniques which provide general information most rapidly.

Steinberg: Dr. Janssen, would you care to describe some of your tests and the profiles you obtain? I believe they are rather different from Dr. Irwin's.

Janssen: It is basically a battery of tests; Dr. Irwin convinced me years ago that his approach to the problem was really better than the one we were following, and the preliminary screening tests we are using now are comparable to those he described. We start by trying to get a profile of various properties by looking at animals. All observations are made simultaneously by two independent observers watching the animals from different points in the laboratory; their subjective impressions are recorded by a code system which is simply a method of expressing the confidence they have in their own judgment. The scoring is therefore somewhat different from Dr. Irwin's system. The results are checked for observer reliability on a sequential analytical basis, and at the end of that test, another series of screening tests is run (see also p. 392).

Dr. Irwin emphasized the need for certain artificial conditions, such as convulsions, in order to screen for anticonvulsant activity, and we are doing this also. The further selection of screening tests depends to a great extent on what has been found in observation tests. If in an observation test the compound seems to resemble chlorpromazine, for instance, producing catalepsy in rats as only neuroleptic agents will do, we screen the compound in a series of tests specifically designed to study these properties further.

Cook: A screening test should eliminate compounds as well as identify active ones. Both speakers have mentioned their observational techniques as well as mentioning that other procedures are used which are more carefully specified. But are observational techniques used to eliminate compounds on the basis of observed effects or on the basis that no effects were seen?

Irwin: This is an important point. Screening procedures must be set up with the elimination of compounds at the earliest possible stage as the major aim; otherwise, the work in drug evaluation would be fantastic. Observational techniques, in my view, can be used to eliminate compounds with greater rapidity and assurance than purely instrumental techniques.

I should clarify our use of the term observation; under this heading, we include instrumental techniques and specific test situations as well as drug-induced changes in which the responses to a drug can be observed and recorded directly. Dr. Cook uses operant conditioning, but this requires an enormous baseline of experience to work successfully, and is limited in the range of information it can provide. One needs other types of measures as well. The pole-climbing procedure which Dr. Cook described is an operant procedure, but it is also an observational procedure used with an instrumental approach, and is considerably more efficient and rapid in operation than the purely instrumental, bar-press approach. There are many valid approaches to drug screening; the important point, however, is that a screening programme requires a more comprehensive battery of tests than instrumental techniques alone can provide to minimize the probability of overlooking a good drug. Nonetheless, there always exists the risk of missing a valuable compound, for there are far more measures of importance than can be studied within the limitations of manpower and time.

In drug screening and evaluation, a multidimension-observational approach is particularly important. Unitary pieces of information separately derived are also necessary, since not all drug effects can be directly observed, but they are relatively less useful than data simultaneously obtained in integrated form, where one can see the quantitative relationships between the various behavioural changes and side effects produced by a drug.

Morse: Dr. Irwin, you said that, in general, larger doses are needed to modify the more stable behavioural performances. As far as the effects of drugs on schedule-controlled behaviour are concerned, that is almost certainly not a valid generalization. If by the dose needed to modify behaviour one means the ability to detect changes at a small dose level, then, in general, the more stable the performance, the greater the likelihood that a small dose will be detectable.

Irwin: I think that psychologists have effectively selected methods which have a reasonable degree of sensitivity, and have discarded those that have not. I grant that the various measures used today, which involve highly stable outputs of behaviour, contain enough features to make them sufficiently sensitive to detect drug effects. Nevertheless, and this has been documented many times, in general the more overlearned a behaviour, the greater is the dose of drug required to influence it. Work has been done by Wikler (Wikler, A. [1948]. *Amer. J. Psychiat.*, **105**, 329; Wikler, A., and Masserman, J. H. [1957]. *Arch. Neurol. Psychiat.* [*Chic.*], **77**, 28) and by Kornetsky (Kornetsky, C., and Dawson, J. [1961]. *Pharmacologist*, **3**, 74) on this point. Outside the field of drug studies, Chapman and Wolff (Chapman, L. F., and Wolff, H. G. [1959]. *Arch. Neurol.* [*Chic.*], **1**, 357) have reported similar findings associated with lesions of the brain. The behaviours first lost are those which are least stably organized. The more stable the behaviour, the more resistant is it to the effects of brain damage; I presume that drug effects operate in an analogous manner.

One may still have, with a particular procedure, a sufficient degree of drug sensitivity, but the overall generalization is still true. If you compare the effects of drugs on conditioned avoidance behaviour during and after the acquisition phase, I think you will find that a smaller dose of drug is required to abolish the behaviour during the acquisition phase than to affect the learned behaviour.

Morse: I am not discussing the gross disruption of behaviour, but the ability to detect drug effects. Consider a classical example—Dews' work on the effects of pentobarbitone on fixed-ratio and fixed-interval performances (Dews, P. B. [1955]. *J. Pharmacol. exp. Ther.*, **113**, 393). At doses of about 2 to 4 mg./kg. the fixed-interval performance is greatly reduced compared with the control level, but the effect of saline is much greater on fixed-interval performance; so the ability to detect an effect of a small quantity of pentobarbitone is actually greater on the fixed-ratio performance. As a general rule, it is not true that the more stable the performance, the less susceptible it is to modification by drugs.

Irwin: I stand by my original statement.

Stein: Dr. Irwin, what *specific* behavioural effect does one see with 3 mg./kg. of imipramine that would enable one to characterize the drug?

Irwin: In the cat one observes increased wakefulness. At that dose, I might add, one also begins to see slight side effects, for example limb weakness, ataxia, mydriasis and an increased respiratory rate.

Bonta: Some three or four years ago, quite independently of Dr. Irwin, we also started a similar programme (Bonta, I. L., and Overbeek, G. A. [1963]. *Proc. Int. Congr. Hormonal Steroids, Milan, 1962*, in press). In the first phase we also use a non-instrumental, observational technique. Working with mice and rats, we found that the route of administration can make marked differences in these animals. We observed that certain 16-amino-substituted steroids, given intravenously, produced convulsions or locomotor excitation, whereas given orally or subcutaneously they produced sedation.

On this question of eliminating the compound in the first phase of the tests, we increase the dose till toxic symptoms appear and we do this because we think that toxic symptoms are often exaggerations of therapeutically useful effects. It is obvious that when one gives a compound in a dose which would kill the animal by respiratory paralysis, convulsions due to anoxaemia will sometimes appear. We eliminate all those compounds which seem to be non-toxic, up to a dose of 500 mg./kg.

Lister: The screening programmes of both Dr. Janssen and Dr. Irwin are presumably directed towards the discovery of compounds which affect abnormal behaviour in man. I wonder if some advantage may be gained by studying the behaviour of abnormal animals rather than of normal animals?

Irwin: I agree that we do not take as much advantage of unusual tendencies in certain strains of animals as we might. We must define what we mean by abnormal behaviour, but if I had a strain which was exceedingly fearful or aggressive, and where this measure was fairly reliable, I would feel more confident using this direct measure of behaviour to assess drug effects than I would in using indirect, instrumental techniques from which one is more likely mistakenly to *infer* a clinical effect. The abnormal behaviour, in this case, would strike me as a more suitable analogue or model of the behaviour that one finds in man and wants to treat.

Janssen: Abnormal animals can certainly be useful; for example, many of our tests involve giving amphetamine first, and an animal which has had amphetamine is not a normal animal. But I want to point out that I have no inborn tendency to prefer abnormal animals to normal animals! Both can be useful.

PREDICTION OF CLINICAL EFFECTS OF PSYCHOTROPIC DRUGS FROM ANIMAL DATA

J. O. COLE AND R. E. EDWARDS

Psychopharmacology Service Center, National Institute of Mental Health, Bethesda

THE prediction of the efficacy of drugs in man from drug effects in animals is particularly difficult in the field of psychiatry. Platitudes which are also partial truths abound, for example:

1. The differences between a rat's brain and a man's brain are both qualitatively and quantitatively much greater than the differences between their livers.

2. Since the aetiology and pathophysiology of almost all psychiatric conditions are unknown, equivalent disease states cannot be created in experimental animals.

3. All our present effective psychoactive drugs either first showed their special properties in man or are closely related to such compounds.

4. Since many factors other than drugs influence the symptoms of mental illness (milieu, psychotherapy, personal misfortunes or windfalls, the "natural history of the disease", the placebo response), it is difficult to be certain whether any drug does or does not show clinical efficacy. If one cannot even demonstrate clinical efficacy readily, how can any series of animal tests ever predict it?

All these statements are at least partially true. In addition, if one tries to derive from the published literature some idea of the measures which predict drug efficacy in man, almost all the available data concern drugs which have been successfully used in the clinic; the comparable data on drugs which were found to be ineffective in man are either nonexistent or are buried in the confidential records of drug companies.

In the face of such difficulties one might well wonder whether the need for valid animal screening procedures is worth the effort required to develop them. We believe that it is. In fact, without such tests we see little hope of correctly selecting for clinical trial a reasonable percentage of useful new compounds from among the 30,000 or more new chemical substances which the chemists of the pharmaceutical industry synthesize each year. The cost of evaluating a single new compound in man is now well over 100,000 dollars and therefore to evaluate all new compounds would cost more than three thousand million dollars a year. Thus it is simply not economically feasible to test more than a small fraction of the available new compounds in patients even if it were possible in terms of facilities and manpower, which of course it is not. Finally, there does not now appear to be any fundamental reason why useful animal tests cannot be developed, provided we devote a sufficient amount of time and effort to this specific task, and to the broader endeavour of creating a science and technology of comparative psychopharmacology.

Four possible courses of action are apparent:

1. To continue to use "promising" (that is, handy and reasonable sounding) methods in the hope that effective new drugs will come to light sooner or later.

2. To attempt to develop in animals conditions that closely resemble human clinical states in the hope of getting closer to a valid animal equivalent in which to assess drug efficacy.

3. To seek compounds which produce a variety of interesting behavioural changes in animals on the assumption that we shall thereby discover more rational methods of selecting compounds for specific clinical needs.

4. To assess empirically the predictive value of a wide variety of animal test measures by using drugs known to be effective in various conditions as standards for the preliminary validation of predictors; these tests can then be refined on newer compounds.

Since most of the literature provides only fragmentary

evidence of the effects of drugs in either animals or man, the synthesis of these data cannot readily be accomplished and the conclusions drawn in this paper will of necessity be tentative.

One of the problems noted above concerned the clinical effects to be predicted, and an attempt will therefore be made to present an ordering of the clinical effects of standard drugs, because these must serve as the criteria to be predicted.

The relative efficacy of psychotropic drugs

The following crude, three-vector system is presented in the hope that its hierarchies may be useful in the statistical analysis of animal predictors of clinical efficacy. The arrangement of the drugs can be fairly well supported by available clinical evidence.

There is overwhelming evidence that chlorpromazine is effective in treating many symptoms of schizophrenia and that promazine and pecazine are less effective. Other phenothiazines, such as thioridazine, fluphenazine, and perphenazine, are of comparable effectiveness to chlorpromazine in the treatment of schizophrenia. Although differences exist between these drugs in effective dose level and in type and incidence of side effects, we contend that significant qualitative differences in clinical efficacy among these drugs have not been demonstrated. Animal measures of the effects of these drugs should, therefore, be examined to determine similarities rather than differences. From this viewpoint the sedative properties of chlorpromazine and the more stimulant properties of fluphenazine are irrelevant to their most important clinical effect.

Reserpine is certainly less effective than the major phenothiazines in controlling schizophrenic symptoms, and haloperidol may also be less effective. Phenobarbitone is clearly ineffective in schizophrenia. Chlordiazepoxide and meprobamate may be slightly superior to phenobarbitone, but they are not usually useful in this condition.

For the treatment of anxiety and tension in neurotics it is

much harder to set up a hierarchy of drugs in order of potency. It may be that clinical evidence will eventually show a continuum of chlordiazepoxide–meprobamate–phenobarbitone, to place the most studied drugs in descending order of efficacy. The position of the other minor tranquillizers on this continuum of efficacy is not clear, nor is the position of the phenothiazines.

In the treatment of depression, a continuum in descending order of efficacy may well be: electroconvulsive therapy, amitriptyline,

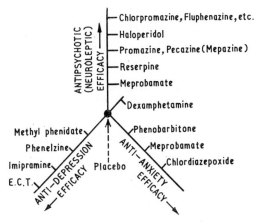

FIG. 1. Relative efficacy of some psychotropic drugs ordered along three clinical dimensions.

imipramine, phenelzine, methyl phenidate and dexamphetamine. The place of placebo in this continuum is not clear. Dexamphetamine may actually be worse than a placebo in treating depression. In endogenous depressions, the placebo may lie somewhere between phenelzine and dexamphetamine. (See also this volume, p. 455.)

Laboratory and clinical data on a new antipsychotic drug

Rather than attempt a comprehensive review of the adequacy of clinical predictability from animal behavioural data for a large number of psychotropic drugs, we shall present the available information on a single new antipsychotic agent.

Fig. 2 shows the structures of two very similar indole compounds, oxypertine and its desmethoxyl analogue. The laboratory behavioural data on these two compounds fairly adequately predicted their suitability for clinical use (Edwards *et al.*, 1962).

In the following discussion we shall refer to several behavioural techniques that one of us (R. E.) has used in the laboratory and

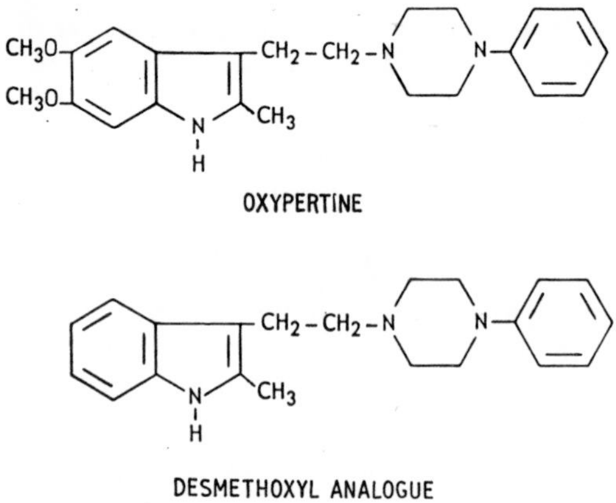

OXYPERTINE

DESMETHOXYL ANALOGUE

FIG. 2. Structures of oxypertine and its desmethoxyl analogue.

which we shall describe briefly. The technique we call "unconditioned avoidance" is simply the avoidance by a rat of a light touch by the experimenter's forefinger and thumb on the vibrissae or nose of the animal. A normal, unmedicated animal will withdraw his head within 5 seconds of the moment when the experimenter makes contact. The medicated animal may hold his position indefinitely, allowing the experimenter to touch him in this manner.

The second test procedure is a method used to detect catalepsy. In Fig. 3 a rat is seen standing on a metal screen, resting his forepaws on a horizontal rod. The electrical contact that he makes between rod and screen is detected by an electronic device which operates an electric stop-clock. The experimenter lifts the rat into position and presses a starting switch; the clock runs until the animal breaks contact with either rod or screen. Rats showing drug-induced catalepsy hold this abnormal position for periods longer than 15 seconds per trial.

Two other procedures used are referred to as "conditioned avoidance" and "conditioned approach". The avoidance procedure consists of presenting a 5-second warning sound and light to a rat in a Skinner box in which he has been trained to press a lever in order to terminate this conditioned stimulus. If the rat responds within 5 seconds he receives no shock. Failure to respond within 5 seconds initiates an electric shock through the grid floor of the box. This unconditioned stimulus can be terminated by pressing the same lever or will be self-terminating within 3 seconds. The positive reinforcement counterpart of this technique is referred to as "conditioned approach" and substitutes for the shock a drop of water as a reward for a thirsty rat for responding during the 5-second warning period. Failure to respond within 5 seconds merely means that the animal must wait approximately one minute until the conditioned stimulus (the sound and light) comes on again. Thus the positive reinforcement is mild compared with the negative reinforcement in the other procedure. Psychotropic drugs delay or abolish the rat's lever-pressing response to the warning signal in both of these tests of learned behaviour.

Median effective doses of the two indole compounds for each of these four procedures are presented in Table I. Different groups of rats were used in the two operant conditioning tests, but the same rats were used for unconditioned avoidance and catalepsy. It is clear that whereas the median oral effective doses of oxypertine are of a reasonable magnitude, the desmethoxyl analogue is virtually inactive. The results obtained with rats were confirmed in a Sidman avoidance situation with rhesus monkeys. Additional comparisons between oxypertine, chlorpromazine and reserpine in the rat are given in Table II. As can be seen, oxypertine has a

Table I

A COMPARISON OF THE BEHAVIOURAL EFFECTS OF
OXYPERTINE WITH THOSE OF ITS DESMETHOXYL ANALOGUE

Behavioural test	Oral effective doses in mg. per kg.	
	Oxypertine	Desmethoxyl analogue
Cond. avoidance	$7 \cdot 6 \pm 1 \cdot 2$	Inactive (50–400)
Cond. approach	$11 \cdot 5 \pm 3 \cdot 4$	Inactive (100 & 200)
Uncond. avoidance	$6 \cdot 9 \pm 1 \cdot 8$	Irregular (25–1600)
Catalepsy	$8 \cdot 1 \pm 1 \cdot 5$	4/10 at 800

Table II

A COMPARISON OF THE BEHAVIOURAL EFFECTS OF
OXYPERTINE WITH THOSE OF CHLORPROMAZINE AND RESERPINE

Test	ED_{50}'s in mg./kg. for rats		
	Oxypertine, oral	Chlorpromazine, oral	Reserpine, s.c.
Cond. avoidance	$6 \cdot 8 \pm 1 \cdot 3$	$11 \cdot 6 \pm 3 \cdot 3$	$0 \cdot 45 \pm 0 \cdot 12$
Cond. approach	$11 \cdot 5 \pm 3 \cdot 4$		$0 \cdot 58 \pm 0 \cdot 08$
Catalepsy	$8 \cdot 1 \pm 1 \cdot 5$	$20 \cdot 5 \pm 4 \cdot 5$	$1 \cdot 6 \pm 0 \cdot 2$
Overt behaviour	$10 \cdot 0 \pm 2 \cdot 7$	$8 \cdot 0 \pm 1 \cdot 5$	$0 \cdot 35 \pm 0 \cdot 07$
Eye closure	$12 \cdot 0 \pm 2 \cdot 1$	$9 \cdot 1 \pm 1 \cdot 0$	$0 \cdot 10 \pm 0 \cdot 01$

behavioural profile that is much more like that of chlorpromazine than like that of reserpine.

The clinical results that were obtained with these compounds are consistent with the laboratory data. Oxypertine gives results in man which are similar in several respects to those obtained with chlorpromazine. However, only undesirable side effects are obtained with the desmethoxyl analogue. The one departure

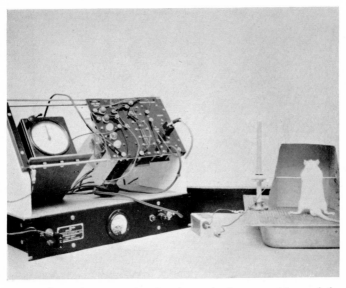

Fig. 3. The catalepsy test, showing the rat in the test position and the associated timing apparatus.

To face p. 292

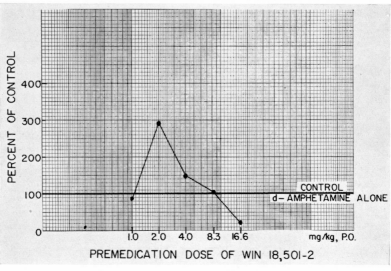

FIG. 4. The potentiation of dexamphetamine by oxypertine (WIN 18,501–2).

from what one would predict from the laboratory findings is that the undesirable side effects of the analogue occurred at low doses, which were even lower than those which would show any effects with oxypertine.

Another interesting property of oxypertine is illustrated in Fig. 4. At a rather low dose, which happens to be the average daily dose for man, this drug will potentiate the stimulant effects of dexamphetamine in a photocell activity cage. Two mg./kg. of oxypertine, given to rats 6–8 hours before medication with dexamphetamine, produces a nearly 300 per cent increase in random activity over that of the group receiving dexamphetamine alone. This is in line with the clinical finding that oxypertine induces a higher degree of tension, anxiety, and akathisia-like extrapyramidal symptoms than one would expect with chlorpromazine.

Recent clinical reports indicate that schizophrenics treated with oxypertine show a decrease in isolation and withdrawal and an increased ability to communicate. Approximately a third of the patients treated in one study also showed motor restlessness, increased muscle tone, a mask-like facial expression, and anxiety approaching panic at doses of 120 mg. or more per day (Durell and Pollin, 1963). In another study (Hollister et al., 1963) it was found that the drug was highly effective in patients classified as "schizophrenic" or "depressive" but not in those classified as "paranoid". This author concludes that oxypertine is an effective antipsychotic agent ranking with the phenothiazine derivatives he has studied.

Both papers note the presence of extrapyramidal effects, which were correctly predicted by the catalepsy test in laboratory animals. Indeed, it appears to us that a comparable incidence of extrapyramidal signs has been observed with oxypertine at one-half to one-fourth of the corresponding dose of chlorpromazine, on the basis of unpublished as well as published reports.

We should like briefly to touch on two matters concerning the relation of laboratory data to clinical results. The first is the relative sensitivity of animal behavioural techniques. Obviously, if very high doses of a drug are required in animals because of insensitive tests, the profile of action measured may correspond only with that obtained at toxic doses in man. Several American laboratory groups have recently reported very encouraging results with the squirrel monkey as a small model of man. In

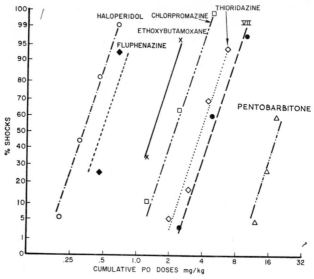

FIG. 5. Dose-response curves for several psychotropic drugs obtained with squirrel monkeys. Cumulative dosing at 90-min. intervals (from Hanson et al., 1962).

Fig. 5 dose-response curves for several tranquillizers are presented. We are indebted to Dr. Harley M. Hanson (Merck Institute of Therapeutic Research) for this figure, which shows his results with squirrel monkeys on a nondiscriminated avoidance schedule (Hanson et al., 1962). The regularity of the drug effect, measured by the percentage of electric shocks received as a function of dosage, is evident. In Table III the mean doses of three pheno-thiazines required to cause monkeys to fail to avoid 50 per cent of the possible shocks are compared with the doses of these three drugs used in a recent double-blind clinical drug study by the Psychopharmacology Service Center. The effective dose in squirrel monkeys, when multiplied by seventy to obtain a value corresponding to the total human dose, compares well with the doses used by the psychiatrists in this study. Even thioridazine, which is usually much less potent than chlorpromazine in animals, is quite effective in this procedure.

Table III

A COMPARISON OF THE DOSES OF THREE PHENOTHIAZINES USED IN A CLINICAL STUDY WITH THE AVERAGE DOSES USED WITH SQUIRREL MONKEYS IN AN AVOIDANCE EXPERIMENT[*]

(from Hanson et al., 1962)

| | Squirrel monkey ($70 \times ED_{50}$) | P.S.C. Collaborative Study | | |
		Minimum	Average	Maximum
Chlorpromazine	154	200	655	1,600
Thioridazine	266	200	700	1,600
Fluphenazine	35	2	6·4	16

[*] Squirrel monkey doses, in mg./kg., were multiplied by 70 to make them comparable with human daily doses.

Our second point concerns the use of laboratory procedures to investigate analytically the consequences of different medications. Steinberg, Rushton and Tinson (1961) have shown that a stimulant does not cancel out all the behavioural effects of a barbiturate, thus helping to explain the clinical value of preparations such as Dexamyl or Irish coffee! Fig. 6 illustrates another experiment with two drugs in which similar behavioural tests can give quite discrepant results when antagonism between the drugs occurs for one type of response and potentiation for another. Here the three test procedures on which we presented data above are used to evaluate the consequences of medicating rats with chlorpromazine, hyoscine, or chlorpromazine plus hyoscine. Hyoscine alone is inactive on the unconditioned avoidance and catalepsy test procedures, and therefore the bars corresponding to a control dose of hyoscine alone are omitted. If doses of chlorpromazine and hyoscine are chosen which will give a small, positive effect in blocking the conditioned avoidance response—that is, doses that will impair the performance of one out of five

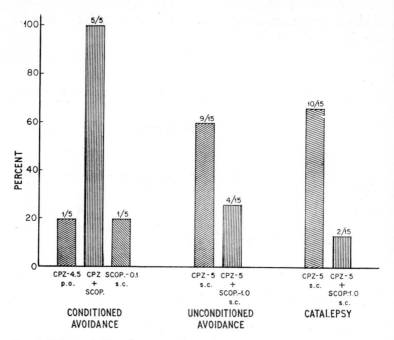

FIG. 6. Effects of chlorpromazine and hyoscine (scopolamine) and of the two drugs given at the same time on three tests of rat behaviour.

rats—and a third group of five rats is then given the same amount of chlorpromazine, but with hyoscine at the same time, all five rats are unable to function at the criterion level. However, hyoscine antagonizes rather than potentiates the disruptive effects of chlorpromazine on unconditioned avoidance and catalepsy. From this one might infer that the perceptual and associative effects of chlorpromazine and hyoscine potentiate each other, but the extrapyramidal effects induced by chlorpromazine are antagonized by hyoscine, an anticholinergic drug.

Summary

To recapitulate, a three-vector, rank ordering of several drugs has been presented as a means of summarizing our current appraisal of the efficacy of psychotropic drugs. This might serve as a system of criteria for evaluating animal test methods for these drugs. A comparison of laboratory and clinical data on a new antipsychotic agent has been presented to illustrate the utility of animal behavioural methods. Data showing the comparable sensitivity of squirrel monkey and man to several drugs have been presented, and an experiment which illustrated the use of behavioural methods in the analysis of drug interactions has been described.

REFERENCES

DURELL, J., and POLLIN, W. (1963). *Brit. J. Psychiat.*, **109**, 687.
EDWARDS, R. E., Moon, L. E., Jr., and PEARL, J. (1962). *Pharmacologist*, **4**, 167.
HANSON, H. M., WILOSLAWSKI, J., and CAMPBELL, E. (1962). *Pharmacologist*, **4**, 152.
HOLLISTER, L. E., OVERALL, J. E., KIMBELL, Y., Jr., BENNETT, J. L., MEYER, S., and CAFFEY, E., Jr. (1963). *J. New Drugs*, **3**, 26.
STEINBERG, H., RUSHTON, R., and TINSON, C. (1961). *Nature (Lond.)*, **192**, 533.

DISCUSSION

Hendry: In your diagram (Fig. 1) you showed as vectors anxiety, depression and psychosis. What evidence have you that these three conditions are in fact orthogonal? Many clinicians regard anxiety as an integral element in all mental disturbances, and there are cases where depression and psychosis are closely connected. I am thinking particularly of postpartum depression and involutionary depression, which may lead to psychoses.

Edwards: We certainly recognize that these three vectors or dimensions are not orthogonal. We proposed them as a preliminary, crude approximation to a scheme for ordering the three important classes of drugs, to give the preclinical investigator something from which to work. I agree that anxiety is involved in schizophrenia, as Dr. Hamilton's paper shows, for instance (p. 299). If a patient on a neuroleptic drug becomes too anxious, phenobarbitone, and now chlordiazepoxide can be given to reduce his anxiety. Obviously these drugs are capable of producing as well as ameliorating abnormal behaviour. However, I think that although anxiety and the psychotic conditions most characteristic of schizophrenia are not completely orthogonal, there is a difference between them. Equally, it seems reasonable to place in a third category those individuals who are depressed, but who do not show anxiety or psychotic symptoms to a marked degree.

Steinberg: I wonder what proportion of the drugs which Dr. Edwards listed as effective were discovered by the three different methods of discovery which have been discussed: the observational method, the operant method, and the *Fingerspitzengefühl* or intuition, to which Dr. Janssen has referred?

Edwards: I believe that the earlier drugs in each category were developed by clinical observation. Later drugs, such as chlordiazepoxide, were detected by various laboratory experiments and observational methods, and then confirmed in the clinic. I am not really depressed by this; I do not think we will really know how successful these preclinical methods are for perhaps another twenty years.

PREDICTION OF CLINICAL RESPONSE FROM ANIMAL DATA:
A NEED FOR THEORETICAL MODELS

M. HAMILTON

Department of Psychiatry, School of Medicine, University of Leeds

MOST of the previous authors have dealt with their subjects in a forthright manner and have talked of practical problems and experimental results. I hope that I shall be forgiven if I emphasize the sub-title of my paper, "A need for theoretical models", and deal with some more abstract aspects of the subject of this section of the symposium.

This paper is going to make only one point in relation to the two major types of psychotropic drugs in clinical use nowadays, the anti-depressives and the tranquillizers. I will start with the most obvious of clinical observations on the action of the anti-depressive drugs, that is, the long delay which occurs before any effect of the drug is noticed; two to three weeks is very common. This is a very remarkable phenomenon, but it is matched by the equally remarkable results which occur, if and when they do occur, when the patient starts to respond to the drug. We then see a virtual disappearance of all the patient's symptoms: not only does he feel less depressed, but he becomes less preoccupied with thoughts of his guilt, he sleeps better, he does not wake in the early hours of the morning, he regains his interest in his work and activities, he goes back to his normal former social life, his appetite is restored, he stops worrying and his weight increases. All this takes place sometimes within a few days, two or three at the most; not always, but often. This suggests that the effects of the drug given are not simply a masking of the symptoms. It would appear that in some way the drug is producing a biochemical change affecting some process which has occurred in the body (perhaps in the brain) and that this latter process is fundamental to the disease.

It seems very simple, in consequence, to postulate a "biochemical lesion" as the basis for depressive illnesses, but such an hypothesis would be more than simple; it would be very naive. We cannot ignore the relation between the depressive illnesses and the manias and anxiety states. Furthermore, we must always bear in mind the self-limiting character of the depressive disorders. No biochemical disorder shows the recurrences which are typical of the depressive disorders, although hyperthyroidism which develops in the third or fourth decades, will go on fluctuating for a period, before it may finally disappear.

Be that as it may, we must now ask how the anti-depressive drugs work. For a start, I suggest that we can postulate two possible modes of action: the first is that these drugs have some stimulating effect on some centre or function which overcomes a block (which forms the "lesion"); and the second is that they produce a compensating lesion. What this means I will deal with a little later; but ignoring the details (and I am well aware that these hypotheses are more stimulant of controversy than anything else), if we devise this theoretical model, it can lead only to one conclusion, and that is that experiments on normal human beings, and even more so on normal animals, are not going to give us very much information on the nature of the effect of the anti-depressive drugs. It is true that biochemical and electrophysiological studies may provide clues to the site of such action, but I think they can do very little more than that. I am quite certain that behavioural studies cannot give us the essential clue, and it is for this reason that at the moment, as we have heard from Dr. Janssen, the search for further drugs must proceed along those extraordinarily laborious empirical lines. Only some sort of theoretical model can give us a guide.

Turning now to the tranquillizers, I should like to remark that never has a group of drugs been more remarkably misnamed. Judging, for example, by their action on anxiety states and on agitated depressions they have almost no tranquillizing effect at all. On the contrary, the toxic appearance of patients who have been well loaded with the phenothiazines in attempts to diminish their anxieties is very characteristic, and so also is the remarkable improvement in their anxiety on stopping the drugs.

The main field of action of the so-called tranquillizers is in the schizophrenias. We do not at present have a drug with a "curative" effect (a very naive term). In view of the remarkable benefits which can be obtained in the chronic schizophrenias by means of social therapy and the various techniques of rehabilitation and psychological treatment, I would suggest that the most useful type of drug in this field is one which would potentiate the effects of such social and psychological treatment.

What clinical research has been done on this point suggests that these tranquillizing drugs have, in fact, the opposite effect (Hamilton et al., 1960, 1963). The few and inadequate investigations which have been done on this do, however, find themselves in agreement with the general consensus of opinion that tranquillizers have very poor results on schizophrenics who are in good environments, undergoing an active rehabilitation programme, and *vice versa* (Little, 1958). In agreement with this, it would appear that these drugs have very little place in out-patient practice, where we can generally assume that patients are in comparatively good environmental conditions (Hordern and Hamilton, 1963).

The general implication of this is that tranquillizing drugs act by producing a "compensating lesion". It is analogous to what the surgeon does when he treats Parkinsonism, that is to say, they work by their toxic effect, and the particular results they have compensate in some way the effects of the schizophrenia. I put it forward for consideration that the main brunt of this toxic effect falls on what might be called, in a Jacksonian sense, the highest faculties.

Once again it must be concluded from this that experiments on normal subjects and on animals will indicate the disturbing effect of these drugs rather than their therapeutic use. It may be argued that there is a need for theoretical models about the nature of these disorders, to be provided by the psychiatrists, and that this might well take first place. I would say on this that there is no difficulty in providing such theoretical models and they can be, and have been, produced like rabbits out of a conjurer's hat. You will probably agree with me that such theoretical models of the nature of these disorders are not sufficient to guide the psycho-pharmacologist in finding new drugs or elucidating their action; and certainly they are not necessary.

To sum up: only a theory can give us a guide to further research and the finding of new drugs. Without it we are forced to go through the endless empirical investigations that have been described and this is not the way for rapid progress.

REFERENCES

HAMILTON, M., HORDERN, A., WALDROP, F. N., and LOFFT, J. (1963). *Brit. J. Psychiat.*, **109**, 510.

HAMILTON, M., SMITH, A. L. G., LAPIDUS, H. E., and CADOGAN, E. P. (1960). *J. ment. Sci.*, **106**, 40.

HORDERN, A., and HAMILTON, M. (1963). *Brit. J. Psychiat.*, **109**, 500.

LITTLE, J. C. (1958). *J. ment. Sci.*, **104**, 334.

DISCUSSION

Stein: Dr. Hamilton, I agree that the phenothiazines do not seem to have a selective effect on anxiety and probably not much effect on schizophrenia. However, are they not specifically effective against manic states, and if so, is this effect due to a toxic action?

Hamilton: The phenothiazines are not uniquely effective on manias, for there are many drugs which sedate the manic patient. Yes, I do think that the effect of the phenothiazines is due primarily to their toxic effect.

Bein: Is every sedative action due to a toxic effect?

Hamilton: That is a loaded question! Consider the sedative action of amylobarbitone sodium. Small doses produce sedation and larger doses increase sedation to the point of hypnosis; the animal or patient falls asleep. Still larger doses produce coma, and larger ones still, death. Do you think that there are two processes here and that the initial sedative action is not the same as the final toxic action? Or is there one continuous, linear process, in which case there is from the beginning a slight toxic effect? When we are dealing with the barbiturates, the toxic effect is in a sense negligible. Damage to the functions of the individual is trivial and temporary, and the therapeutic effect, which is the one we are looking for, happens to be critical: the patient can now sleep. However, if he takes amylobarbitone sodium and then wants to solve a mathematical problem or drive a car, he may find that the effect is perhaps toxic after all.

When we are dealing with the phenothiazines this sedative-hypnotic effect is very small indeed. What I am suggesting is that the effects of these drugs on the symptoms of the schizophrenic are very close to those effects which produce a disturbance on what might be called a physiological level. The effects are already toxic on some of the higher functions. I base this theory on the fact that chronic schizophrenics, who are responding well to their environment and whose behaviour is reasonably adequate at a relatively low level, do not show any benefit from these drugs. On the contrary, with high doses they show the toxic effects only; whereas in those who are more acutely ill, grossly hallucinated and disturbed and deluded, the effect of the drug is to damp down these manifestations. I suggest that the beneficial effect is seen because the toxic effect on the brain happens to balance these symptoms. I gave as an analogy the example of the surgeon who operates on the brain in order to relieve Parkinsonism. The patient will certainly be pleased when his tremor has gone, but nobody would dream of suggesting that the brain is now functioning better than it did before.

Bein: I am not competent to argue about the clinical treatment, but I think that to regard every pharmacological action as a toxic one is too broad a generalization. There is also some confusion over the terms therapeutic index and specific effect. For instance, is the action of a barbiturate the same at both low and high doses? Dr. Bradley has shown that barbiturates block arousal in doses which are considerably smaller than the normal anaesthetic dose. One should not generalize about the mode of action of any drug without specifying first, the dose used, and in addition, the system in which it was tested.

Bonta: I think that this distinction of toxic and therapeutic psycho-pharmacological effects is largely artificial. A careful study of toxic effects can give us very useful information, because even the toxic effect of a drug could be very characteristic, or unique—no other drug might produce this type of toxic effect. The effects of aspirin, for example, can be demonstrated in animal experiments only at nearly toxic dose levels. Furthermore, "toxicity" depends greatly on the experimental conditions. At a dose in which analeptics are toxic to normal animals, they would be absolutely non-toxic to depressed or sedated animals.

Joyce: Surely it is not enough to define operationally what we mean by toxic. We have to go further and also define what we mean by the right dose. In animal experiments this might be defined as the dose to alter behaviour on a fixed-ratio schedule, but that might be quite a different dose, and hence the wrong dose, from that which alters behaviour on, say, a fixed-interval schedule. It seems that we have to draw up a balance sheet of those human responses which are helpfully acted upon by each drug at doses between x and $10x$, and those which are interfered with by the same drug for the same dose range.

Gaddum: Dr. Hamilton seemed to suggest that we could not discover anything about a drug which would be useful in man by experiments on normal animals. Theoretically, it is possible to make an animal abnormal by giving it some other drug. For example, you can make it resemble a schizophrenic patient, and then find something which can cure it of this state. Many people hoped that LSD-25 would lead in this way to the discovery of new drugs which would be of use in schizophrenia.

Collier: It is quite common practice to use animals treated with reserpine or tetrabenazine as models of depressed man. The main justification for this has been that reserpine occasionally produces something like melancholia in patients. Certainly those drugs which are reputed to be anti-melancholic generally reduce reserpine or tetrabenazine depression in animals; although with drugs like imipramine, pharmacologists have to work hard to show this effect.

Hamilton: Thank you, Dr. Gaddum; this was precisely my point, that we need theoretical models. If we are going to investigate drug action we must devise some hypothesis as to how these drugs are going to work. You have suggested that we should take one step further, and not only decide what lesion the drug is going to work on, but produce the lesion also! I think this is an excellent suggestion but I do not think anybody has yet succeeded.

Brown: Have pathological mutants ever been considered as experimental animals for screening tests before clinical trials?

Bein: Unfortunately there are very few animals which can be used suitably in such tests. Experiments with mutants such as circling mice or waltzing mice have not led to more informative results than pharmacological experiments in normal animals.

Janssen: There are also a certain number of animals which are known to be spontaneously abnormal in their behaviour. For example, there are individual rats and also dogs which have the inborn tendency to kill mice. It is rather exceptional; only 5 per cent of our rats have this tendency. It is an all-or-nothing affair and they either kill mice from the first trial or they will starve rather than devour mice with which they come in contact. I think there are many analogous possibilities which may be interesting to test.

It is clear that we should all like to have models and to arrive at solutions logically. But in fact practically no useful drug has been developed in a logical way. We cure diseases with drugs which we know hardly anything about. So far as mental disease is concerned, where we have no immediate hope of achieving this goal of Dr. Hamilton's, we have to take some action in the meantime. This empirical approach can be fruitful, as the history of medicine has shown.

Chance: I think we should be clear about what we regard as normal in an animal. In regarding the eating of mice by 5 per cent of rats as abnormal, you are neglecting the well-known fact that in biological populations hereditary differences between members of a population establish different food habits and other differences of behaviour in order that the population can quickly change to different sources of food in times of ecological disturbance and stress. Therefore this particular variation is not necessarily in any sense "abnormal" in a population. I have shown that the same explanation may well apply to audiogenic seizures in mice. Whether or not you regard them as useful tools for examining anti-epileptic drugs is a different matter altogether. But the distinction between normal and abnormal in this context needs further clarification.

If we are going to make models which are interpretable both in animal terms and in human behavioural terms, there has got to be a considerable reorganization of the conceptual formulations we have inherited from medicine, because these are not capable of being directly interpreted in biological terms. On the other hand, it is possible to observe human beings and to see if the observations can be organized on theoretical models which approximate more closely to those models you can develop when you observe animals. I have tried to show that one way of doing this in animals produces a different kind of knowledge about an animal. We have already begun to observe human beings from this same point of view, and it is possible to see forms of behaviour which show striking similarities with animals. I am not yet prepared to say whether we shall be able to make models which have any general validity in this connexion.

Cook: We have had a varied discussion of screening procedures and the relevance of the findings of such procedures to the clinic. I think it is appropriate to ask the question—screening for what effect? The one thing lacking seems to have been a definition of the clinical syndrome which we are attempting to treat with drugs. Although Dr. Hamilton referred to our lack of models—I was not quite sure whether he was providing them or saying they did not exist—I think we lack primarily a definition of those relevant criteria in a particular syndrome which can be used by the preclinical pharmacologist. It is wrong to consider the field of psychopharmacology as something unique. We are dealing with an aspect of pharmacology in which behaviour is the substrate. In a symposium of cardiovascular pharmacology we would perhaps make a greater attempt to establish the relevance of not only preclinical but also clinical criteria, than we have done here.

Joyce: There is one paradoxical "disadvantage" under which we all labour who work in the fields of psychiatry, psychology and psychopharmacology, which is that with a few exceptions—and I agree with Dr. Cook that one must define what one is talking about here—patients do not die as a result of their mental disease, or not very directly or not very soon. If you have heart failure and it is not treated you die, and so it becomes extremely necessary to study the drugs which can reverse heart failure. We, on the other hand, work in this very amorphous area in which all we know is that behaviour is disturbed, but, as Dr. Chance pointed out, we do not really know what normal behaviour is. Many of us are loath to risk giving drugs or taking other therapeutic measures which may leave the patient in a worse state than he was in in the first place.

Miller: It is perhaps a little discouraging to end on the topic of the human applications. I am reminded of somebody's definition of schizophrenia as a secret society to which people are elected by unknown rules which change from time to time! I think it is no fault of clinicians that some of the gravest mental illnesses are still a great mystery, but as long as we do not really understand them, it is quite difficult to select animal tests from which to predict how drugs will act upon this unknown state of affairs. Nevertheless, much progress has been made on a relatively blind, empirical basis. For the first time the number of people in mental hospitals is being reduced. This reduction saves enough money, and produces enough relief of human misery, to justify all our research.

PREDICTION FROM MAN TO ANIMALS

C. R. B. JOYCE

Department of Pharmacology, The London Hospital Medical College

ONLY about ten per cent of the 3,000 or so papers noted in *Psychopharmacology Abstracts* for 1961 were mainly concerned with behavioural studies (clinical and biochemical or pharmacological work accounted for about 40 per cent each). A random sampling suggests that, whereas a large number (although still a minority) of the clinical papers were stimulated by findings with animals, not more than one in ten of the behavioural papers, at most, had observations originally made on man as one of their immediate causes. The proportion in the present symposium does not seem so very dissimilar.

Man may not be unique, but he is somewhat different from most other animals, especially in those ways which make him peculiarly interesting to himself. If the psychopharmacologist of the rats is a rat, he may be wondering if his predictions of drug effects in his fellow rats have been so unsuccessful because they were mainly based on experiments with man. Humans use time, social contacts and experience in ways that are more complex than those of animals. They also have more alternative ways of organizing the attainment of a given objective. All these aspects pose special problems, and are often considered together as constituting human variation, or error.

Pharmacodynamics and pharmacotherapeutics cannot be separated, although their methods and their criteria of progress are rather different. The success of one is hard to judge in relation to that of the other, but psychotherapeutic advances are undoubtedly more likely if pharmacodynamics is able to offer useful explanations of the way in which drugs produce their behavioural effects. This in turn depends upon the ability of experimental psychology, neurophysiology and biochemistry to provide testable hypotheses, and we have been privileged to hear about this during this symposium.

But it is plain that the development of therapeutically useful substances is an empirical business at the moment, and a rather inefficient one at that. Not more than one in from a half to two million substances given a cursory preliminary screening is considered worth submitting to clinical trial: and of about twenty such substances reaching clinical trial, only one is judged by reputable manufacturers to be useful enough for marketing. A cynic might say (à propos of Professor Miller's plea for the publication of more negative results) that this proportion is about what one would expect to occur by chance at the 5 per cent level anyway. An unknown number of useful compounds is certainly jettisoned and it is now common knowledge that the life-time of the survivors is short. The half-life, in fact, is agreed to be about five years.

Perhaps it is time for therapy to repay its debt to pharmacodynamics by making some extrapolations from human to animal behaviour, rather than the other way about.

Variability. Human beings are different from each other and from themselves at other moments in time. This variation is itself interesting; it often swamps drug effects when these are evaluated over whole groups, and is presumably similar to that which occurs in animals, despite attempts to reduce it, for example by inbreeding or homogeneous environments. The latter gives rise to both Type 1 and Type 2 errors, namely, rejection of useful, and acceptance of useless compounds. Both kinds of error are responsible for an unknown wastage of human work. This is certainly increased by generalization to the sick human population from an illicit sample of usually healthy animals. The occasional rediscovery of substances originally rejected, such as cycloserine or phenylbutazone, is a haphazard affair, and suggests that the frequency with which the wrong hypothesis is rejected in man may be very great. There is already some evidence that there are drugs for individuals: this appears to be true for analgesics (Jellinek, 1946; Newton and Tanner, 1956) and antidepressants (Pare, Rees and Sainsbury, 1962) at least. The study in animals of such individual variation might profitably use the "single-case" approach. It seems likely that a study of the interactions between tests, drugs and individuals, analogous to that of Lehmann and Knight (1961) on humans, in terms of increment and decrement liabilities, would also be worth while in animals. Dr. Stein and Dr. Irwin have both suggested that basal levels of responding can modify apparent or true drug effects—and human beings have very different basal levels of responding.

Time relations. Many psychotherapeutic agents begin to have an effect, if at all, after the lapse of some weeks. On the other hand, some effects may last for months, or even into the next generation, although the drug was withdrawn long before (Freedman and Benton, 1961;Werboff and Kesner, 1963). Over what time-scale should which species be examined, not merely for toxic but for potentially useful effects? Irwin (1959) has reported that the effect of iproniazid on running activity may take several days to develop, and Miller (1961) has shown that the "therapeutic" effect on conflict behaviour of chlorpromazine given for one day carries over into the period after the drug is withdrawn, although this does not happen with amylobarbitone. Dr. Bureš and Dr. Steinberg have told us how the exact point during the learning experience at which the drug is given modifies subsequent behaviour. But most sick human behaviour is already established, and very likely "strongly engaged" as well, by the time it comes up for treatment.

Social relations. Just as the results of even a double-blind clinical trial sometimes depend quite dramatically upon the individual therapist (Joyce, 1962), different experimenters obtain different conditioning curves in rabbits (Brogden, 1962), and apparently in planarians as well (Rosenthal and Halas, 1962). Have such observations on man and animals a common basis? Participation in a group, especially if some of the other members have been given the same, or especially different, treatments, can change the magnitude of the drug effect (Joyce, 1963), and even its direction (Starkweather, 1959). Human beings, after all, whether as patients in hospital or as out-patients at home, are members of groups in which drug treatment is very heterogeneous. Animal analogies are obviously available here. Is the dolphin, maybe, the ideal animal for such studies since, so far, he alone can fully share his environment with the experimenter and can communicate with him (Lilly, 1962)?

Experience. Expectations based upon previous acquaintance with drugs, reading about them, or, presumably, with other people's beliefs about their actions, can modify what actually occurs inside the subject, or what he observes of these occurrences, or perhaps what he reports of them to the experimenter. First-term preclinical students, asked to state in advance what they expect to observe in themselves after taking an unspecified drug, anticipate dry mouths, increased heart-rates and sleepiness. The operant rat learns after one experience with hyoscine to behave when subsequently given saline as if he had had hyoscine again (Herrnstein, 1962), and Steinberg, Rushton and Tinson's (1961) results with barbiturate and amphetamine mixtures for naive rats point the same way. Experience is also involved in the development of alternative pathways to the same end. This is characteristically human, but as Dr. Chance has beautifully shown, not exclusively so. Where there are such alternatives, a drug that interferes with only one route may appear inactive, although if the same response also occurs on the way to other goals, and is there much less easily substituted, the drug might be seen to be active if tested on a response related to this other part of the route. It is also very striking that so many dose-response curves, for so many different drugs, show an initial departure from control values, followed by a reversal of the direction of the effect at higher doses. Probably all animals, ourselves included, perform most specific responses sub-optimally: and it looks as if any single response can be improved by throwing any spanner into the works so long as it is a small one. But what is the cost to the accurate performance of other, unmeasured responses?

Complexity. In one last area, we may look for animal tests of the claim to man's uniqueness. This is in the field of complexity which distinguishes so much of human activity. The effect of most drugs at ordinary doses is easier to demonstrate upon simple than upon complex tasks, for example, upon mathematical addition rather than upon differentiation (Smith and Beecher, 1962), although one may suspect that it is on the more complex tasks that most social effects of such substances (both for and against society) are shown. Smith, Weitzner and Beecher (1963) elsewhere observed the effects of amphetamine more sensitively upon trained than upon untrained athletes. Is the human patient's sick response to be regarded as simple or complex, as trained or untrained? What about healthy man's ability to be "original" when influenced by drugs? Can rats or other animals be trained to produce a rich repertoire of operant responses, so that the effect of drugs in increasing or decreasing the less probable of these may be studied as an analogy to human originality?

What I am pleading for is the analysis in operational terms of all kinds of human behaviour, as Skinner and Ferster, especially, have suggested. Schedules are important in determining drug effects, and many of those important for human behaviour are VI, VR with collateral chaining and plenty of TO; timing of drug administration is important; and the identification of the reinforcing stimulus is also vital, but frequently, in the human situation, very doubtful. What, for instance, reinforces the interrupter at a political meeting, or perhaps the last speaker at a symposium? Not, I suspect, the answer to the question he takes so long to ask. I think it important to be clear that the aims of therapy and of pharmacodynamics are different and their languages are so as well. "Standard rats" will not answer the problems of pharmacotherapy nor will the mere identification of sources of variation and interaction. We need to *use* these factors.

No doubt it will be a very long time before the psychiatrist can set up in his laboratory a carefully selected individual animal model for each of his patients, on which the effect of each possible treatment intended for the patient can be predicted: but this day will, at least be more congenial to me than another which we have at times seemed likely to reach much sooner—the day when, as with iodine today and primaquine in parts of Africa, chlordiazepoxide will come in the salt and imipramine in the pepper.

REFERENCES

BROGDEN, W. J. (1962). *Psychol. Rep.*, **11**, 239.
FREEDMAN, D. X., and BENTON, A. J. (1961). *New Eng. J. Med.*, **264**, 529.
HERRNSTEIN, R. J. (1962). *Science*, **138**, 677.
IRWIN, S. (1959). *Fed. Proc.*, **18**, 406.
JELLINEK, E. M. (1946). *Biometrics Bull.*, **2**, 87.
JOYCE, C. R. B. (1962). *J. chron. Dis.*, **15**, 1025.
JOYCE, C. R. B. (1963). *Proc. Soc. psychosomat. Res.* In the press.
LEHMANN, H. E., and KNIGHT, D. A. (1961). *In* Neuro-Psychopharmacology, **2**, 291, ed. Rothlin, E. Amsterdam: Elsevier.
LILLY, J. C. (1962). Man and Dolphin. London: Gollancz.
MILLER, N. E. (1961). Discussion of the paper by Amedeo S. Marrazzi. *Ann. N.Y. Acad. Sci.*, **92**, 1028.
NEWTON, D. R. L., and TANNER, J. M. (1956). *Brit. med. J.*, **2**, 1096.
PARE, C. M. B., REES, L., and SAINSBURY, M. J. (1962). *Lancet*, **2**, 1340.
ROSENTHAL, R., and HALAS, E. S. (1962). *Psychol. Rep.*, **11**, 251.
SMITH, G. M., and BEECHER, H. K. (1962). *Pharmacologist*, **4**, 166.
SMITH, G. M., WEITZNER, M., and BEECHER, H. K. (1963). *J. Pharmacol.*, **139**, 114.
STARKWEATHER, J. (1959). *In* A Pharmacologic Approach to the Study of the Mind, p. 165, ed. Featherstone, R. M., and Simon, A. Springfield: Thomas.
STEINBERG, H., RUSHTON, R., and TINSON, C. (1961). *Nature (Lond.)*, **192**, 533.
WERBOFF, J., and KESNER, R. (1963). *Nature (Lond.)*, **197**, 106.

Ciba Foundation Sessions on Intermediation between Administered Drugs and Behavioural Effects

SESSION 1: THE BIOCHEMICAL APPROACH

CHAIRMAN: Dr. J. M. Barnes

INTRODUCTION

McIlwain: I thought it appropriate in opening this discussion to choose a subject with some biochemical coherence even though its reference to behavioural matters might be indirect, and with that in mind I have chosen two approaches, one of which emphasizes more the drug and the other the neural system upon which it acts.

Neural mechanisms. Considering first such neural systems, one of their outstanding biochemical characteristics is the special use made of the differential sodium and potassium concentrations common to all cells. Neuronal polarization, the nerve impulse, standing potentials in the cortex, or the electrocorticogram are largely manifestations of sodium and potassium ion movements, variously restrained and permitted by nerve cell membranes. Moreover, the movements have many characteristics of their own independently of the part of the brain or of the organism in which they take place, and I propose to begin by describing a few such characteristics, observed in isolated mammalian cerebral cortex. Here, movement of sodium and potassium ions on electrical excitation is found susceptible to many centrally acting substances, in concentrations in which they act as drugs (Table I). Changes in membrane polarization occur in association with these movements and, secondarily, the tissue's energy-rich phosphates and respiration are involved as part of recovery processes.

A basis for modified ion movement as part of the action of many substances is thus evident.   Of those compounds without effect in such a system, some may act specifically in connexion with synaptic phenomena and transmitter substances, which appear not to be limiting factors in the electrically stimulated tissues. Thus, reserpine has no action, though chlorpromazine acts (McIlwain and Greengard, 1957). The transmitting agents themselves probably act by modifying ion movement. Sodium and potassium movements in such systems thus merit further consideration, and aspects to which I wish to draw attention are

Table I (McIlwain) .

IONIC AND METABOLIC ACTIONS OF DRUGS ON ISOLATED MAMMALIAN CEREBRAL
TISSUES

An asterisk (*) means that the depolarization was either smaller in content or briefer in duration.

Compound	Actions during excitation		
	Na entry or K loss	Depolarization	Phosphocr. loss or respiration
Phenobarbitone 0·1–0·3 mM	↓	↓ *	↓
Diphenylhydantoin 0·1–1 mM	↓	—	↓
			at certain frequencies
Chlorpromazine 5–50 μM	↓	↓ *	↓
Haloperidol 10–100 μM	↑	—	↓
Protoveratrine 1–5 μM	↑	—	↑
Cocaine 10–50 μM	—	↓ *	↓
Pentylenetetrazole 0·1–1 mM	0	0	0

(Based on data in McIlwain, H., and Rodnight, R. [1962]. Practical Neurochemistry. London: Churchill; Hillman, H. H., Campbell, W. J., and McIlwain, H. [1963]. *J. Neurochem.*, **10**, 325.)

the speed and extent of the changes resulting from excitation. Our discussions at the Middlesex Hospital have already emphasized how such time factors could link actions exhibited by a drug at very different biological levels: chemical and behavioural. The data of Fig. 1 show the manner in which different, sustained levels of stimulation gradually make corresponding, sustained changes in the level of cerebral sodium and potassium, and also in membrane potentials. When stimulation ceases, return is gradually made to the previous composition and potential.

The data thus show that quite moderate levels of stimulation—of, for example, only 5 pulses/sec.—alter sodium and potassium ion gradients at excitable cerebral cells, alter membrane potentials, and hence alter the cells' readiness to respond to associated stimuli. Further, the changed state persists for some time after stimulation is stopped, or is changed in rate. Perhaps in the discussion it can be considered whether this gives a basis for the adjustment of firing rate or threshold in groups of cells, in a fashion relevant to conditioning and behavioural change.

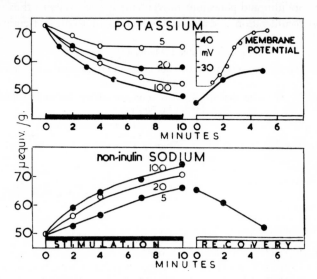

FIG. 1 (McIlwain). Changes in sodium, potassium and membrane potential on stimulating isolated guinea pig cortex. Frequency/sec. shown against curves. Based on data in McIlwain and Joanny (1963) and Hillman, Campbell and McIlwain (1963).

It should be noted at this point that regrettably little is known in chemical and physical detail of how sodium and potassium ion movements are controlled at neural membranes, though this is now receiving increasing attention.

I wish now to comment on the speed of the changes illustrated in Fig. 1, and to emphasize that the central nervous system involves cognate processes which operate at a wide variety of speeds, and so give a basis for changes in function which persist for periods of varying duration. The pattern of the displacement and recovery is dependent on (*a*) the existence of a moderately-sized reservoir of the substances which are changing, in relation to the change per stimulus; and (*b*) the processes of recovery proceeding at rates not overwhelmingly greater than those of the initial displacement. Alteration of the size of the reservoir,

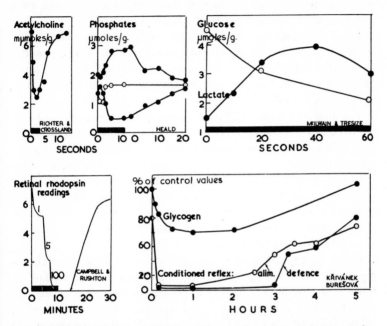

FIG. 2 (McIlwain). Time-course of change in neural constituents during or after stimulation. The period of stimulation is indicated by a black bar; data refer to rat or guinea pig cerebral tissue electrically stimulated, except as stated. Acetylcholine: *in situ*. Phosphates: from above; inorganic phosphate, adenosine triphosphate, and phosphocreatine; tissue *in vitro*. Rhodopsin: stimulus by light. Glycogen: stimulus by potassium salts. (For references, see p. 320.)

the speed of depletion and of re-assimilation or resynthesis will all affect the length of time for which a cerebral system is altered by a given period of activity. Fig. 2 shows that the mammalian brain has chemical systems taking from 5 sec. to 5 hr. for recovery, and these are unlikely to represent the maximum range, for investigation has not been extensive.

It may be noted that the availability of several of the substances which only gradually recover, such as glucose, lactate, and energy-rich phosphates, can all be expected to condition cerebral performance. Phosphocreatine represents an interesting extension of the reservoir of adenosine triphosphate, of known variability and connected to it metabolically by a specific enzyme. Recovery of cerebral glycogen in rats after spreading depression has been concluded (Křivánek, 1958) to be correlated with recovery of conditioned reflexes. Another process of loss and resynthesis, of visual purple in the retina, has been interpreted as a major factor in sensory adaptation of the retina (Davis, 1961; Wald, 1959).

The findings with acetylcholine remind us that transmitter substances are open to comparable processes of depletion and resynthesis; in this case, very rapidly. Both these processes, in acetylcholine and in other substances which may be central transmitters, are known to be inhibited by drugs affecting behaviour. I am saying relatively little about transmitting agents, as others here can say much more, but these considerations may be relevant to the connexions reported between cholinesterase and behaviour (Krech, Rosenzweig and Bennett, 1956; Russell, Watson and Frankenhaeuser, 1961).

With respect to changes of longer persistence—with aspects of learning which last a lifetime—I think it is significant that the level of activity of a neurone will modify its content of the carbohydrates and phosphate intermediates shown, and that these are major sources of energy for biosynthesis and for maintenance of cell constituents as well as for the second-by-second performance of the cell. Lack of knowledge still leaves a very wide choice with respect to mechanisms. Ribonucleic acids contribute much to protein synthesis, and have been proposed as involved in long term changes on grounds which I will not discuss in detail (Hydén, 1960; Deutsch, 1962). It may however be noted that much ribonucleic acid is found, in neural systems also, in membrane-derived fractions (Hanzon and Toschi, 1959; Wherrett and McIlwain, 1962), and thus in some physical association with the major site of ion movement. A basis is thus provided for local modification in the synthesis of membrane-components; phospholipids and protein constituents undergo appreciable turnover.

Perhaps this is the point at which one should note that there is still, inherently, a greater complexity among the atoms and molecules of one neurone than among the 10^{10} neurones of the brain.

Production of drugs affecting behaviour. It merits comment that most of the discoveries about how to isolate and to guide the synthesis of drugs in general were made with the use of tests of animal behaviour. It was the behaviour of experimental animals which guided Stertuner's isolation of morphine in 1806 and which at several points determined the selection of volatile anaesthetics between 1840 and 1860. Simple reflexes in animals, drowsiness, reaction to pain, were the tests used when chemical structure was being compared with biological action in producing hypnotics and mild analgesics between 1870 and 1890: during these times were developed the techniques of synthesis of small groups of substances, their testing and the synthesis of further substances related to the most active ones (McIlwain, 1957).

It is therefore not surprising that this technique—of synthesis, testing and guidance of further synthesis—has continued to be applicable to producing drugs which affect the brain. (Subsequently, of course, the technique has been applied in other fields, as the synthesis of antimicrobial agents.) It is intriguing that more recent investigations which have led to the introduction of new chemical classes of centrally acting drugs, have in a sense recapitulated, rapidly, the 100 years of development which I have briefly sketched.

Thus (1) among phenothiazines, selection was made first on the basis of potentiating barbiturates and lowering body temperature, and produced chlorpromazine. Only subsequently has selection among chlorpromazine analogues been made on the basis of more elaborate tests of behaviour. Also (2), if I may take Dr. Janssen's development of haloperidol as an example, you will recall that he initially examined substances related to pethidine, with tests for analgesia and mydriatic action (Janssen *et al.*, 1959*a*). This led to selection of piperidinobutyrophenones, and among them the choice of haloperidol was made by examination of righting reflexes, and of co-ordinated activity (rotating rod) as well as potentiation of barbiturates and an analgesic assay (Janssen *et al.*, 1959*b*). Subsequent selection has used learned avoidance-escape habits (Janssen and Niemegeers, 1961). This is the way his procedure has appeared from his publications; I will leave him to comment further.

I regret that in their papers Dr. Janssen and Dr. Irwin did not say more about the tactics of planning synthesis and screening tests; as they say, little is published, but this is just the point; and to know the practice of two or three laboratories would be better than knowing of none. My interest springs from my belief that working habits in this regard condition the sort of compounds which are produced. If there are a number of successive phases of synthesis and screening, then such methods are most unlikely to produce a substance in which sharp structural specificity is demanded: because these methods involve making the most active substance by a gradual approach through compounds of lesser, but measurable, activity. Those finally chosen are not, therefore, likely to be metabolites, coenzymes, or transmitting agents, for these are usually of high structural specificity. But the action of a specific metabolite or transmitter substance can be disturbed or modified in many ways, and some of the drugs produced can block such agents. It is natural, in view of my foregoing remarks, to consider that drugs may have such effects at the mosaic of polar groups presented by the excitable cell membrane; and this constitutes at present a major working hypothesis. For at this point a drug may modify the ion movements whose importance was outlined earlier. At present it is only too easy to make such suggestions, and our need is for more detailed knowledge of neural membranes, which will probably be obtained only after much discussion and experimental work.

REFERENCES

BUREŠOVÁ, O. (1956). Personal communication quoted by Křivánek (1958).
CAMPBELL, F. W., and RUSHTON, W. A. H. (1955). *J. Physiol. (Lond.)*, **130**, 131.
DAVIS, H. (1961). *Physiol. Rev.*, **41**, 391.
DEUTSCH, J. A. (1962). *Ann. Rev. Physiol.*, **24**, 259.
HANZON, V., and TOSCHI, G. (1959). *Exp. Cell Res.*, **16**, 256.
HEALD, P. J. (1954). *Biochem. J.*, **57**, 673.
HILLMAN, H. H., CAMPBELL, W. J., and MCILWAIN, H. (1963). *J. Neurochem.*, **10**, 325.
HYDÉN, H. (1960). *Acta Univ. Göteborg*, **66**, 3.
JANSSEN, P. A. J., JAGENEAU, A. H. M., DEMOEN, P. J. A., VAN DE WESTERINGH, C., RAEMAEKERS, A. H. M., WOUTERS, M. S. J., SANCZUK, S., HERMANS, B. K. F., and LOOMANS, J. L. M. (1959a). *J. med. pharm. Chem.* **1**, 105.

JANSSEN, P. A. J., VAN DE WESTERINGH, C., JAGENEAU, A. H. M., DEMOEN, P. J. A., HERMANS, B. K. F., VAN DAELE, G. H. P., SCHELLEKENS, K. H. L., VAN DER EYCKEN, C. A. M., and NIEMEGEERS, C. J. E. (1959b). *J. med. pharm. Chem.*, **1**, 281.

JANSSEN, P. A. J., and NIEMEGEERS, C. J. E. (1961). *Arzneimittel-Forsch.*, **11**, 1037.

KRECH, D., ROSENZWEIG, M. R., and BENNETT, E. L. (1956). *J. comp. physiol. Psychol.*, **49**, 261.

KŘIVÁNEK, J. (1958). *J. Neurochem.*, **2**, 337.

McILWAIN, H. (1957). Chemotherapy and the Central Nervous System. London: Churchill.

McILWAIN, H., and TRESIZE, M. A. (1956). *Biochem. J.*, **63**, 250.

McILWAIN, H., and GREENGARD, O. (1957). *J. Neurochem.*, **1**, 348.

McILWAIN, H., and RODNIGHT, R. (1962). Practical Neurochemistry. London: Churchill.

McILWAIN, H., and JOANNY, P. (1963). *J. Neurochem.*, **10**, 313.

RICHTER, D., and CROSSLAND, J. (1949). *Amer. J. Physiol.*, **159**, 247.

RUSSELL, R. W., WATSON, R. H. J., and FRANKENHAEUSER, M. (1961). *Scand. J. Psychol.*, **2**, 21.

WALD, G. (1959). Handbook of Physiology; Section 1, Neurophysiology, 671. Washington: Amer. Physiol. Soc.

WHERRETT, J. R., and McILWAIN, H. (1962). *Biochem. J.*, **84**, 232.

CAUSE–AND–EFFECT RELATIONSHIPS

Irwin: Let us start with the heart of the matter. We are interested in the general problem of behaviour and the relationship that biochemical events might have to behaviour. This assumes that one can somehow establish a cause-effect relationship between events at one level of organization with those at another. In the biochemical literature there is a great deal of information on what might be considered to be correlated or associated events, but one sees very little in the way of studies so organized and designed as to reveal a cause-effect relationship. Professor McIlwain, could you comment on how a biochemist ought to proceed to demonstrate a cause-effect relationship between what *he* is measuring and what the psychologist presumes he is measuring.

McIlwain: The general question of cause-and-effect relationships I would see as an interference by the drug with sodium and potassium movement in some way, facilitating or blocking it through combination of the drug molecule with molecules which act at neural membranes. This combination may not be covalent, but may be rather the type of association compound which already exists in the membrane between cholesterol, lecithin, cerebrosides and other membrane constituents in the underlying protein. A great deal of both the metabolism and structural alteration which permits ion movement must occur in a highly structured membrane. It is at this point that I picture drugs acting, thereby altering sodium and potassium concentrations, membrane potentials, the ability of the cell to react and its time-characteristics when it does react. When it fires, the electrical sign which one sees as an electrocorticogram or a nerve impulse is a secondary phenomenon, a manifestation of the movement of sodium or potassium ions, restrained and permitted by the characteristics of the membranes through which they pass. It is those characteristics I believe the drug to be altering.

Irwin: This is a hypothetical construct which sounds very attractive since, ultimately, membrane changes such as you describe must be affected. But if we are to try to correlate events at a membrane level in various parts of the brain with the complexity of behaviour observed, taking into account the enormity of the pathways and functions of the brain, then what you are essentially projecting is the impossibility of ever establishing anything of a more specific nature in the way of a cause-effect relationship to account for the complexity observed. What biochemists have generally attempted to do, for example, is to take events at a more varied biochemical level, such as an increase in brain serotonin or noradrenaline, as being possibly correlated with certain of the behavioural effects of a drug. But what are biochemists actually doing to distinguish whether they are simply measuring a fortuitously associated event, or an actual cause-effect relationship? I submit that in order to do this, one cannot do group studies. One has to consider individual differences, and to correlate observed changes in an individual animal.

For example, in group correlations comparing the biochemical and behavioural effects of monoamine oxidase inhibitors (MAO-I), we have been able to show a significant positive correlation between brain amine levels of serotonin or noradrenaline and the increase in locomotor activity produced by the chronic administration of the drugs in rats (Irwin, S., and Tabachnick, I. A. [1961]. *Fed. Proc.*, **20**, 396). The correlation included group responses to three MAO-I's, isoniazid as a positive control, and saline, with two dose levels of each treatment. Thus, a positive, highly significant correlation of group responses was obtained even when mixing up treatments and doses in a single comparison. However, when similar data were evaluated on an individual animal basis, even with the same drug and dose, we failed to observe any semblance of a correlation between the biochemical and behavioural effects, indicating the absence of a cause-effect relationship. I submit, therefore, that the approach of the biochemist to a cause-effect relationship must always proceed from individual animal correlations of the data; I have yet to see biochemists do this.

McIlwain: Perhaps it is inevitable that the biochemist deals with groups of animals, presumably groups of selected strains in which individuals are similar. He must initially answer the question of how such strains differ one from the other either in transmitter-substance concentration, in endocrinological characteristics or perhaps in organization of membrane structure. For example, strains of rats selected for differences in behaviour differed in thyroid function (Feuer, G., and Broadhurst, P. L. [1962]. *J. Endocr.*, **24**, 127). Note that the biochemical observations that arose during the behavioural discussions were naturally sporadic. During the present symposium there may have been some biochemical logic, but less interpretation in terms of behaviour. This, I think, indicates the problems that lie before us, that will have to be solved experimentally.

Miller: I think that perhaps some of us are asking for a less elegant application of lower-powered biochemistry to certain grosser problems of behaviour. One notices sometimes that a very aggressive strain seems to have an unusually active adrenal–pituitary axis. Is any work being done on problems such as this or are such problems not defined as biochemistry?

McIlwain: I am very happy to include them in the description of biochemistry. When correlations are found between, say, the endocrinological differences between two strains and their behavioural characteristics, this again sets a problem which is due to be resolved at the level of transmitter substance or membrane phenomena. It is certainly important to collect observations of that sort, because they give a most valuable biochemical entry into the subject.

VARIABILITY IN RESPONSE OF NERVOUS TISSUE TO STIMULATION

Irwin: In studying the external behaviour of organisms one finds a great deal of variability, as well as species and strain differences. However, one has the feeling in biochemical studies, and sometimes in neurophysiological work, that one is dealing with a standardized animal. Professor McIlwain, would you tell us whether in your studies with isolated tissues you find strain, species or individual differences in the response of the tissues to changes in the frequency or intensity of stimulation, and also whether differences in stimulus requirements affect the responsiveness of the tissues to drugs.

McIlwain: This has been studied in a relatively sporadic fashion. Certainly one would find some differences between human cerebral tissues and those of the lower animals which can be exhibited by techniques such as these (McIlwain, H., and Rodnight, R. [1962]. Practical Neurochemistry, p. 177. London: Churchill); there are differences in substrate utilization between human cerebral tissues and those of the rat or guinea pig which are seen best in electrically stimulated, isolated tissue. For instance, glutamic acid will serve more effectively as a substrate for human cerebral tissue than it will for those of the rat or guinea pig.

There are certain species differences in metabolic rate, which are fairly well tabulated, the smaller experimental animals having in general rather higher concentrations of energy-rich phosphates, and rather higher rates of respiration (Krebs, H. A. [1950]. *Biochim. biophys. Acta*, **4**, 249; Tower, D. B., and Elliott, K. A. C. [1952]. *Amer. J. Physiol.*, **168**, 747). Some of these characteristics have been followed during development, so that the coming into being of the differential ion concentrations and the response to stimulation which depends on them have been followed in the guinea pig, rat and other species, over the point at which there is initially in newly-born rats a relatively low differential concentration of sodium and potassium salts in comparison with the external fluids. In the newborn there is no real metabolic response to electric stimulation—this can be seen to develop in the course of the first ten or twenty days of life (Greengard, P., and McIlwain, H. [1955]. *In* Biochemistry of the Developing Nervous System, pp. 251–260, ed. Waelsch, H. New York: Academic Press).

Irwin: Can you offer any concrete examples of differences in evoked responses? Are there any characteristic changes due to different frequencies or intensities of stimulation that you observe between species? I am particularly interested in the variability you might observe with a single strain of animal, and whether you can detect the equivalent of the rather marked differences between individuals that we observe in overt behaviour.

McIlwain: These differences have not been sought, and among relatively normal animals I am not aware of any incidental observations that would point in this direction, although they would be well worth looking for. However, a dozen or more nutritional, metabolic or toxic factors have been described which can result in varying degrees of epileptogenicity in mammalian species (Tower, D.B. [1960]. Neurochemistry of Epilepsy. Springfield: Thomas) and it is likely that some of these would afford examples of changed reactivity in cerebral tissues themselves.

Summerfield: May I first refer back to Dr. Irwin's earlier question about individual differences, which seems to me extremely important? It is, after all, through observations of individual differences in behaviour that psychiatric patients are identified. Perhaps relative measurement of changes, whether electrical or biochemical, may obscure signs of individual differences at this level of observation. The sort of thing that would be indicative would be, for example, correlations between baseline levels and amounts of change. Professor McIlwain, is there any evidence of that sort?

McIlwain: Animals treated in various ways *in vivo* have yielded cerebral tissues that have behaved differently in experimental situations later; tissues, for instance, from hypoglycaemic sheep behave differently from those of normal animals (Setchell, B. P. [1959]. *Biochem. J.*, **72**, 265, 275; Brierley, J. B., and McIlwain, H. [1956]. *J. Neurochem.*, **1**, 109). Tissues from animals treated with certain persistent drugs will also behave differently.

Irwin: I want to project this line of thought one step further to another point. We know that baseline value is an important factor in the response to a drug; perhaps, in some cases, almost a determining factor in the ability to respond. In your preparation you have the possibility of manipulating the level of activity, by driving the neural tissue at different levels, and I wonder to what extent a certain level of drive—affecting baseline level of activity before a drug is added—will affect the response of the tissue to that drug?

McIlwain: The best example of neural drive in this sense affecting markedly the response to a drug is given by protoveratrine, which has no effect on a tissue which is already maximally stimulated electrically, but which is very much more effective under sparse stimuli at one or two per second.

Jarvik: I want to ask a question about Table I, Professor McIlwain. I take it that the chemical concentrations, for example, of chlorpromazine, were equivalent to the pharmacological concentrations ordinarily used. One wonders whether the change in ion fluxes could be related perhaps to a local anaesthetic property of the compound, perhaps to a stabilizing influence on the membrane permeability. Are you inclined to think that somehow this tells us something of the mode of action of these drugs? For example, it would be interesting to know why cocaine resembles chlorpromazine, since cocaine and chlorpromazine produce rather different effects on behaviour.

Stein: Haloperidol is similar therapeutically to chlorpromazine, but one of your tests showed that these drugs had opposite effects.

McIlwain: The main point to note is that the experiments show a direct cortical action of the substances concerned at the concentration at which they exist in the brain during their action as drugs. Chlorpromazine was acting at 5 μM. If one takes the molecular weight as approximately 300, that implies a concentration of 1·5 mg./l.

SPREADING DEPRESSION

Bureš: I should like to show you some results similar to those mentioned by Professor McIlwain but involving only a *single* wave of

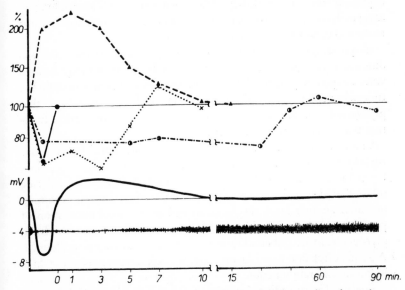

FIG. 1 (Bureš). Chemical changes accompanying cortical spreading depression. Above: percentage change in lactic acid (triangles), phosphocreatine (dots), glycogen (black-white circles) and glucose (crosses). Below: the slow potential change and EEG depression. Abscissa: time after repolarization of the negative slow wave. (Křivánek, J. [1962]. *Physiol. bohemoslov.*, **11**, 383.)

spreading depression. Spreading depression is a peculiar phenomenon that can be evoked in the cerebral cortex by certain direct stimuli such as electrical stimulation or local application of potassium chloride. A depression of EEG activity starts at the point of application of the stimulus and spreads very slowly, at approximately 2–5 mm. per minute, through the entire neocortex in the rat (Fig. 1). The front of the spreading depression wave is accompanied by a very striking slow potential change, a negativity which attains some 7–10 mV. followed by a lower positivity. The upper part of the diagram shows the biochemical changes corresponding to various phases of this slow potential in small pieces of cerebral cortex obtained from heads fixed by liquid nitrogen (Křivánek, J. [1962]. *Physiol. bohemoslov.*, **11**, 383). The phosphocreatine content practically follows the course of the slow potential. The lactic acid content, on the other hand, returns to the pre-depression level more slowly. The glucose content is approximately as rapid in recovery as the lactic acid content, whereas glycogen returns to the pre-depression level only after 30 minutes.

If spreading depression is evoked in a rat with established conditioned reflexes, the conditioned reactions disappear and after a single wave of spreading depression are fully recovered at approximately the time when full recovery of glycogen is attained. This may mean that glycogen is a better indicator of complete recovery of cortical function than other brain constituents.

The work of Dr. Křivánek ([1958]. *loc. cit.*) mentioned by Professor McIlwain referred, not to a single wave of spreading depression, but to the application to the cortex of concentrated potassium chloride solution, which evokes a series of waves of spreading depression coming one after another from the focus created by the local application of potassium chloride; in this case, of course, the effects on the EEG, glycogen content and conditioned reflexes are much more prolonged. A good correlation nevertheless exists between recovery of these three indicators of brain function.

Bradley: The spreading depression is the negative wave, isn't it? Are the conditioned reflexes blocked during the positive after-potential as well?

Bureš: Yes. They are blocked for about 20 minutes after a single wave of spreading depression.

Russell: Do you interpret these electrophysiological changes as reflecting a composite picture of the biochemical processes that you indicated in the upper part of Fig. 1?

Bureš: I think the basic change is ionic, because what really happens during spreading depression is a depolarization of cells in the region of the primary stimulus. This depolarization greatly increases the extracellular potassium concentration which in turn may cause depolarization of the adjacent cells, and thus we get further depolarization spreading throughout the cortex.

Hamilton: Am I to understand that when you put a drop of potassium chloride solution on *one* point of the cortex, there is a loss of glycogen in *all* parts of the cortex?

Bureš: Yes, in all parts of the same hemisphere that are reached by the spreading depression. In the rat all parts of the neocortex in the affected hemisphere are reached in approximately 3 minutes. It should be stressed that lateralization of spreading depression is very convenient for the biochemist, because he can use the symmetrically opposed area of the other hemisphere, which is not invaded by the spreading depression process, as control.

Cook: What is the criterion of spreading depression?

Bureš: What we are doing essentially is to make a recording of EEG activity, and especially of the slow potential change, because this is a virtually unique change characterizing spreading depression. It does not matter where we apply the stimulus, but we usually place the potassium salt on either the occipital or rostral pole of the hemisphere in the parietal region of which we are making the EEG recordings.

Cook: And it works the other way round too?

Bureš: Yes, it is just the same in one region as in another. We kill the rat by throwing the whole animal into liquid nitrogen; then under continuous cooling the frozen head is cut through with an electric saw, again immersed in liquid nitrogen, and small pieces of the cortex, approximately 1 mm.^{3} in volume, are taken out and analysed. As the brain is exposed through a trephine opening about 5 mm. in diameter and the dura is very thin, the superficial layers of the cortex must be frozen in a few seconds, before there has been time for any significant biochemical change.

McIlwain: An interest of these observations is that they exhibit in the whole cortex a correlation between excitation and chemical change which during the normal behaviour of the cortex happens only locally. That is to say, each stimulus normally does alter at a cellular level the ionic balance which is altered grossly for experimental purposes in the whole cortex during spreading depression.

Bureš: In his classical paper, Leão used faradic stimulation to elicit spreading depression (Leão, A.A.P. [1944]. *J. Neurophysiol.*, **7**, 359). This has the disadvantage that it may start an excessive after-discharge. Another way is to use direct current. However, we prefer to use potassium chloride because it is very efficient, and it has no such side effects that may obscure the result.

Summerfield: Could we go back to Professor McIlwain's Fig. 2 (p. 317) and ask Dr. Bureš again what the conditioned reflexes were which he investigated?

Bureš: It was a simple runway experiment, in which the animal started from a particular point and ran to the goal for food; similarly the defence reaction involved a running situation where the rat was put into the starting box and had 5 seconds in which to reach the safe goal compartment, before electric shocks were applied through the floor grid.

Feldberg: I find it difficult to associate the biochemical changes observed here and the changes involved in the spreading depression with conditioned reflexes. If you had done the same experiment on spreading depression, without testing for conditioned reflexes, you would still have obtained these biochemical changes. They are only a sign that during spreading depression the cortex doesn't work in the usual manner. Is that correct?

Bureš: Yes. I think the only conclusion we can draw from this experiment is that after spreading depression there is some correlation between the recovery of the cortex from the behavioural point of view and recovery of such cortical constituents as glycogen. Of course, it is not possible to draw any far-reaching conclusions from this.

Jarvik: You need not have used conditioned reflexes as a behavioural index. Might you not have used unconditioned reflexes as a measure of cortical function?

Bureš: The animal is quite normal from the point of view of the postural reflexes with the exception of the placing reaction described by Magnus. When stimulated, the functionally decorticated rat moves around quite normally.

Jarvik: But the placing reaction shows the same kind of changes as the conditioned reflexes?

Bureš: Yes. They have approximately the same dynamics.

Russell: Dr. Bureš has shown that this is a very interesting technique for studying some psychological problems as well as physiological ones.

Following his lead, Professor Oakes at our medical school has been using the technique in conjunction with instrumental conditioning procedures. For example, one may expose an animal to an instrumental conditioning procedure after spreading depression has been induced on one side of the cortex, in order to see what happens later in another test session when the other side of the cortex is inactivated in this way. This technique offers interesting possibilities for further studies of correlations between behaviour and activity in the cortex.

Miller: How many times can you repeat the application of potassium chloride without damaging the cortex significantly?

Bureš: Of course, when you apply a 25 per cent solution of potassium chloride to a point on the cerebral cortex the point of application is damaged, but this is limited to a depth of about 0·5 mm. and nearby parts of the cortex are completely normal. Usually one can still get spreading depression quite consistently from the same point for 2 days. There is a general tendency to develop techniques which make it possible to use spreading depression as a more chronic procedure, but there are still some technical difficulties.

Chance: May I recall my work on changes in the concentrations of glycogen and lactate in the brain in convulsing mice? (Chance, M. R. A., and Yaxley, D. C. [1950]. *J. exp. Biol.*, **27**, 311.) There we had a corresponding correlation between the period of glycogen depression and the recovery of activity from a collapsed state following the convulsion; the glycogen recovery took approximately 5 minutes in the post-convulsive period of the mouse. Would you like to comment on the possibility of using that preparation in the same way? I am not sure how far the results stand up to present changes in technique, but I used approximately the same methods that you have described.

McIlwain: The major difference in technique was that you sampled the brain of your animals *without* the procedure of fixing which Dr. Bureš described, and this has certainly produced different results. Those produced by Dr. Bureš' method are inherently likely to give a more straightforward biochemical picture. I felt that there was some correlation of glycogen loss and recovery during your work and I would like to see the cortex sampled after being fixed *in situ* by Dr. Bureš' method, by dropping the whole animal into liquid nitrogen without prior decapitation.

Gaddum: Can you tell what part of the brain the drug is acting on by testing it on slices from different regions?

McIlwain: It would be attractive to do that. A difficulty one foresees after administering a drug *in vivo* is that it would be necessary to re-establish an equilibrium between the portion of the tissue taken out and the fluid into which it is put. In handling tissue in these experiments it is important to replace the bloodstream by a solution that supplies glucose and oxygen in a balanced salt mixture and, of course, in placing tissues that have picked up a certain amount of drug into such a fluid, there is a disequilibrium between the drug in the tissue and that in the fluid which ordinarily results in loss of drug to the fluid, so that it would be necessary to make allowance for this in some way, for example by bringing the drug in the solution to the same concentration as that in the blood *in vivo*. There are, of course, other situations in which the drug is not diffusible.

The work I quoted was done entirely with slices of cerebral cortex. There are some observations also with parts of the hypothalamus, parts of the mid-brain, and subcortical white matter, which have not added much in principle except that in the subcortical white matter one finds some evidence for transmission of effect from the local stimulus, as one might expect.

We and a few others have examined human cerebral tissues from neurosurgical operations with the intention of seeing whether their behaviour in isolation did show characteristics that could be related to the conditions of the patients from whom they were removed. I found very little difference except when the tissue was seen to be damaged histologically through neighbourhood to a tumour; how-ever, Tower has reported differences in the acetylcholine system of tissues from epileptogenic foci (Tower, D. B. [1956]. *Progr. Neurobiol.*, **I**, 169).

Gaddum: Quite a lot of these drugs do act on one part of the brain more than another, I think?

McIlwain: Yes, I agree with that, and with the limitation it implies in the interpretation that should be put on experiments with a single type of tissue.

Bradley: The biochemist is certainly getting further when he takes a piece of cortex instead of the whole brain. It would be nice to see different areas studied in this sort of way, particularly subcortical structures.

McIlwain: Yes, there is certainly every possibility of doing this. Indeed before concluding that we could detect no action of reserpine in circumstances such as this, we did actually study several regions of the brain, including the mid-brain and hypothalamus (McIlwain, H., and Greengard, O. [1957]. *J. Neurochem.*, **1**, 348).

Bradley: Studies with radioactively labelled chlorpromazine, for example, have shown that it is concentrated in the mid-brain, and therefore this would be an interesting region to look at.

Barnes: Professor McIlwain, you said that reserpine had no effect on your cortical slices. Have you considered the possibility that this might be because reserpine has to be metabolized in the animal before it becomes an active drug?

McIlwain: It has a defined action which we are not observing in our portion of tissue because we do not take the appropriate part of the brain, and when we do take the appropriate part of the brain, we are not making the measurement, say, of serotonin displacement, that is known to be most connected with the pharmacological action of reserpine. I was quoting it merely as an example of the way in which the system I used will give only certain sorts of information. Not all substances act in the way in which the few that I illustrated act. There is, too, a specificity in action which can be exhibited at the level of the isolated tissue.

Bein: Should you have added reserpine *in vitro*? Reserpine has a very low solubility, especially when compared with chlorpromazine. Could this be the reason why you find no action?

McIlwain: At the very low concentrations involved, I believed the solubility to be adequate, but I will reconsider this.

Dews: How about the partition coefficient? Will it not penetrate the tissue? There may be a 100-fold or more difference between the concentrations of reserpine and chlorpromazine in the tissue depending on the partition coefficient, even though the concentrations in the bathing fluids are approximately the same.

McIlwain: These are certainly important factors, and the comparison between tissue–drug relationships *in vitro* and *in vivo* can be made, in general, on two bases; one is to compare the concentration in the brain itself during the action of the substance as a drug with the concentration in the tissue at the end of the experiment *in vitro*. The second is to compare the blood concentration with the concentration in the fluid surrounding the tissue. Wherever possible we made both comparisons, and when I indicated that the concentrations employed in the experiment were comparable with those *in situ*, I was using one or both, according to which was available.

Janssen: I should like to support Dr. Bein's idea that the insolubility of reserpine might be responsible for its lack of activity *in vitro*, by analogy with many insoluble antihistamines that are extraordinarily potent *in vivo*, but apparently have no activity whatsoever *in vitro*.

I take it that Dr. Bureš' results show that in all probability spreading depression reaches the mid-brain; otherwise it would be difficult to understand why the conditioned reflexes disappear, because this type of conditioned reflex is preserved to a very large extent in decorticated animals.

Bureš: No, I think not. The neurophysiological basis of spreading depression is quite well known, and we really have electrophysiological evidence of the exact extent of spreading depression. In the rat it is limited to the neocortex only, and to the adjacent primitive cortex (the cingulate, entorhinal and pyriform cortex). Spreading depression does not enter the hippocampus or the thalamus and certainly not the mesencephalic reticular formation.

Janssen: However, these conditioned defence reactions to simple motor tasks do persist in decorticated animals!

Summerfield: Yes, but these were running responses in both cases. Leg flexion persists in decorticated animals, but not running responses.

Bureš: There is a big difference between functional decortication and surgical decortication. The main difference is that with functional decortication, achieved by spreading depression, one has an immediate effect. With surgical decortication one has to wait at least a few days for the animal to recover so as to be able to continue the experiment and of course, during this time a lot of vicarious functions are probably developing. According to the classical experiments of Lashley, previous conditioned reflexes are lost after extensive decortication. Usually retraining takes a much longer time than original training and the more complicated functions are normally lost for ever. So our results are quite consistent with the findings of Lashley even with spreading depression limited to the neocortex. We must, of course, take into account the remote effects of elimination of so important a part of the brain as the cerebral cortex. [The subject of Spreading Depression is resumed on p. 373.]

RIBONUCLEIC ACID AND BEHAVIOUR

Bein: The behavioural effect of RNA described by Dr. Cook (pp. 35–9) raises some quite important questions, some of which have already been mentioned. First, it implies that such a highly complex molecule actually enters the brain, and has an action on the central nervous system. Secondly, the psychologists use either shock avoidance behaviour, food motivation or self-stimulation. If the technique of food motivation is used, then the animals are undernourished from a very crude point of view. As RNA is more or less an impure extract of yeast, is it possible that its pharmacological effect on behaviour is mediated through a general effect on metabolic status?

Cook: The mechanism of action of RNA is still obscure. Our data were presented to show that the administration of RNA to rats facilitates the rate of acquisition and prolongs the extinction rate of conditioned avoidance escape responses. In this particular study, the animals received food and water *ad libitum*, so no deprivation was involved. With regard to the possibility of a large molecule such as RNA entering the brain, present evidence suggests that it is unlikely that it would. However, it should be borne in mind that our RNA preparation is really a tetranucleotide with a molecular weight of about 1,300. This is not to say, of course, that this can enter the brain intact. The probable metabolism of this RNA preparation would be from RNA to the individual nucleotides or nucleosides and possibly to purines and pyrimidines. Whether this effect on learning is due to any of these metabolic factors, or to a resynthesized molecule, we do not know.

Gaddum: Have you done experiments with hydrolysed RNA? Does it have the same effect?

Cook: We are at present studying the effect of the administration of nucleotides themselves upon behaviour. With respect to the reported activity of RNA, others have indicated that if a train of stimuli is sent into the central nervous system, RNA levels are increased in those areas of the brain primarily affected by the stimuli. Other studies have shown that by using inhibitors of RNA, certain behavioural patterns can be disrupted. Our studies were designed to investigate the administration of a purified RNA preparation to intact animals and to see whether there would be a change in behaviour. It is altogether premature to conclude which factor of the RNA is responsible. It is also premature to assume anything whatever with regard to the mechanism involved. It might not even be a direct effect on learning or memory—it may well turn out to be an interaction of RNA with some of the parameters of the experimental situation.

Bergel: There are many examples in which it has been shown that not only RNA but also DNA will penetrate into cells, and even into the cell nucleus. The transforming principle illustrates that it is effective, principally in micro-organisms, of course, but the Szybalskis in the United States have recently shown that one can even transform human cells in certain respects by DNA (Szybalska, E. H., and Szybalski, W. [1962]. *Proc. nat. Acad. Sci.* [*Wash.*], **48**, 2026). Alick Isaacs and his colleagues have also recently found that foreign RNA promotes the formation of interferon in certain cells, namely in chick cells with RNA from the mouse and in mouse cells with RNA from the chick, so the idea that large molecules could not reach the cortex is a little premature (Rotem, Z., Cox, R. A., and Isaacs, A. [1963]. *Nature* [*Lond.*], **197**, 564).

Dr. Jarvik mentioned experiments with actinomycin D as an inhibitor. Of course, it inhibits only one specific process, namely, the DNA-directed synthesis of messenger RNA, and nothing else. Now, it is quite feasible that the production of RNA or DNA which might be necessary for laying down the biochemical factors responsible for memory, is not interrupted by actinomycin D, and I think such experiments ought to be repeated with combinations of actinomycin D, puromycin, and similar compounds which interfere at different points of the chain of molecular events.

Jarvik: Yes, I think Professor Bergel's suggestion is important. Now that fairly specific chemical antagonists are available, substances that will interfere with synthesis in various stages of the process, it would be useful to try combinations. Recently Flexner and his co-workers (Flexner, J. B., Flexner, L. B., Stellar, E., De La Haba, G., and Roberts, R. B. [1962]. *J. Neurochem.*, **9**, 595) reported that puromycin did not interfere with learning in mice, even though protein synthesis was interfered with to the extent of 83 per cent. Now, one might guess that in learning there is some kind of synthetic process, and it is reasonable to assume that either proteins are being synthesized, or nucleic acids. It is possible, of course, that other substances, fats perhaps, are involved, and at this stage it is just as important to eliminate possibilities as it is to show that they exist. There was an interesting study by Dingman and Sporn using 8-azaguanine, a purine antagonist; they reported that this substance interferes with learning, but not with the performance of a well-learned task (Dingman, W., and Sporn, M. B. [1962]. *J. Psychiat. Res.*, **1**, 1). It is hard to understand the significance of these findings at this stage; we must simply follow them up and see where they lead.

McIlwain: I am a little uncomfortable about the certainty with which these effects can be ascribed to ribonucleic acid, and the certainty with which one can speak of RNA as a chemical entity. It is no more a chemical entity than, say, yeast protein, and like yeast protein it could very well still have associated materials, or act in a way dependent on its being a polyelectrolyte, rather than on its detailed chemical structure.

Barnes: Have you ever got a pathologist to look inside the peritoneum of these animals, Dr. Cook?

Cook: As I mentioned, one of the first studies we carried out was to administer RNA (160 mg./kg.) intraperitoneally for one month to normal rats. They were observed daily, and no observable symptoms were produced that could distinguish them from untreated rats. At the end of a month they were sacrificed and no gross changes were observed in the peritoneal cavity. However, occasionally some irritation was seen. An important point is, what is the appropriate agent for a control injection? We tried such things as tragacanth and various concentrations of saline. I should mention that we have also administered RNA orally, and have seen similar effects to those produced after intraperitoneal administration. I feel that these findings eliminate the possibility that intraperitoneal administration as such caused the effect we have seen. [See also discussion following p. 40.]

SESSION 2: THE ELECTROPHYSIOLOGICAL APPROACH

Chairman: Dr. J. M. Barnes

INTRODUCTION

Bradley: In these opening remarks I want to touch on some further topics which relate electrophysiology to behavioural studies. I was gratified earlier in this symposium when the importance of negative findings was emphasized because most of the results I wish to discuss now are negative.

When the rôle of the cerebral cortex in behaviour was emphasized earlier, I was very interested in Dr. Bureš' findings concerning spreading depression and conditioned responses. We have attempted to study drug-induced changes in the electrocorticogram which are within the normal range of the electrical patterns recorded from the cerebral cortex in the sleep-wakefulness transition, and I now want to discuss an example of the disparity between the results obtained by electrophysiological and behavioural studies of drug action respectively.

I have already referred to the pharmacological dissociation between the electrocorticogram and behaviour which occurs when certain drugs are used. It has been suggested that the behavioural state of arousal and the presence of an activation pattern in the EEG is an essential prerequisite to an orienting response and Morrell (Morrell, F. [1961]. *Physiol. Rev.*, **41,** 443) has postulated that the activation pattern may in fact be a component of orienting behaviour. Others have equated these two phenomena but I would question whether this is justified. However, it is difficult to understand why an animal's behaviour is apparently unchanged when the electrocorticogram is dominated by high-amplitude slow waves, such as appear when atropine is administered in sufficiently large quantities. One can think of three possible explanations for this: (1) that behavioural changes do

occur, but cannot be detected by simple observation; (2) that the presence of slow waves in the electrocorticogram has no significance for
behaviour; and (3) that the cortical mechanisms affected by atropine are
not those concerned with behavioural responses.

We can rule out the second possibility because we know that
normally the presence of slow waves in the EEG reflects a pronounced
change in the behavioural state.

So far as the first possibility is concerned, we had, of course, been
looking for changes in the state of wakefulness and were quite sure that
there were no behavioural signs of increased sleep following the
administration of atropine. In fact, the reverse was often true. We
decided, therefore, to see if any changes in behaviour could be detected
after atropine administration in animals, using more refined methods
for measuring behavioural effects. The experiments were carried out
by Mr. T. Hollingworth. Since these experiments were to be carried
out on rats, it was first of all necessary to establish that the slow wave
pattern could be induced by atropine in these animals. Cortical recording electrodes were chronically implanted in adult rats and, following
recovery from the operation, atropine sulphate was administered in
varying doses.

It was found that high-amplitude slow waves which were not
blocked by the sensory stimuli that normally produced arousal responses and a corresponding activation pattern in the EEG appeared
approximately 20 minutes after the injection of a dose of 15 mg./kg. of
atropine by the intraperitoneal route (Fig. 1). So far as could be seen by
simple observation, the behaviour of the animals was unchanged. Lower
doses caused the slow activity to appear in intermittent bursts and these
could often be blocked by sensory stimulation. The larger dose was
therefore used in these investigations and it was found that the peak of
the electrophysiological effect appeared about 20 minutes after the
injection and recovery was complete in 24 hours.

Three behavioural experiments were carried out:

(a) The first consisted of a simple conditioned avoidance response.
Animals were trained to avoid an electric shock applied to the floor of a
box by jumping on to a vertical grid and were conditioned to an
auditory stimulus, a bell. Spontaneous jumping was eliminated by
electrifying the vertical grid during the inter-stimulus period. When

the conditioned stimulus was presented, the vertical grid became uncharged and 5 seconds after the end of the conditioned stimulus the
floor became charged. After a group of animals had been trained to

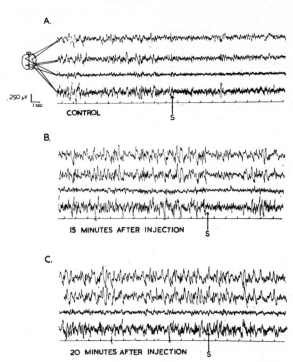

FIG. 1 (Bradley). Records of the electrocorticogram of an
unrestrained conscious rat with implanted electrodes, showing
the effect of 15 mg./kg. of atropine on the response to auditory
stimulation.

give 95 per cent correct responses, half of them were operated upon and
had cortical recording electrodes implanted. Both groups were then
given a further training session and half of each group was injected with
atropine sulphate, while the other half was injected with normal saline.
The EEG was monitored in the animals with implanted electrodes and

when the slow activity in those treated with atropine had reached a peak, all the animals were tested again for the conditioned avoidance response. The EEG was recorded again after the behavioural test to ensure that the atropine activity was still present and 24 hours later the whole test was repeated. During each session the number of correct and incorrect responses was recorded, together with the reaction time,

Table I (Bradley)

SIMPLE CONDITIONED AVOIDANCE SITUATION: INCORRECT RESPONSES

| | Treatment | | | |
	Operated + Saline	Operated + Atropine	Saline	Atropine
A				
Litter 1	1	2	1	1
Litter 2	2	0	2	1
Litter 3	2	2	2	1
Litter 4	1	2	2	1
B				
Litter 1	1	1	1	1
Litter 2	1	1	0	1
Litter 3	1	2	2	2
Litter 4	2	6	1	3
C				
Litter 1	1	2	1	1
Litter 2	0	0	2	0
Litter 3	1	1	1	2
Litter 4	2	2	1	1

Number of incorrect responses to the conditioned stimulus (all figures are out of 20 trials): A, Before treatment; B, Twenty minutes after treatment; C, Twenty-four hours after treatment.

defined as the time elapsing between onset of the conditioned stimulus and the animal jumping on to the vertical grid to avoid the shock.

Four litters were used in this experiment, and the analysis of the results (Table I) from the whole group showed that there was no significant difference in the number of incorrect responses between the animals treated with atropine compared with those treated with saline, and no difference between the animals with implanted electrodes as compared with those without electrodes. There was some scatter in reaction times but no consistent trend occurred.

(b) The second experiment consisted of a conditioned avoidance test which involved a discrimination between two auditory stimuli. First a group of animals was trained for simple avoidance as described in the previous experiment, again using the bell as the conditioned stimulus (CS). This became the positive CS, and when the animals had reached 95 per cent correct responses a second stimulus (a buzzer) was introduced into the training schedule as the negative conditioned stimulus. As before, to prevent spontaneous jumping the vertical grid was electrified during the inter-stimulus periods and was uncharged when the positive CS was applied. When the negative CS was applied, however, the vertical grid remained charged and the floor uncharged. Thus, the correct response was for the animal to jump for the bell (positive CS) and remain on the floor for the buzzer (negative CS). Training was continued until a 95 per cent correct response level was reached for both stimuli presented randomly. Any animals failing to reach this level after 60 trials were rejected for the drug experiment. The rest of the experiment was carried out much as before; half the animals were operated, and the electrocorticogram was monitored before, during and after the animals were tested. They were also tested 24 hours after the drug was administered. Three litters were used in this case and again there was no significant difference in the responses of the atropine treated animals compared with the saline treated controls, nor in the operated animals compared with the unoperated animals (Table II). Nor was there any significant change in the reaction time.

(c) Since the conditioned avoidance response represents a very rigid type of behavioural response, with a strong motivational aspect, it was thought that a different kind of test involving a different form of motivation might show up some effects of atropine on behaviour. The third test therefore consisted of a maze experiment in which the animals were required to run from one end of the maze to the other for a food reward. Both the running times and the reaction times were measured and the mean for 10 trials taken for each animal. Once again half the animals were operated on and had cortical recording electrodes implanted so that the atropine activity could be monitored before and after testing. No significant changes in either the running times or in the reaction times were produced by atropine in doses which induced slow wave activity in the electrocorticogram.

Thus it appeared from the results of these three experiments that the presence of the slow wave activity, induced by atropine in the electro-corticogram, had no effect on the performance of the animals in the particular tests used. Higher doses of the drug, of the order of 25 to 35 mg./kg., have been found to cause a depression of the rate of lever pressing to avoid electric shock in rats (Carlton, P. L., and Didamo, P. [1961]. *J. Pharmacol.*, **132,** 91) and in the number of correct responses in an avoidance situation which involved pole-climbing. Presumably

Table II (Bradley)

CONDITIONED DISCRIMINATION AVOIDANCE SITUATION: INCORRECT RESPONSES

| | Treatment | | | |
	Operated + Saline	Operated + Atropine	Saline	Atropine
A				
Litter 1	0	1	1	0
Litter 2	0	0	0	1
Litter 3	0	0	1	1
B				
Litter 1	0	1	0	2
Litter 2	0	2	0	2
Litter 3	0	1	1	0
C				
Litter 1	1	1	1	0
Litter 2	0	0	0	0
Litter 3	2	1	0	0

Number of incorrect responses in a series of 20 positive conditioned stimuli: A, Before treatment; B, 20 minutes after treatment; C, 24 hours after treatment.

these higher doses also induce slow wave activity in the electrocor-ticogram, but the dose we used was what we thought to be the minimal effective dose for producing this effect, and we found no changes in behaviour. It is still possible that the methods we have used in this study were insufficiently sensitive to demonstrate behavioural effects of this drug, and other tests involving perhaps more complicated sensory discrimination might be worth using. It might also be interesting to look, not at the performance of an established response, but at the acquisition of such responses, and the findings which Dr. Bureš has reported on the effects of physostigmine on the acquisition and reten-tion of conditioned responses suggest that cholinergic mechanisms may be important. It would be interesting to know if atropine blocks the effects he obtained with physostigmine. We are including these two drugs, atropine and physostigmine, in a study of the effects of drugs on recent memory in primates, but these experiments have only just begun and the only effect we have obtained so far with atropine is a complete blocking of responses. Certainly we cannot rule out the possibility that the presence of atropine-induced slow waves in the cerebral cortex reflects a change in cerebral function which may manifest itself at some level in the behaviour of the organism. However, so far as learning processes are concerned, it is possible that the neocortex may not be the right place to look, and the work of Adey (Adey, W. R. [1961]. *In* Physiologie de l'hippocampe, pp. 203–222. Paris: C.N.R.S.) and others suggests that the limbic system and the hippocampus in particular may have an important rôle. For example, it has been found that the presence of the rhythmic activity in the hippocampus is associated with goal-directed behavioural responses and drugs which block these responses abolish the rhythmic activity at the same time: on recovery the behavioural response and the rhythmic activity returned together (John, E. R., and Killam, K. F. [1959]. *J. Pharmacol.*, **125**, 252).

DISSOCIATION OF EEG AND BEHAVIOUR

Bureš: Our experience with over-trained avoidance behaviour is exactly the same as Dr. Bradley has reported. With smaller doses of atropine evoking the same EEG effects, the firmly established avoidance behaviour is not changed at all. Longo and Sadowski (Sadowski, B., and Longo, V.G. [1962]. *Electroenceph. clin. Neurophysiol.*, **14**, 465), who used instrumental conditioning for food reward in rabbits, claimed that after dosages of hyoscine which elicit EEG patterns of sleep there is a decrease or even a complete cessation of bar pressing which reappears after administration of a compensatory dose of physostigmine. This may indicate that operant behaviour is perhaps more apt for showing these changes than behaviour which is only responsive to external stimuli.

Stein: Dr. Bradley, P. L. Carlton has recently reported a series of experiments (see Carlton, P. L. [1963]. *Psychol. Rev.*, **70**, 19) which showed in a variety of operant behaviour tests that moderate doses of the anticholinergic drugs could have profound behavioural effects. The conclusion they drew was that if non-reinforcement is important in the test, then the behaviour can be markedly influenced by atropine and hyoscine. That is, there appears to be a cholinergic system involved in the mediation of the effects of non-reward.

There is, however, one caution here. Centrally-active anticholinergic drugs also inhibit thirst (Stein, L. [1963]. *Science*, **139,** 46), so that if the behaviour is reinforced by water one may encounter a satiation effect. Incidentally, these drugs also inhibit food intake, but by a peripheral effect such as drying of the mouth.

Dews: Boren (Boren, J. J., and Navarro, A. P. [1959]. *J. exp. Anal. Behav.*, **2,** 107) has also published effects of atropine on simple fixed ratio responding, and he got very marked effects with doses something like one-tenth of those you were using.

Miller: We should not lose sight of this striking negative result, namely that these animals which show the EEG pattern of sleep are obviously not behaviourally asleep. This shows clearly that, although there is often a correlation between behavioural arousal and specific EEG waves, this is not an inevitable correlation.

Bradley: I should like to say something about hyoscine, to which Dr. Bureš referred. We have found, in a study of a range of atropine-like drugs, that atropine is the most effective in producing this dissociation, and with hyoscine some sedation occurs. Examining their effects on arousal thresholds, we found that although there was a difference between the EEG and behavioural threshold in the case of hyoscine, nevertheless there was some sedation of behaviour.

Feldberg: We know of three drugs which produce this dissociation between sleep and the EEG pattern, namely atropine, physostigmine and morphine. Are there any other drugs or conditions which result in this dissociation?

Bradley: We have only studied the effects of atropine and physostigmine. I agree that morphine is another example. I mentioned earlier our study of a wide range of atropine-like compounds, and it seems that atropine is the most effective. There is also the condition of so-called paradoxical sleep, that I mentioned in my paper (p. 120), where the EEG shows desynchronized activity in deep sleep, but it is rather difficult to study behaviourally.

Irwin: Isn't reserpine another example?

Bradley: Quite possibly.

Cook: Are there any examples of non-correlation on the other side, where you get behavioural effects with a drug without concomitant changes in the EEG?

Bradley: Reserpine would be such an example.

Summerfield: Is anyone willing to suggest any relation between these effects observed in the lower brain, and the observations to which Dr. Bradley referred first, of the deactivation pattern of the EEG?

Bradley: We have been administering drugs systemically, and I believe I am right in quoting Dr. Janssen, who observed the effects of atropine on the learning process, but said that if one examined fully-trained animals there was no effect.

Janssen: Yes, we confirmed your experiments.

Bradley: So far as systemic administration is concerned, therefore, it looks as though there are effects on learning but not on established responses. The reports from Professor Miller and Dr. Stein suggest that there may be localized mechanisms, so that local application of anti-cholinergic drugs is effective. I cannot see at the moment how to relate these two.

Summerfield: Is it known whether the deactivation pattern in the EEG can be disrupted by electrical stimulation of any part of the lower brain?

Bradley: Yes, this is a well-known phenomenon.

Dews: It seems to me that the use of the term "dissociation" is to some extent evading the issue. This has been well brought out by Wikler who discovered the phenomenon (Wikler, A. [1957]. The Relation of Psychiatry to Pharmacology, p. 173. Baltimore: The Williams and Wilkins Company). The original hypothesis as I understood it was that these specific electrical changes in the brain were a direct manifestation of the neurological substratum of sleep. It was regarded as a cause-effect relationship, and it seems to me that these dissociation experiments are crucial in the sense of disproving this hypothesis. People avoid saying this and facing up to the fact that it is no longer tenable.

Bradley: No, I don't think this is so, because the hypothesis is well-established and supported by a great volume of evidence. These are special cases.

Dews: The evidence is for concomitant variation; if you once find an absence of concomitant variation you disprove causal relationship.

Feldberg: Call it correlation if you like. It is certain that sleep is associated with these EEG changes. They appear to be a sign of sleep, in the same way as a slow pulse.

Miller: There is a big difference between a sign and a cause!

Bradley: G. Moruzzi and H. W. Magoun ([1949]. *Electroenceph. clin. Neurophysiol.*, **1**, 455), and later other workers, showed that the arousal system is located in the brain stem, and that this region is responsible for maintaining wakefulness and sleep. The activity at the cortex normally reflects the level of the ascending influence from the brain stem. But this is not *necessarily* true; you can interfere with this relationship, as we are presumably doing with these drugs.

Gaddum: Perhaps one can safely say that sleep causes these effects in the cortex, but that this cortical activity does not cause sleep.

Dews: Dr. Bradley, is dissociation seen in electrical recordings from the brain stem? You are suggesting that the dissociation is due to a block of the effects of the ascending system on the cortex, but if dissociation is also seen at the postulated origin of the activating system, this would not be tenable.

Bradley: The atropine activity can be recorded from the thalamus and limbic system (Bradley, P. B., and Nicholson, A. N. [1962]. *Electroenceph. clin. Neurophysiol.*, **14**, 824). Since it is still present after mid-brain transection (Bradley, P. B., and Elkes, J. [1957]. *Brain*, **80**, 77), the origin of this particular activity (atropine slow waves) cannot be the brain stem.

Dews: Is it not also true that J. M. Sprague, W. W. Chambers and E. Stellar ([1961]. *Science*, **133**, 165) have destroyed a large part of the area that was supposed to be essential for wakefulness and later observed a gradual return of alertness?

Bradley: I don't know this work, but in the earliest work of Lindsley and other associates of Magoun, in which they produced chronic somnolence by chronic lesions in the brain stem, there certainly was a measure of recovery after a time (Lindsley, D. B., Schreiner, L. H., Knowles, W. B., and Magoun, H. W. [1950]. *Electroenceph. clin. Neurophysiol.*, **2**, 483).

Irwin: Rinaldi and Himwich (Rinaldi, F., and Himwich, H. E. [1955]. *Arch. Neurol. Psychiat. [Chic.]*, **73**, 387) have shown that the mesodiencephalic arousal mechanism is under cholinergic control. Atropine completely abolishes the cholinergic mechanism and EEG arousal without producing sleep. Behavioural arousal and the sleep-wakefulness cycle seem to involve another system, possibly an "adrenergic" one.

Bradley: Himwich has suggested that these two systems exist but I do not think that he has sufficient evidence for them. What we have suggested is that the arousal system at the brain stem level is not predominantly cholinergic insofar as behavioural changes in wakefulness and sleep are concerned and that the pharmacological mechanisms responsible for the atropine activity are either localized elsewhere or are not those concerned with behaviour.

Bureš: Perhaps this discrepancy may be resolved by supposing that there are two synchronizing systems, which may both be activated during natural sleep. Atropine may affect only that system which is not connected with behavioural sleep. Perhaps barbiturates affect both these systems in a deeper way, and induce, therefore, both the electrophysiological and behavioural signs of sleep.

Bradley: One can still get the effects of both atropine and physostigmine after removing the influence of the brain stem, which would accord with this suggestion.

Feldberg: There is as yet no evidence that there are any adrenergic neurones in the central nervous system. So we should be cautious when referring to such neurones and be aware that their existence is still hypothetical. Even the evidence for central cholinergic neurones is only established for a certain number of regions.

Bradley: We have found (Bradley, P. B., and Wolstencroft, J. H. [1962]. *Nature* [*Lond.*], **196,** 840, 873) by applying noradrenaline and acetylcholine by iontophoretic injection, using multibarrelled microelectrodes, that there are certain cells in the brain stem of which some are unaffected by these two drugs, some are affected by one or the other, and some are affected by both. The effects can be either excitatory—an increase in the rate of discharge—or they can be inhibitory. There are some neurones, affected by both noradrenaline and acetylcholine, which may be inhibited by one and excited by the other and *vice versa*. None was inhibited by both. So far we have only examined neurones in the brain stem.

Miller: Some were excited by both?

Bradley: Yes, a relatively small proportion. Something like 20 per cent of the neurones examined were affected by acetylcholine.

Jarvik: Dr. Stein, since you suppose that there is a muscarinic system responsible for the cholinergic effects, have you tried injection of atropine or of curare alone, to see what effects these will produce?

Stein: We used atropine, but because the animals were water satiated to start with, it would have been hard to demonstrate any further blocking of thirst. Did you report, Professor Miller, that you could block drinking with local injection of atropine?

Miller: Yes, in thirsty animals. It was just a unilateral injection, but we made a big lesion in the other side of the hypothalamus so that the side we were operating on was all the animals had left.

Feldberg: One cannot use curare for the same purpose in the central nervous system as in the peripheral one because it is a central excitatory substance. We would have to use erythroidine if we wanted to follow your approach, Dr. Jarvik.

Barnes: Dr. Bradley, are there any *positive* correlations between electroencephalographic changes and behaviour?

Bradley: I presented purely negative findings because I was trying to provoke discussion of the rôle of the neocortex in behaviour. So far as the positive side is concerned, there is quite a lot of information, and a good deal of work has been done not only with the EEG but with evoked responses.

Summerfield: The positive side is relatively uninteresting.

Dews: It seemed to me that here one had the first clear-cut relationship between a change in the EEG on the one hand and an unequivocal change between sleep and wakening on the other. Because of its simplicity, this idea spread not only through neurophysiology but also through psychology. The implication was that this was a causal relationship; these changes happen in the brain, and as a consequence the animal exhibits behavioural sleep. But once you have shown that these characteristic changes can occur with no change in the behaviour, the main appeal of the hypothesis is destroyed. Perhaps because it was such a simple hypothesis, people have been hesitant to accept that the new evidence destroys it.

Stein: Are we all agreed that there is dissociation between subcortical activity and behaviour? There is clear dissociation between cortical activity and behaviour. But how about mid-brain activity, for example?

Bradley: This is what I attempted to present. I don't think mid-brain activity has been studied sufficiently carefully to say.

Miller: Certainly we have to discriminate between two aspects. One is the EEG activity as a causal mechanism, and the other is the rôle of the arousal and sleep systems, which I think remains standing. Indeed there is the additional convincing evidence that you can put animals behaviourally to sleep by stimulating the areas that ordinarily produce the spindle bursts as a *sign* of sleep, although not as a part of the *causal* mechanism of sleep. Hess's old work has thus been confirmed and extended, so the thalamo-cortical inhibitory system is well supported by evidence. The reticular arousal system is also well supported. Again, there is convincing evidence that stimulation in a different place, the lower pontine system, will produce a different kind of sleep, the deep sleep that is characterized by the fast-wave EEG activity which looks as though it were arousal. Behaviourally this is a deeper kind of sleep from which it takes much more stimulation to wake the animal; indeed a normal animal in a deep fast-wave sleep always goes through a stage of lighter spindle-burst sleep on its way to a state of arousal, which is characterized by fast waves.

Feldberg: I want to draw attention to the fact that both atropine and hyoscine, which produce this dissociation, also produce unconsciousness when given in large doses, so that the difference may not be so great as it might appear at first sight. Perhaps we should not immediately give up an hypothesis because there are one or two opposing facts. Ultimately they may be explained in quite a different way without really undermining the basic idea originating from the experiments of Moruzzi and Magoun (Moruzzi, G., and Magoun, H. W. [1949].*Electroenceph. clin. Neurophysiol.*, **1,** 445).

Summerfield: Atropine and hyoscine seem to be different from other drugs that produce unconsciousness. Barbiturates and similar central depressants seem to have more continuously graduated effects on behaviour.

Bureš: Surely to get a synchronized EEG it is enough to have only a part of the cortical cells in synchronized activity. It would be important to know what other cortical units are doing. Maybe a smaller part of the cortical nerve cell population is affected by atropine than by barbiturates. A local synchronized activity may mask the behaviour of other parts of the cell population.

Bradley: If we accept the hypothesis that the slow potentials in the EEG are dendritic potentials, then we would not necessarily see any change in unit activity. It may be that atropine is acting specifically, not directly necessarily, but affecting the dendritic potentials and not the neurones themselves.

Miller: The work of E. V. Evarts ([1960]. *Fed. Proc.,* **19,** 828; [1962]. *J. Neurophysiol.,* **25,** 812) has shown that Sherrington's beautiful analogy between sleep and the lights of the city going out is simply not true. When you record with microelectrodes you find the brain is just as active, if not more so, in sleep. Under external stimuli, the signal-to-noise ratio may be different, but there is certainly no activity decrement in sleep; if anything, there is an increment, which means that there may be more noise in the system so that the signal comes through less clearly. Therefore, microelectrical recording of single cells by itself may not be a particularly good way of finding out whether an animal is asleep.

Bradley: We have found (Bradley, P. B., Eayrs, J. T., Glass, A., and Heath, R. W. [1961]. *Electroenceph. clin. Neurophysiol.,* **13,** 577) in experimentally induced hypothyroidism, which changes the structure of the cortex, in particular the branching of the dendrites, that this does affect the slow potentials in the cortex, whereas the neuronal populations are very little changed.

Edwards: It has been mentioned that atropine, physostigmine and morphine produce a dissociation effect. Can anyone explain why morphine should be grouped with these two others? How does morphine have a similar action?

Gaddum: Morphine certainly does prevent the liberation of acetylcholine in the gut (Paton, W. D. M. [1956]. *Brit. J. Pharmacol.,* **112,** 119).

Edwards: This possible similarity between hyoscine and morphine is interesting in view of the additional similarity shown in Table I. This is the similarity of the ratios obtained by comparing the effects of drugs on both a conditioned avoidance test and its positive reinforcement analogue, which I refer to as the conditioned approach test (see p. 291).

Various kinds of drugs disrupt these learned responses, and this disruptive effect is quantified by scoring a performance marked by a significant increase in the number of failures to respond appropriately as a positive drug effect. The results, thus dichotomized, are used to compute the median effective dose and its standard error by the Miller-Tainter graphic method (Miller, L. D., and Tainter, M. L. [1946]. *Proc. Soc. exp. Biol. (N.Y.)*, **57**, 261).

The first compound which I tested on approach as well as avoidance was morphine (Edwards, R. E. [1961]. *Fed. Proc.*, **20**, 397) and I thought that the resulting large ratio might be evidence of a tranquillizing or analgesic effect, but by testing other compounds, this theory was

Table I (Edwards)

RATIO OF THE MEDIAN EFFECTIVE DOSES OF A DRUG REQUIRED TO PRODUCE A SIGNIFICANT DECREMENT IN PERFORMANCE ON TWO BEHAVIOURAL TESTS

Drug	Conditioned avoidance	Conditioned approach	$\dfrac{CAv}{CAp}$
	(ED_{50} *in mg./kg., s.c.*)		
Alvodine	1·8 ± 0·6	2·2 ± 1·0	0·8
Dexamphetamine SO_4	inactive	inactive	—
Chlorpromazine HCl	0·86 ± 0·05	1·00 ± 0·43	0·9
Morphine SO_4	2·9 ± 0·4	0·37 ± 0·17	7·8
Hyoscine HBr	0·16 ± 0·6	0·022 ± 0·006	7·3

disposed of. When I found that hyoscine had a similar ratio, I began to look for any action which these two drugs might have in common. It would be desirable to test more standard drugs in this manner, but your comment, Dr. Gaddum, concerning Paton's demonstration of the blocking by morphine of acetylcholine release from the vesicles in the peripheral autonomic system, suggests one way of accounting for the similarity.

Feldberg: This suggestion could be tested experimentally. When we perfuse the cerebral ventricles with eserinized saline solution we observe a steady output of acetylcholine; it should be easy to find out if the addition of morphine to the perfusion fluid reduces this output. We may be able to do this experiment in the near future.

Edwards: I should be delighted to have the answer; it would be very helpful to have that information.

DOSE LEVELS IN ANIMALS AND MAN

Feldberg: The effects of atropine on behaviour and the associated changes in the EEG pattern could perhaps be studied in human beings. Ostfeld, Machne and Unna have given atropine by mouth to humans and found that the peripheral effects are over earlier than the central effects, so that there need be no interference between them. The behavioural effects and the associated EEG changes are at a maximum three to four hours after administration, and persist up to seven hours, whereas the peripheral effects are maximal after two hours and gone after four hours (Ostfeld, A. M., Machne, X., and Unna, K. R. [1960]. *J. Pharmacol. exp. Ther.*, **128**, 265).

Bradley: The difficulty is that in animals at any rate, you need very large doses, and one wonders whether one can get up to the sort of dose level needed to produce this dissociation in man.

Feldberg: Unna and his colleagues seem to have been successful in producing changes in the EEG by giving atropine by mouth.

Miller: My son was given too much atropine in his eyes which produced transient hallucinations. This is interesting because that is what you get with sleep. You get dreams which are similar to hallucinations. He obviously was not asleep, but had vivid dream-like experiences.

Feldberg: It is well known that hyoscine produces hallucinations, and there is a resemblance to acute psychosis. The mediaeval stories attributed to witches are quite possibly based on the experience of atropine and hyoscine poisoning.

Hamilton: It is difficult to relate the dose that you gave these animals to the equivalent dose in man. But before you get toxic hallucinations in man surely the dose would have to run up to 50 to 100 times more?

Herxheimer: Not necessarily; with 2–4 mg. you already begin to get central effects in man.

Feldberg: Some animals, like the rabbit, have a very active atropinase, so that large doses of atropine can be given before effects are obtained. Therefore, one cannot easily estimate from animal experiments the dose required for human beings.

Janssen: We conducted a series of experiments in rats with tertiary amines and also with several quaternary amines, all with anticholinergic activity. There is at least one test where one can show profound behavioural effects with atropine at dose levels that produce hardly any mydriasis at all, of the order of o· 1 mg./kg. given subcutaneously every day. Certain behavioural effects can be observed with tertiary amines in rats at these dose levels, and not with quaternary amines, so that in all probability these effects are of central origin. The experiment involves a kind of shuttle box with three compartments instead of two. At any given moment one compartment is dark, another is green, and the third is yellow, the yellow light being somewhat brighter than the green light, because as you know, although rats are colour blind, they can distinguish between a dim and a bright light. In order to avoid an electric shock the rat has to escape under auditory stimulation with a cut-off time of 15 seconds by jumping from the dark compartment into the green one. Then he must wait in the green compartment until the next auditory stimulus one minute later. This process is repeated for a session of ten consecutive cycles in which the conditions are changed at random so that the green light appears sometimes to the left and sometimes to the right. We have studied the effect of these drugs on the speed of learning of rats in these conditions.

What atropine-like substances do, rather specifically, is not so much to interfere with avoidance learning (because atropine-treated rats learn almost as fast as controls so far as performance is concerned) but rather to hinder the rats from learning to wait for the next stimulus to occur. They make what we call paradoxical errors, for after arriving in the safe compartment they do not wait there for the next auditory stimulus, but continue to jump into another compartment where they are punished, and then come back eventually to the safe compartment. Atropine-like substances will do this at very low dose levels; they seem to be the only drugs that do precisely this.

Edwards: This occurs with o· 1 mg./kg. atropine?

Janssen: If given every day 1 hour before the experiment. This is the lowest active dose, but at the very high dose level of 15 mg./kg. the effects are extraordinarily pronounced.

There is one particular experiment which does give central effects with atropine at levels around 10–20 mg./kg.; below these dose levels we can detect almost no effect with atropine sulphate. If you provoke a state of very pronounced catalepsy with chlorpromazine-like compounds, you can break this catalepsy or prevent it by pre-treating the rats with approximately 15 mg./kg. of atropine.

Edwards: Is there perhaps a cumulative effect at low doses with daily medications?

Janssen: No, I don't think so, because at 0·1 mg./kg. atropine we can measure these effects over a period of 5–8 hours.

Edwards: Why doesn't it occur on a single acute medication?

Janssen: It lies in the nature of the test itself—we are studying the effect of these drugs on *learning* so we have to do it several times. The rats are tested in these conditions three times a week and they get the injections every day.

EFFECT OF DRUGS ON EATING AND DRINKING

Janssen: There is another simple experiment which shows, in rats at least, that some behavioural characteristics are profoundly affected by atropine at very low dose levels. This is an experiment with rats trained to feed on a 24-hour deprivation schedule. After a period of training these rats eat a constant amount of food every day, of the order of 15 g. per rat, but this feeding habit can be blocked almost completely by atropine at dose levels of the order of 0·3 mg./kg. Of course, this might be a peripheral effect due to drying of the mouth.

Steinberg: Do they stop eating altogether, or do they eat irregularly?

Janssen: No, they won't feed during the 2-hour period which is allowed for them to eat. The rats are treated only half an hour before the session. The strange thing here is that this is much more effective in rats that are trained on a food deprivation schedule than in ordinary rats.

Stein: My rats ordinarily would eat, say, 8 g. of dry food in half an hour. When pretreated for half an hour with atropine, they would always start to eat but leave off after about 1 g. In similar tests on water intake, however, some animals would not start to drink at all.

Miller: It may be relevant here to describe some research from my laboratory on central effects of certain transmitter and certain blocking agents. One of my students (Grossman, S. P. [1960]. *Science*, **132**, 301; [1962]. *Amer. J. Physiol.*, **202**, 872) studied the effects of introducing crystals of the sympathomimetic substances, adrenaline or noradrenaline, or of parasympathomimetic substances, acetylcholine or carbamyl-choline chloride, into the lateral feeding area of the hypothalamus. He tapped minute amounts of the crystals into the cannula, which was a

No. 27 syringe needle with its hub turned down so that it could be screwed inside a No. 24 needle that was permanently implanted in the rat's skull after its hub had been reduced in size and threaded within. He found that adrenaline and noradrenaline elicited eating, whereas acetylcholine and carbamylcholine chloride (commonly called carbachol) elicited drinking, when introduced at different times via the same cannula into the same place in the same rat. The rats had been trained also to press one bar for food and another bar for water. When both bars were present simultaneously, noradrenaline elicited pressing the bar for food whereas carbamylcholine chloride elicited pressing the other bar for water, showing that the effects of two types of chemo-stimulation have the characteristics of hunger or thirst respectively, in that they can elicit learned responses as well as consummatory ones.

Mrs. Gottesman and I made a dose-response study using liquid, instead of crystalline, chemostimulation, and replacing solid food with slightly salty Metercal, so that normal animals when deprived of food would drink the salty Metercal instead of water, but when previously deprived of water, would drink it rather than the salty Metercal. We compared a liquid food with water in order to rule out the possibility that one form of chemostimulation elicited chewing, while another elicited lapping responses. We found that with carbamylcholine chloride, drinking of water begins to be elicited at a dose of approximately 3×10^{-10} moles, and is maximally elicited by a dose of approximately 24×10^{-10}, while larger doses tend to elicit convulsions. Drinking of liquid food begins to be elicited at a dose of 24×10^{-10} moles of noradrenaline, with a maximum effect at approximately 650×10^{-10} moles, beyond which higher doses seem to elicit lethargy instead of increased eating. In the motor cortex, no obvious effects are elicited by noradrenaline, while the first effects of carbamylcholine chloride, which are motor movements or convulsions, appear at from 200 to 650×10^{-10} moles, with no appreciable drinking being elicited. Thus, the place as well as the substance seems critical in determining the effect.

In the lateral hypothalamus, noradrenaline potentiates the amount of food eaten after 24 hours of food deprivation, but carbamylcholine chloride drastically reduces the amount eaten. Conversely, carbamylcholine chloride increases the drinking of a rat after 48 hours of water deprivation, and noradrenaline reduces it. These results make me think that the well-known interference between hunger and thirst is at least in part a central, rather than a purely peripheral, phenomenon.

Now we come to the part that is most interesting. S. P. Grossman ([1962]. *Amer. J. Physiol.*, **202**, 1230) used a lot of controls but the most interesting ones were blocking agents. With too low a dose of blocking agent there is no effect, with too high a dose the animal is sick and does nothing, but at the maximally differential dose given intraperitoneally, atropine sulphate produces little, if any, decrease in the amount of eating elicited by noradrenaline in the hypothalamus, whereas ethoxybutamoxane produces a very strong reduction in food intake. With exactly the same intraperitoneal doses the opposite action on drinking is elicited by carbamylcholine chloride in the hypothalamus. Atropine blocks this drinking entirely, but ethoxybutamoxane does not produce nearly so big an effect. Furthermore, with normal hunger and thirst you get a similar differential effect. Finally, with normally thirsty or hungry animals you can get a similar differential effect by introducing the blocking agents—atropine sulphate or dibenzyline—via the cannula directly into the lateral feeding area of the hypothalamus. Perhaps this technique would be useful in testing for central effects of new blocking agents, employing the convenient quantitative behavioural index of the amount of water drunk or food eaten.

Stein: We have extended some of the work that Professor Miller has described and have shown, I think, that the cholinergic drinking effect is a muscarinic and not a nicotinic one (Stein, L., and Seifter, J. [1962]. *Amer. J. Physiol.*, **202**, 751). We adapted the cannula system from the one that Professor Miller uses. It is a concentrically-mounted double cannula, the inner one being removable so that finely powdered crystalline substances can be tapped into it and applied to a specific brain region by replacing the cannula.

Pharmacologists have found it useful to classify the peripheral actions of acetylcholine into two types: "muscarinic" actions which are duplicated by muscarine and blocked by atropine and "nicotinic" actions which are duplicated by nicotine and blocked by curare. This classification is not ordinarily applied to the central actions of acetylcholine, but it seems reasonable to do so.

First we compared muscarine and nicotine with carbachol (in the periphery, carbachol has both muscarinic and nicotinic effects).

Muscarine was as active, or even slightly more active, than carbachol, while nicotine had no more activity than a sodium chloride control (Fig. 1). We showed also that atropine, applied to the hypothalamus 30 minutes before testing, largely blocked the effects of carbachol and muscarine on drinking. We concluded from these results that muscarinic synapses in the hypothalamus can be chemically activated to induce drinking.

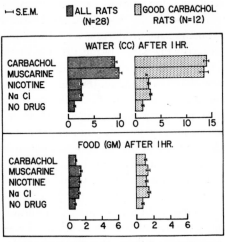

FIG. 1 (Stein). Effect of carbachol, muscarine and nicotine on food and water intake in rats.

Miller: As A. E. Fisher and J. N. Coury ([1962]. *Science,* **138,** 691) and others have shown, this carbachol effect can be obtained from other areas of the brain, especially from the pre-optic area. Dr. G. Wolf and I found that if you make lesions in the lateral hypothalamus, when the animals recover from the operation they never fully recover their drinking elicited by carbachol in the pre-optic area, which suggests that the lateral hypothalamus is a way-station through which this process goes.

Stein: Fisher's largest effects—with animals drinking fantastic amounts of up to 50 ml. water—were obtained after injection of carbachol in the dorsomedial hippocampus. It would be interesting to see whether lesions in the lateral hypothalamus would eliminate these effects.

Miller: That the effects we have been studying are governed by a chemical-times-place code is quite obvious, because if you give noradrenaline systemically you tend to *interfere* with eating in hungry animals, rather than to *elicit* eating in satiated animals. Furthermore, immediately after seeing our cannulae and results, R. Hernandez-Peon ([1963]. *In* The Physiological Basis of Mental Activity, ed. R. Hernandez-Peon. *Electroenceph. clin. Neurophysiol.,* Suppl. 24. In press) tried acetylcholine in the forebrain and secured sleep there, in contrast with our drinking from the lateral hypothalamus or motor effects from the motor cortex. Although drinking can be elicited by carbachol in quite a few regions of the hypothalamus, the effects of noradrenaline are much more specific; you must be in exactly the right places, which I trust is why they have failed to repeat the results from our laboratory!

Stein: I am glad you pointed out that the noradrenaline effect (eating) is not as easy to obtain as the carbachol effect (drinking). It may be that you have to present the animals with non-preferred food (salty Metercal) or food that they have been exposed to for quite a while, as Grossman did. It is as though they have picked through the more desirable pieces, and now, having only less desirable food available, allow themselves to become slightly hungry. Under these conditions of slight hunger, noradrenaline will induce them to eat. We have tried 200 brain points with fresh food with almost no success.

Miller: The trouble is that if you give a satiated animal fresh food he will start to eat it; it is hard to get a satiation end-point. That is why you cannot use food freshly put into the rat's cage.

There are probably also species differences. With cats one is so likely to get a rage response that it is difficult to elicit anything else.

Feldberg: In connexion with Professor Miller's experiment, I want to point out that one region of the brain, the hypothalamus, is particularly rich in noradrenaline and also in acetylcholine. I wonder, Dr. Gaddum, if one knows how far beneath the surface of the hypothalamus these substances can be found in strong concentration?

Gaddum: I have no experience or knowledge of the hypothalamus in that respect. I have had some experience of the cortex, where the cholinergic mechanism in cats is about 1 mm. below the surface. There is a cholinoceptive system there where one can get release of acetylcholine.

SESSION 3: THE NEUROPHYSIOLOGICAL APPROACH

CHAIRMAN: Dr. J. M. Barnes

INTRODUCTION

Feldberg: The conventional neurophysiological approach to behaviour, excluding the electrophysiological contributions which have been dealt with in Session 2, would be to try to pinpoint given changes in behaviour to special regions of the brain. The two classical methods used are to stimulate or to place small lesions in different parts of the brain, and then to see what happens. Both methods are successful when applied to some structures, but fail when applied to others, although these other structures are not unaffected by the stimulation or lesions. I shall illustrate this difference with reference to two structures: the hypothalamus and the hippocampus.

I have not used either of these methods. My experience is confined to observing effects produced by drugs introduced into the cerebral ventricles, where the outcome is the same. And again, when dealing with our experiments, I shall limit myself to the hypothalamus and the hippocampus which lie close to the ventricular surface and thus are easily reached by the intraventricular route.

I shall begin with the classical experiments of Hess in which he stimulated discrete regions of the brain in the conscious cat. He introduced his electrodes point by point through the diencephalon, filmed the effects, killed the cats and then examined the stimulated points histologically. Dr. Sherwood and I went to Zurich in 1954 to study his records and we took with us a film showing the effects we had seen in our cats of intraventricular injection of drugs. I remember well that when we showed Hess our film he remarked that he had seen all our effects in his stimulation experiments. The effects of intraventricular injections of drugs are summarized in the three columns of Table I. Most of the behavioural changes are listed in the third column, but the other two columns contain a number of responses which can be components of behavioural reactions.

It is not surprising that many of the effects listed in the table were also obtained by Hess by electrical stimulation. The responsive areas in the

Table I (Feldberg)

Blood pressure changes
Vascular changes
Tachy- and bradycardia
Sinus arrhythmia
Pilo-erection
Hyperglycaemia
Pupillary changes
Withdrawal and protrusion of nictitating membranes
Salivation
Tear secretion
Defecation. Micturition
Licking. Swallowing
Mastication. Snapping
Retching. Vomiting
Eye movements
Widening, narrowing, spasm of palpebral fissure
Nystagmus
Tachy- and bradypnoea
Panting
Laboured respiration

Muscular inco-ordination
Loss of placing reactions
Ataxia. Muscular weakness
Trembling. Tremor
Abolition of tremor
Reflex hyperexcitability
Spasticity
Ear flutter. Facial contractions
Erection of penis
Washing movements
Scratching bouts
Circling
Miaowing. Calling
Growling
Blind charging ahead
Myoclonus
Tonic and clonic convulsions
Changes in electrical activity of brain:
Sleep pattern. Seizure discharges. Augmentation of evoked responses. After discharge

Drowsiness. Apathy. Lethargy
Unresponsiveness
Sleep and anaesthesia-like conditions
Hyperphagia
Analgesia
Catatonic stupor
Heightened alertness
Excitement. Restlessness
Agitation
Sham rage
Anger. Hostility. Tail lashing
Playful. Affectionate
Fear. Apprehension. Anxiety
Appearance of having hallucinations

diencephalon, as mapped out by Hess, lie predominantly within 3 mm. of the mid-line. When his electrodes were implanted more laterally, stimulation was usually ineffective. When we measured the distance substances had penetrated through the walls of the third ventricle, following perfusion through the ventricular cavities, we found that substances in the third ventricle easily reached points within 3 mm. of the mid-line.

I shall discuss three behavioural reactions which are obtained from the hypothalamus:—(1) Vocalization, (2) Hyperphagia or bulimia, and (3) Mating behaviour.

Various drugs injected intraventricularly into cats produce loud calling and miaowing and, according to Hess, this is also a frequent response to electrical stimulation of areas in the wall of the third ventricle, from the level of the subthalamus above to the infundibulum below. But—and this shows the difficulty in interpreting stimulation experiments and in assessing the site of action of drugs penetrating the brain from its inner surface—the hypothalamus is not the only site from which facio-vocal responses are obtained on electrical stimulation.

On the one hand, they are obtained from various mesencephalic structures, on stimulation of the peri-aqueductal grey matter, of the tegmental reticular formation, or of the tectum (Ingram, Ranson, Hannett, Zeiss and Terwilliger, 1932; Magoun, Atlas, Ingerson and Ranson, 1937; Jenkner and Ward, 1953). On the other hand, they are obtained from structures situated more rostrally in the neuro-axis; Gastaut (1952) as well as MacLean and Delgado (1953) described occasional vocalization on stimulation of the amygdala, and according to de Molina and Hunsperger (1959), growling is a typical response to stimulation of certain areas of the amygdala and along the pathway of the stria terminalis. Therefore if we obtain a facio-vocal response on intraventricular injection of drugs we cannot say with certainty where the drugs act, but for some we know at least that their action is at central synapses and not on fibre tracts, a distinction not always possible with stimulation or lesion experiments.

Hyperphagia, or bulimia, was obtained by Hess on stimulation of the hypothalamus caudal to, and partly overlapping, the zone from which the defence reaction is obtained. The cat not only lapped up milk eagerly but exhibited compulsive biting and gnawing of inedible objects. In our experiments with intraventricular injections, compulsive biting was occasionally observed. The most common effect was that the cat voraciously devoured a pot of meat. The point I want to stress is that the hyperphagia obtained by Hess was the result of stimulation, whereas in our experiments it was the result of intraventricular injections of anaesthetics, substances which are usually regarded as central depressants. An explanation of this discrepancy is provided by the lesion experiments of Anand and Brobeck (1951).

Fig. 1 is from their paper. It is a diagram of a cross-section of the rat's brain stem. The black areas represent electrolytic lesions in the hypothalamus and the dorsal projections are the electrode tracts. In rats, and the same applies to cats, small bilateral lesions close to the wall of the

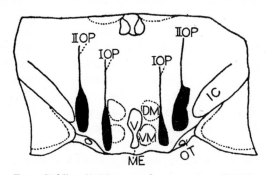

Fig. 1 (Feldberg). Diagram of cross-section of a rat's brain stem. The black areas represent electrolytic lesions in the hypothalamus and the dorsal projections are the electrode tracts. The medial lesions (I OP) induced hyperphagia and obesity, the lateral lesions (II OP) inhibition of food intake. DM and VM, nucleus dorso- and ventro-medialis of the hypothalamus; V, third ventricle; ME, median eminence; OT, optic tract; IC, internal capsule. (From Anand and Brobeck, 1951.)

hypothalamus at I OP lead to hyperphagia. But lesions placed more laterally at II OP have the opposite effect; they inhibit food intake. According to Anand and Brobeck the lateral areas must be regarded as the actual feeding centres responsible for the central hunger reaction and the urge to eat, whereas the ventro-medial nuclei exert an inhibitory influence on these feeding centres. We can thus expect hyperphagia to occur either on stimulation of the lateral areas—this may have happened in the experiment of Hess—or on inhibition or depression of the medial nuclei, which may have been the effect of the anaesthetics on their intra-ventricular injection. There is another possibility. Green, Clemente and de Groot (1957) have shown that lesions in the amygdala also produce hyperphagia, so the anaesthetics may have acted from the lateral ventricle.

I might, before I continue, reply at once to a question Professor Miller has not yet put to me!* That is—what is the effect of adrenaline and acetylcholine given intraventricularly? With both these substances we have never seen any sign of hyperphagia, but that may be because they do not penetrate deeply enough to reach the lateral areas. Interestingly enough, adrenaline injected intraventricularly has a soporific effect, yet does not produce hyperphagia.

The third observation concerning behavioural changes associated with the hypothalamus is one that has been dealt with by Harris, Michael and Patricia Scott in a previous Ciba Foundation Symposium (1958). It is the effect produced by implants of oestrogens into the hypothalamus on the mating behaviour of ovariectomized cats. The reason for discussing these experiments again is that they illustrate an important concept for behavioural studies, namely, that the central nervous system is the target organ for hormonal action and that such action may be restricted to small regions of strategically important neuronal structures.

In spayed female cats mating does not occur, because the female cat does not accept the male in the absence of oestrogens. Harris, Michael and Scott devised a method by which a small amount of solid hormone was implanted at selected sites in the brain of the cat. They deposited or fused a small amount of stilboestrol on to the tip of a stainless steel needle and introduced it into the brain by means of a Horsley-Clarke apparatus. Only when the implant was in the posterior hypothalamus did they obtain a sustained sexual receptivity lasting for months, during which the cat accepted the male although her genital tract had remained anoestrous. The receptivity was assessed in daily 10-minute mating tests with trained male cats.

Making use of radioautography and stilboestrol labelled with carbon-14, Michael (1961) measured the extent of the spread of the hormone from the implant. Only a minute area immediately adjacent to the implant was exposed, but for a prolonged period, to a steep concentration gradient of the hormone. So it is a very restricted area in which the hormone acts.

* This refers to the experiments discussed on pp. 355–357.

I said that mating occurred only when the implant was in the hypo-thalamus. There was one exception. In one experiment in which they had aimed for the cerebellum, mating occurred, but the implant was later found to be situated in the cisterna and the stilboestrol must have been released into the cerebrospinal fluid. This experiment has a special appeal to me since the amounts released would have been too small to produce a positive mating response if the stilboestrol had first to be absorbed into the blood stream. According to Michael and Ryman (1959) only about 1–3 μg. are released per day from the implant, which has a surface area of about 2 square millimetres. Recently, Sproull (1963) has shown in anaesthetized cats that the main stream of the cerebrospinal fluid from the cisterna is towards the tuber cinereum, so that the released stilboestrol might have reached and penetrated the hypothalamus from its outer surface.

There is an earlier observation which shows that sex hormones are more active from the liquor spaces than from the subcutaneous tissue. Kent and Liberman (1949) produced psychic oestrus in the oestrone-primed, ovariectomized hamster, by injecting progesterone into the lateral ventricle in amounts too small to be effective on subcutaneous injection. After the intraventricular injection the female exhibited lordosis when presented with males and mating occurred. The effect of the progesterone here too appears to have been on the hypothalamus, which in these experiments must have been reached and penetrated from its inner surface.

In connexion with the concept that the central nervous system is a target organ for hormones, I should like to point out that several naturally occurring steroids exert strong central actions following intravenous or intraperitoneal injection; some produce anaesthesia, others convulsions, and, as shown by Heuser and Eidelberg (1961), the EEG changes associated with the convulsive activity begin in the hippocampus.

This brings us to the hippocampus. Here the position is different. We cannot attribute with certainty specific behavioural functions to this structure as we can to the hypothalamus. Yet it is easy to stimulate the hippocampus and to produce profound changes in its electrical activity. Its main fibre connexions run in the fornix which contains more fibres than the pyramidal tract, as shown by Daitz (1953), who counted them in man. However, section of the fornix apparently produces no behavioural changes in man (see Green, 1960).

Green (1960) in his review in the *Handbook of Physiology* states that no clear rôle has been attributed to this large part of the brain. However, many attempts have been made to do so, one of the latest being that of Votaw (1959) who suggests that the hippocampus probably acts as an independent supplementary motor area related to emotional expression. He obtained a definite pattern of somatic motor movements on electrical stimulation of points along the hippocampus in monkeys, the area for the face being very large, that for the upper extremity being small, and no area existing for the lower extremity.

The hippocampus has an extremely low threshold for stimulation, electrical or otherwise, and responds to electrical stimulation with a characteristic pattern which consists of a train of high frequency and high amplitude spikes which spread to other parts of the brain, and for which the terms "after discharge" or "seizure discharge" have been used. Andy and Akert (1955) recorded this discharge in unanaesthetized cats using implanted Hess needle electrodes for stimulating and recording. As long as the seizure discharge was confined to the hippocampus there were no overt alterations in behaviour or motor effect. Activation of the hippocampus does not therefore produce changes in behaviour which are revealed simply by observing the animal. However, when the hippocampal discharge spreads to the association areas of the cerebral cortex, there is arrest of all activity, the cat stares or looks about in apparent bewilderment, and when presented with a mouse it takes no notice. When the seizure discharge spreads to the motor and sensory areas as well, the cat develops generalized convulsions.

The results obtained with lesions in the hippocampus are very much the same. Ablation of this part of the brain has not been feasible, but local injuries, whether electrolytic, surgical or chemical, produce changes which are strikingly similar to those seen on electrical stimulation, probably because in this part of the brain any lesion, in whatever way it is produced, acts as a focus of irritation. I think the latest experiments of this kind are those of Blum, Magnes, Bental and Liban (1961) in which small cystic lesions were produced in the ventral hippocampus of cats by unilateral injection of $0 \cdot 025$ to $0 \cdot 03$ ml. of a cold gel of 5 per cent sodium tungstate.

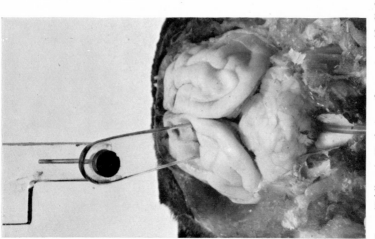

FIG. 2 (Feldberg). Exclusion of posterior half of left lateral ventricle during perfusion of the cat's cerebral ventricles. *Left:* position of lowered Perspex strip with resulting compression of left hemisphere. Brain perfused with formalin from aorta; skull and dura removed; both inflow cannulae taken out; aqueductal cannula *in situ. Right:* difference in staining of the walls of the lateral ventricles after perfusion with bromophenol blue. Roof of both lateral ventricles removed. From Carmichael, E. A., Feldberg, W. and Fleischhauer, K. (1963). *J. Physiol. (Lond.),* **165,** 53P.

We can also elicit a hippocampal seizure discharge by perfusing drugs, for instance, tubocurarine, through the cerebral ventricles. The evidence that this discharge, which we record from the cerebral occipital cortex, originates in the hippocampus is twofold:

(1) It does not occur when the inferior horn of the lateral ventricle is excluded from the perfusion with tubocurarine. The method we use is to compress the body of the lateral ventricle with a Perspex strip through a hole in the skull. Fig. 2 shows the position of the strip after removal of the skull. In this cat both ventricles had been perfused with the dye bromophenol blue. On the right the caudate nucleus and septum and also the hippocampus remained unstained. When we perfused tubocurarine through a lateral ventricle with the compression on, the seizure discharge did not develop.

(2) The second method is to record not only from the cerebral cortex but also from the hippocampus by inserting a needle electrode into this structure in order to find out where the discharge originates. Fig. 3 shows that it begins in the hippocampus, and spreads to the cortex and then to the amygdala.

These results obtained by stimulation or with lesions, or with drugs applied intraventricularly, do not give us information about the function of the hippocampus, but they are valuable because they reproduce some aspects of clinical disorder, namely, certain forms of epilepsy, psychomotor or temporal epilepsy. And in fact such experiments have been described as hippocampal epilepsy in animals. But to elucidate the physiological function of the hippocampus we need other methods, and here those used by psychologists may be most fruitful.

One attempt of this kind is seen in the experiments of Bureš, Burešová, Weiss, Fifková and Bohdanecký (1961). They obtained in rats a "pharmacological ablation" of the hippocampus by producing a spreading depression in this structure with implanted crystals of potassium chloride. They then examined its effects on the learning of a simple avoidance reaction, or on re-learning it, in order to discover the rôle of the hippocampus in various aspects of higher nervous activity.

I have chosen the hypothalamus and the hippocampus because applied to the one, the classical methods of neurophysiology reveal

specific changes in behaviour, whereas applied to the other they fail to
do so. The amygdala lies perhaps between these extremes. The classical

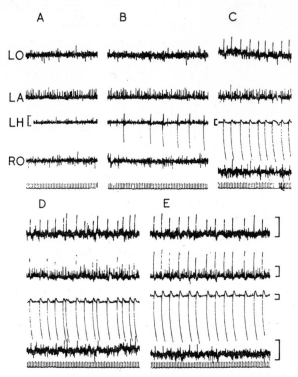

FIG. 3 (Feldberg). Monopolar records of electrical activity of
the cortex, amygdala and hippocampus in a cat anaesthetized
with chloralose. Record *A* taken during perfusion of artificial
cerebrospinal fluid from both cannulated lateral ventricles to
aqueduct. Records *B*, *C*, *D* and *E*, taken 16, 25, 28 and 35 min.
after beginning of perfusion with tubocurarine 1/20,000 from
the left ventricular cannula. LO and RO, left and right occipital
leads, LA and LH, left amygdaloid and hippocampal leads.
Calibration 1 mV. Time marker in seconds. (From Feldberg and
Fleischhauer, 1963.)

methods enable us to obtain some information about its function,
but a seizure discharge is easily elicited, not only by electrical stimulation but also with lesions, so preventing the full elucidation of the

physiological function of this structure, but again providing us with information for the understanding of certain aspects of some forms of epilepsy.

When I think of how physiologists sometimes look on psychologists, and psychologists on biochemists, I cannot resist concluding with a remark by the American philosopher, W. Durant, who says that to speak ill of others is a dishonest way of praising ourselves. Thus, physiologists studying behaviour should beware of neglecting the methods of the psychologists.

REFERENCES

ANDY, O. J., and AKERT, K. (1955). *J. Neuropath.*, **14**, 198.

ANAND, B. K., and BROBECK, J. R. (1951). *Yale. J. Biol. Med.*, **24**, 123.

BLUM, B., MAGNES, J., BENTAL, E., and LIBAN, E. (1961). *Electroenceph. clin. Neurophysiol.*, **13**, 340.

BUREŠ, J., BUREŠOVÁ, O., WEISS, T., FIFKOVÁ, E., and BOHDANECKÝ, Z. (1961). *In* C.N.R.S. Int. Coll. Physiologie de l'hippocampe, pp. 1–15. Paris: Centre National de la Recherche Scientifique.

DAITZ, H. (1953). *Brain*, **76**, 509.

FELDBERG, W. (1963). A Pharmacological Approach to the Brain from its Inner and Outer Surface. London: Edward Arnold.

FELDBERG, W., and FLEISCHHAUER, K. (1963). *J. Physiol. (Lond.)*, **168**, 435.

GASTAUT, H. (1952). *J. Physiol. Path. gén.*, **44**, 431.

GREEN, J. D. (1960). *In* Handbook of Physiology, p. 1373, ed. Field, J., Magoun, H. W., and Hall, V. E. Baltimore: Waverly Press.

GREEN, J. D., CLEMENTE, C. D., and DE GROOT, J. (1957). *J. comp. Neurol.*, **108**, 505.

HARRIS, G. W., MICHAEL, R. P., and SCOTT, P. P. (1958). *Ciba Found. Symp. Neurological Basis of Behaviour*, p. 236. London: Churchill.

HEUSER, G., and EIDELBERG, E. (1961). *Endocrinology*, **69**, 915.

INGRAM, W. R., RANSON, S. W., HANNETT, F. I., ZEISS, F. R., and TERWILLIGER, E. H. (1932). *Arch. Neurol. Psychiat. (Chic.)*, **28**, 513.

JENKNER, F. L., and WARD, A. (1953). *Arch. Neurol. Psychiat. (Chic.)*, **70**, 489.

KENT, G. C., Jr., and LIBERMAN, M. J. (1949). *Endocrinology*, **45**, 29.

MACLEAN, P. D., and DELGADO, J. M. R. (1953). *Electroenceph. clin. Neurophysiol.*, **5**, 91.

MAGOUN, H. W., ATLAS, D., INGERSOLL, E. H., and RANSON, S. W. (1937). *J. Neurol. Psychopath.*, **17**, 241.

MICHAEL, R. P. (1961). *In* The Regional Chemistry, Physiology and Pharmacology of the Nervous System, p. 465, ed. Kety, S. S., and Elkes, J. London: Pergamon.

MICHAEL, R. P., and RYMAN, B. (1959). *Fed. Proc.*, **18**, 1669.

DE MOLINA, A. F., and HUNSPERGER, R. W. (1959). *J. Physiol. (Lond)*, **145**, 251.

SPROULL, D. H. (1963). *J. Physiol. (Lond.)*, **169**, 538.

VOTAW, C. L. (1959). *J. comp. Neurol.*, **112**, 353.

DEPRESSANT EFFECTS OF INTRAVENTRICULAR ADRENALINE

Jarvik: Professor Feldberg, have you any idea how the sedation that intraventricular adrenaline produces can be mediated? It is a rather paradoxical effect, is it not, when compared with the results reported by Dell and his colleagues or by Rothballer, of local injections of adrenaline (Dell, P., Bonvallet, M., and Hugelin, A. [1954]. *Electroenceph. clin. Neurophysiol.*, **6**, 599; Rothballer, A. B. [1959]. *Pharmacol. Rev.*, **11**, 494).

Feldberg: The two depressant effects obtained with intraventricular adrenaline are (*a*) a sleep-like condition, and (*b*) the ability to prevent or abolish tremor produced by other drugs. Adrenaline, given in minute amounts by the intraventricular route, prevents or abolishes tremor in cats: the tremor elicited by intraventricular tubocurarine or the pentobarbitone sodium tremor. The amounts of intraventricular adrenaline that produce this effect are minute, sometimes less than 20 nanograms (20. 10^{-9}g.).

These are certainly central depressant effects. If we inject adrenaline intravenously we get alerting. The question is: is this alerting response a direct central effect of adrenaline? Certain observations suggest that it is not. V. G. Longo and B. Silvestrini ([1957]. *Proc. Soc. exp. Biol. (N.Y.)*, **95**, 43) as well as P. Mantegazzini, K. Poeck and G. Santibanez ([1959]. *Pflügers Arch. ges. Physiol.*, **270**, 14) did not observe this effect on injection of adrenaline into the carotid or cerebral arteries. So it may be that the effect is not a direct central one, but mediated by excitation of sensory nerve endings somewhere in the body, initiating afferent impulses to the brain. Or if it is a direct central effect, it is probably one acting on other structures than those affected by intraventricular adrenaline. In this connexion I would like to recall the observations reported earlier by Dr. Marley that in chicks in which the blood-brain barrier is not yet established, intravenous adrenaline produces profound sleep; but not in the adult chicken (p. 176).

Miller: Our dose-response curve for the effect of noradrenaline on eating turned down at the higher levels. I believe this was because the animals became sleepy and lethargic. So, there is no doubt in my mind that central adrenaline in certain parts of the brain can have exactly the effects you observed, Professor Feldberg. Again, the systemic effects may be exactly opposite to the central effects; just as the systemic effect of noradrenaline is anti-appetite while the effect in the lateral hypothalamus is pro-appetite, so the systemic effect is alerting whereas the effect on at least certain regions of the brain is to make the animal lethargic. It is very important in studying these drugs' effects to remember that it is not only a chemical code, but a chemical-times-place code.

Feldberg: I confess I do not know how easily adrenaline passes the blood–brain barrier.

Bradley: There is some evidence that adrenaline penetrates into the brain relatively slowly and appears only after a matter of some hours (Weil-Malherbe, H. [1960]. *Ciba Found. Symp. Adrenergic Mechanisms*, pp. 421–423. London: Churchill). There is one other point about intra-arterial injections: if enough adrenaline is injected into the carotid artery alerting occurs, but only after a time delay which corresponds roughly to the circulation time. Thus it is possible that the adrenaline is being changed into something else which acts on peripheral structures. Nevertheless, with iontophoretic applications of noradrenaline in the brain stem, the activity of single neurones can be modified.

Dews: Experiments with tritiated adrenaline suggest that only very small amounts get through the blood–brain barrier of cats (Weil-Malherbe, H., Axelrod, J., and Tomchick, R. [1959]. *Science*, **129**, 1226). More enters some areas, such as the area postrema and the pineal body and the hypothalamus. One is always up against the problem that Dr. Marthe Vogt has emphasized: you do not know how much is enough, so however little goes through you are never quite comfortable that even this minute amount might not be sufficient to produce profound changes inside the central nervous system.

Jarvik: In line with what Professor Miller has said about opposite effects, intravenous adrenaline has been reported to produce a tremor, so it is interesting that Professor Feldberg should find that it combats tremor when given intraventricularly.

Feldberg: Yes, this is a question of dosage. V. E. Hall and P. B. Goldstone ([1940]. *J. Pharmacol.*, **68**, 247) showed in cats that intravenous infusion of adrenaline first enhances and then abolishes pentobarbitone sodium tremor. That could mean that the enhancement is an indirect effect of small amounts of adrenaline, the abolition a direct effect on the central nervous system. Further, in Parkinsonism, tremor is increased by a slow intravenous infusion of adrenaline, as shown by Barcroft and his co-workers (Barcroft, H., Peterson, E., and Schwab, R. S. [1952]. *Neurology*, **2**, 154). The fact that intravenous adrenaline has an enhancing action on tremor is certainly true, but whether it is a direct central action or not, and if a central action, whether one on the hypothalamus or on other structures, is not known.

Bein: A recent paper by Schaefer (Baust, W., Niemczyk, H., Schaefer, H., and Vieth, J. ([1962]. *Pflügers Arch. ges. Physiol.*, **274**, 374) claims that the alerting action of adrenaline is an indirect one, due not to its direct action on the reticular ascending system but rather perhaps to its action on the blood pressure.

SPREADING DEPRESSION

Bureš: We have been working for some time on the effect of hip-pocampal damage on conditioned reflexes. As already stated in the discussion on the biochemical approach (see p. 327), spreading depression can be used to achieve "functional decortication", or functional elimination of particular brain structures. I will now attempt to describe what happens in the depressed structure from the neurophysiological point of view.

Fig. 1 shows the slow potential change on the surface of the cerebral cortex during cortical spreading depression in the rat. During this slow potential change, the spontaneous firing of practically all cortical neurones is depressed almost to zero and only after about five to ten minutes is there a recovery to the pre-depression level. We can therefore assume that the part of the cortex where the spreading depression occurs is severely impaired, so that it loses its normal functional connexions with the other parts of the central nervous system. This justifies our use of spreading depression as a functional decortication procedure.

Spreading depression may be evoked not only in the cerebral cortex, but in some other structures as well: Fig. 2 shows the spatial distribution of the maximal negativity of cortical and hippocampal spreading depression recorded with deep capillary electrodes in the different layers of the cortex and of the hippocampus. There is no transition of spreading depression between these two structures; selective elimination of either the neocortex or the hippocampus can be obtained, therefore, by injecting concentrated potassium chloride into one or other region.

What happens to the animal during spreading depression evoked in

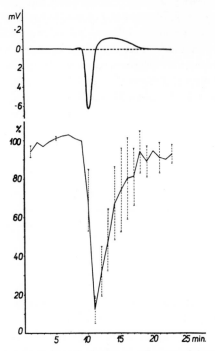

FIG. I (Bureš). Decrease of spontaneous activity of cortical neurones during cortical spreading depression. Above: the slow potential change, negativity downwards. Below: average firing rate (spikes/minute) of 14 cortical units. 100 per cent—mean frequency of the 10 min. control interval. Dotted vertical bars indicate the standard errors of the means.

the cortex or in the hippocampus? We do not see much change in the overt behaviour of the rat; the postural reflexes are preserved, and the animal will respond to painful stimulation. This is true both for cortical and for hippocampal spreading depression. But there is a very clear-cut impairment of the primitive conditioned reflexes, during both cortical and hippocampal spreading depression. With bilateral spreading depression in the hippocampus a simple avoidance reaction is depressed, to much the same extent as with cortical spreading depression.

I want to mention some examples of possible uses of spreading depression in pharmacological research. My colleagues in Prague, Dr. Weiss and Dr. Bohdanecký, have used functional decortication in

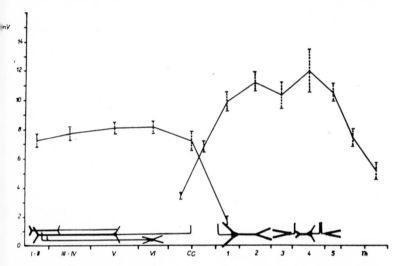

FIG. 2 (Bureš). Spatial distribution of the negative maximum of the slow potential change in the neocortex and hippocampus. Average values obtained from 92 cortical and 100 hippocampal points. The dotted vertical bars indicate standard errors of the means. (According to Monakhov, K. K., Fifková, E., and Bureš, J. [1962]. *J. cell. comp. Physiol.*, **59**, 155 and *Physiol. bohemoslov.*, **11**, 269.)

studying the neural circuits mediating the effect of barbiturates or atropine on the central nervous system. Similar results were obtained with both drugs. EEG changes obtained from the hippocampus of the rat, after a dose of barbiturates sufficient to evoke a classical synchronization effect in the cortex, were compared with those obtained after the same dose in a rat in which a cortical spreading depression was evoked. In the latter case no synchronizing effect was found. It seems that when the cortex is eliminated, the synchronizing mechanism is severely impaired, probably because the diencephalo-cortical circuits, which may play an important rôle in sustaining the synchronized activities, are impaired in some way. However, in contrast, cortical spreading depression does not affect the action of physostigmine. After application of physostigmine a typical theta activity develops in both hippocampus and reticular formation. As this theta activity in the hippocampus is not changed during cortical spreading depression, functional decortication apparently does not interfere with the synchronizing effect at the hippocampal level. This is quite consistent with the results of surgical decortication, for example with the data of Green and Arduini (Green, J. D., and Arduini, A. [1954]. J. Neurophysiol., 17, 533).

It is interesting that some theta activity survived in the reticular formation even during functional elimination of the hippocampus. This probably means that the hippocampus may not be absolutely essential for sustaining theta activity in other parts of the brain.

Now, two more examples—both on rats—of a simple use of spreading depression. If one investigates the sleeping time after administration of different drugs in normal animals and in animals during bilateral spreading depression, one finds that during spreading depression the sleeping times are enormously prolonged with thiopentone, ether and a variety of other drugs (Bureš, J., and Burešová, O., [1956]. Physiol. bohemoslov., 5, 26; Bohdanecký, Z., and Nečina, J. [1963]. Physiol. bohemoslov., 12, 55). In this way, therefore, it is quite simple to study the participation of the cortex in the drug effect.

It is similarly possible to follow the effect of spreading depression on the convulsive thresholds of caffeine, leptazol and strychnine (Bohdanecký, Z., and Nečina, J., loc. cit.). In this experiment there is continuous intravenous injection of the drug until convulsions are evoked. In spite of the fact that conventional pharmacology classifies caffeine as a cortical and strychnine as a subcortical convulsant, in both cases during cortical spreading depression there is a clear-cut increase of the threshold.

In the same way the effects of several analgesics were studied. Again, most analgesics are enhanced in their action during cortical spreading depression.

Dr. J. Nečina (1962, personal communication) also tested the effect of spreading depression on the aggregation toxicity of dexamphetamine. We were surprised to find that mice are not less susceptible during spreading depression to aggregation. The typical enhancement of the dexamphetamine effect in groups of mice remained the same even when the mice were functionally decorticated. This surely means that the effect is localized in some lower regions of the central nervous system.

Herxheimer: I thought from your previous remarks that spreading depression does not last very long—only a matter of minutes. Did these sleeping times, for example, also only last such a short time? How do you make them fit together?

Bureš: A single wave of spreading depression does really last a short time. The negative slow potential wave lasts only 2 minutes and full recovery of the EEG after a single wave of spreading depression is attained after 10, or at most 20 minutes. But in these experiments on, say, the effect on sleeping time, we apply a concentrated potassium chloride solution. This creates a focus in the cortex from which one wave of spreading depression after another is started, at 5-, 7-, 10- minute intervals. This keeps the EEG activity down quite efficiently for up to 4 hours.

Irwin: What concentration and volume of potassium chloride do you use?

Bureš: We use a piece of filter paper, 2 mm. × 2 mm., with approximately 5 mg. of 25 per cent potassium chloride.

Summerfield: So a much bigger lesion is produced in these cases than the ones you spoke of earlier, when you gave the dimensions as within 0·5 mm. of the point of application of the potassium chloride?

Bureš: Yes, I am now talking about direct application of this filter paper to the cerebral surface, exposed through trephine openings approximately 5 mm. in diameter. When we evoke spreading depression in subcortical structures—and so far, we have tried the hippocampus, the caudate nucleus and the striatum of birds—we use micro- injection or implantation of potassium chloride crystals. Both methods are quite efficient. Of course, with micro-injection you get a single wave of spreading depression with 0·1 or 0·2μl. of potassium chloride, and the initial lesion is quite negligible.

Janssen: Dr. Bureš, is the production of spreading depression in the caudate nucleus an efficient way of blocking avoidance habits or not?

Bureš: So far we have not used this technique with conditioned reflexes in rats, but I can tell you about the results in pigeons. Dr. Shima has shown that during bilateral striatal spreading depression keypecking for food reward is severely impaired in pigeons. Of course the rôle of the striatum in pigeons cannot be directly compared with the rôle of the caudate in the rats.

Janssen: What is the visible effect when you produce spreading depression in the caudate nucleus in rats? Do they become catatonic?

Bureš: I cannot say, because so far we have studied the effect of caudate depression only in anaesthetized animals, from the electrophysiological point of view. We have no information on the behavioural effects of caudate spreading depression in the rat.

Janssen: Would it be difficult to do it in normal animals?

Bureš: No. The only difficulty is that caudate spreading depression in rats may spread also to the neocortex, and this may obscure the results. Perhaps from this point of view a better animal for experiments on caudate spreading depression would be the cat. In the cat you can get very nice spreading depression in the caudate and the danger that it will affect the cortex is very much less, because the brain is so much bigger.

Cook: Dr. Bureš, as you know, many neurotoxic drugs and other deficiencies affect conditioned avoidance behaviour. Within your test procedure, is there any way to measure whether this was a selective action, or whether the animal's general behaviour was so grossly impaired that perhaps the description "inhibition of conditioned avoidance" was not a proper evaluation of this effect on behaviour? Do you know whether escape behaviour remained intact? When one speaks about "inhibition of conditioned avoidance" what is meant is that avoidance behaviour is affected in some reasonably selective way. If the animal is asleep, of course avoidance is decreased, but the animal is exhibiting many kinds of neurotoxic effects.

Bureš: We used different conditioned reflexes, not only the avoidance type but some approach behaviour as well. Even very primitive avoidance behaviour is severely depressed in general.

Cook: Are any other primitive behaviours maintained?

Bureš: I can give you the example of the rat in a runway situation. The rat has to run from the electrifiable part of the apparatus to a safe compartment within 5 seconds of the conditioned stimulus. During spreading depression, even when this habit was previously overtrained, the conditioned avoidance behaviour is completely lost. This means that the rat is no longer able to escape during the 5 seconds; it just stays on the start point until it receives shocks. Also the conditioned components of escape behaviour (correct orientation of flight) are lost. The rat just produces chance behaviour. Sometimes after 30 seconds or one minute it finds its way to the safe side; but the escape latency is usually longer than in a completely naive animal put into the same situation.

LOCALIZATION OF BRAIN FUNCTION

Chance: I would like to mention some work with which I have been associated. Dr. Segaar has been working on the social behaviour of the stickleback (Segaar, J. [1961]. *Behaviour*, **18**, 256). He has located the areas in the prosencephalon which control the behaviour of the fish towards its mate. These are in an area which has a circular structure, which facilitates the approach and the ongoing part of the behaviour, and a central part, which is inhibitory of this. He also located what he calls "parental behaviour" in the mesencephalon. However, I would like to suggest that this is not correctly termed because the "parental behaviour" of the stickleback is oriented towards the nest; it is therefore essentially behaviour oriented to the physical environment and not to a moving social object, as the rest of the behaviour is. Dr. Irwin has already suggested that the distinction between physical and social behaviour is a fundamental one. It is just possible that this type of study would locate a fundamental division between the prosencephalon and the mesencephalon. This is extremely interesting work; to what extent it stands up to anatomical investigation I am not in a position to say, but the ethological side of the work is very well done.

The other point that I would like to refer to is the question of brain structures which give a discrete phenomenon which can be attached to a stimulation or activation of that area, and those brain areas which appear to have less clearly-defined functions. I have published a theoretical structure for the analysis of behavioural movements in monkeys in a social context (Chance, M. R. A., and Mead, A. P. [1953]. *Symp. Soc. exp. Biol.*, **7**, 395). Some of you may think that this sort of analysis is difficult to do; actually the idea that analysis of behaviour is more complicated than analysis of, say, cellular structure, or of any physiological mechanism, is entirely spurious. It is perfectly possible to analyse any level of organization with some confidence; it merely depends on whether one is prepared to pay attention to the requisite entities.

Thus it is conceivable that in the brain stem there are circumscribed centres which are control mechanisms for the simple forms of approach behaviour. But when you get a neopallium, the problem becomes complicated and you will see if you watch rats, for example, in which we have analysed movements, that a great deal of the behaviour is by no means complete. In fact, most of the time, the behaviour is a question of modulation of tendencies which increase or decrease approach tendencies towards completion of the situation within which the final consummatory act can take place. Ethologists distinguish appetitive behaviour, which means going out to locate the right situation in which the final consummatory acts can take place. I would very much like to examine that prodigious list of behavioural elements which we were given by Professor Feldberg, because I fancy we would find a heavy predominance of consummatory-act components. What I am suggesting is that in a social context you will find a very large number of situations in which a modulation of the approach and of appropriate postural gestures are *also* required for that situation. Indeed, this is an essential prerequisite for the success of courtship; an animal cannot get close enough to mate in most situations, without a sufficiency of signalling to reduce the aggressive components. In these situations animals have to modulate their approach and avoidance tendencies very carefully. So avoidance is not just an "all-or-nothing" phenomenon and approach is not an "all-or-nothing" phenomenon; the whole thing is a balanced system, which requires some sort of "feedback" to govern it.

There is just one other point: as you go up the evolutionary scale, that part of the amygdala which is not concerned with smell gets progressively greater. In primate social life more and more of the life of the animal is concerned with its social interactions and with fitting itself appropriately into the hierarchical structure. In the social monkeys it is impossible to consummate any act whatever without it taking place in the correct social situation. In such circumstances you require a heavily-modulated sign stimulus *output* as well as ability to differentiate between stimuli. These are the contexts within which some of these brain structures may eventually find their behavioural outlet.

Stein: Dr. Bureš, do you know the recent study (Isaacson, R. L., Douglass, R. J., and Moore, R. Y. [1961]. *J. comp. physiol. Psychol.*, **54,** 625) in which it was shown that bilateral hippocampal ablation facilitated the acquisition of an avoidance response? This seems to be in conflict with your report that impairing the hippocampus inhibits the acquisition of conditioned behaviour.

Bureš: The evidence on the hippocampal ablation effects on conditioned behaviour is not yet clear. For example, a study by Thomas and Otis (Thomas, G. J., and Otis, L. S. [1958]. *J. comp. physiol. Psychol.*, **51,** 130) claims that there is, on the contrary, a big impairment of learning of an avoidance response after a dorsal hippocampectomy. There is similar evidence by Kaada and his colleagues on maze learning in rats (Kaada, B. R., Rasmussen, E. W., and Kveim, O. [1960]. *Acta. physiol. scand.*, **175,** 82).

Stein: Possibly those were *passive* avoidance tests, that is, tests where behaviour is *inhibited* by punishment. Isaacson studied *active* avoidance, where behaviour is facilitated by avoidance of punishment, and found that hippocampal lesions improved acquisition. McCleary and others have shown the utility of distinguishing between active and passive avoidance in interpreting such studies (McCleary, R. A. [1961]. *J. comp. physiol. Psychol.*, **54,** 605).

Miller: If I may rise to the level of human work for once, Brenda Milner ([1959]. *Psychiat. Res. Rep. Amer. psychiat. Ass.*, **11,** 43) has reported that hippocampal lesions do not seem to affect performance much, but they do seem to affect the *acquisition* of new long-term memories, though not new short-term ones.

Bradley: Might not these differences in the effects of hippocampal ablation depend upon the particular area; because one cannot really ablate the whole hippocampus?

Stein: Isaacson made rather extensive ablations of both dorsal and lateral hippocampus.

Bureš: I want to stress that with spreading depression there is this big difference, that it acts immediately. This may explain a lot of discrepancies; one cannot compare it directly with any form of surgical ablation.

McIlwain: It is believed to be analogous with migraine in man. Are there cognate observations on behaviour in these conditions?

Bureš: There is an interesting observation by Lashley on himself. He had a travelling scotoma accompanying migraine, which travelled across his visual field at a velocity comparable with the rate of spreading depression through the visual cortex. This was later calculated by P. M. Milner ([1958]. *Electroenceph. clin. Neurophysiol.*, **10**, 705). There are similar observations by B. Szabuniewicz ([1959]. *XXI Int. Physiol. Congr.*, Abstracts, p. 268). Perhaps a local impairment of circulation may start spreading depression. But it must be stressed that spreading depression is an unnatural phenomenon which probably plays no rôle in normal brain function.

Janssen: Professor Feldberg, I did not quite understand your interesting remarks concerning hyperphagia and compulsive biting obtained by stimulating certain areas of the hypothalamus. Would you tell me whether the hypothalamus is the only region of the brain that produces such effects; and also whether you think that the compulsive biting is only an exaggeration of what you call hyperphagia, or whether you have seen animals that have suffered from compulsive biting without actually swallowing what they were biting?

Feldberg: I have little experience myself. Compulsive biting has been described on hypothalamic stimulation by Hess, and we have found it a considerable nuisance that animals with implanted electrodes sometimes start to bite the leads. But this is not frequently observed on intraventricular injection of small amounts of anaesthetics, such as choral or chloralose. The usual effect is vigorous eating and swelling of the abdomen because the animals eat more than they can stand and in the end they may even vomit. I have no means of discriminating between hyperphagia and compulsive biting. Professor Miller, in your experiments in which you distinguish between drinking and eating, did you see any indication of compulsive biting if you proffered a pencil or something like that?

Miller: I do not think we get appreciable compulsive biting from chemical stimulation of the brain, but if you strongly stimulate the lateral hypothalamus electrically, you get this compulsive biting that

Hess describes. At lower levels you do not get it, but perhaps the placement of the electrodes plays some rôle, because my student, W. W. Roberts, found a lot of compulsive biting.

Janssen: When we give a big dose of amphetamine our animals do show compulsive chewing, as we call it, but they do not swallow or eat what they bite. There are early studies by Amsler (Amsler, C. [1923]. *Arch. exp. Path. Pharmak.*, **97,** 1), in which he described these phenomena with apomorphine and also with amphetamine in rats; he claimed that destroying the caudate nucleus caused these phenomena to disappear. He also said that decortication and removal of the thalamus and various other regions of the brain had no such inhibitory effects. Unfortunately he said nothing about the hypothalamus, and that was why I asked whether you had any information.

Feldberg: No, but I think it would be interesting to investigate whether amphetamine, given by the intraventricular route, will produce compulsive biting.

Chance: Is this biting like chewing or is it a repeated snapping together of the teeth?

Feldberg: I only know that if you proffer a pencil they bite it, and if they can reach a lead from an electrode they bite that; but they do not try to swallow the pencil or the lead. It is a type of gnawing.

Miller: If you make lesions in the ventromedial nucleus of the hypothalamus, these animals will sometimes come out of the ether biting, so it looks as if there may be a compulsive biting element in that case as well as the hyperphagia. Did you inject amphetamine systemically?

Janssen: Yes, 10 mg./kg. intravenously.

Bradley: We have injected amphetamine into the ventricle in large doses of the order of 10 mg. and could find no change in either behavioural or electrophysiological activity.

Chance: There are several different ways in which the jaws can be used; they are superficially similar but behaviourally they are quite distinct. If an animal is eating, it gnaws with the incisors; the two jaws are brought together quickly and with some force. The back molars are sometimes used with an oscillating movement, in triturition, and the teeth are brought together slowly. Again, if the animal uses its jaws as an aggressive instrument it gnaws at the same time, but in a social situation the teeth are barely allowed to touch; they simply come together so that they give a nip. Finally, in an audiogenic seizure the teeth are brought together once and for all, and the animal hangs on to whatever it is biting. These are four distinct ways and there may be others; they look superficially rather similar except for the last one, although they are not so really.

Miller: W. W. Roberts studied the compulsive gnawing produced by various levels of electrical stimulation of the brain to see whether it was due to hunger. As you know, rats do a certain amount of gnawing in order to prevent their teeth growing through their lips. His animals were slightly hungry and eating syrupy food in a cage which had wooden slats for them to gnaw on. When he stimulated them, they left the syrupy food to bite on the slats, which seems to indicate that it was not just a hunger response, but was a different, gnawing response. They would also, incidentally, learn to choose the correct arm of a metal T-maze in order to reach these wooden slats (Carey, R. J., and Roberts, W. W. [1962]. *Amer. J. Psychol.*, **17**, 375; abstract).

Steinberg: In your own experiments, Professor Miller, when you found that if rats had been given amphetamine you then had to apply a bigger electrical stimulus to initiate the behaviour, was that gnawing behaviour or eating ?

Miller: That was eating. After systemic amphetamine the lateral hypothalamus has to be stimulated with a higher electric current in order to induce eating, which is, of course, completely in line with the anorexic properties of amphetamine. The effects of amphetamine on Roberts' gnawing have not been studied. It might be interesting as a possible further way of differentiating gnawing from hunger, but it has not been tried.

Herxheimer: Could this gnawing of slats be a textural effect ? If you gave the rats two foods that taste similar, one of the syrupy kind and the other rat cakes, would they then prefer the one that was tougher and better for their teeth, so that there would not be a complete disjunction of eating and biting ?

Miller: My general impression is that a normally hungry rat will prefer wet mash. This is perhaps not quite as syrupy as the food Roberts used; but they prefer wet mash to the laboratory chow pellets, if given the choice. However, if you fed them on this continuously it is conceivable that they would build up a need to gnaw and so change to the pellets. Anyhow, in Roberts' case it was not hunger, because they would leave the food to gnaw at inedible wood.

Chance: You would obtain an increase in gnawing activity in a cage merely by decreasing the temperature, because the need to build a nest then requires the breaking up of any materials available to do it. Rats will gnaw the cage bars if you do not provide them with any nesting material. So here gnawing is being organized by a totally different set of behaviour; just as we use our mouths for talking and also for eating.

Miller: Yes, this is a little complicated. B. Andersson and B. Larsson ([1961]. *Acta. physiol. scand.*, **52,** 75) found that cooling the pre-optic area makes goats eat and warming it makes them drink, so temperature regulation is certainly a factor.

SESSION 4: THE PHARMACOLOGICAL APPROACH

Chairman: Dr. J. M. Barnes

INTRODUCTION

Gaddum: The most important contribution of pharmacology to the subject of this symposium has been the discovery of drugs with powerful actions on the brain. Many of the best drugs, like alcohol, and opium, and mescaline, and cannabis, were discovered by chance before pharmacology became a science, and pharmacologists have continued with the same method of discovering drugs since. LSD-25 was discovered accidentally during work on the peripheral effects of ergot alkaloids. Iproniazid was introduced for the treatment of tuberculosis, and it happened to have effects on amine oxidase, and chlorpromazine was originally famous as a drug which would lower the body temperature and was then found to have other effects. The best way of discovering something really new is to look for something else.

Screening tests have become more elaborate during the past twenty years. The original pharmacological method of doing a toxicity test was to inject a series of doses of drugs into animals, and come back next morning, and count the corpses. Then somebody found out that you could tell a little more by watching whether the animals went to sleep, or whether they had convulsions. Since then the matter has been much improved in all sorts of ways. A committee under Professor Russell wrote a very good review of screening tests (see p. 389); I hope we shall hear more about these things later from Drs. Irwin and Janssen. I think that screening tests are not things you can devise by logic. If you discover a screening test which will detect a new kind of action on the central nervous system and a compound that gives some effect on the screening test, then you can collaborate with chemists to concoct something a hundred times more active. By that time, you have

386

something really worth investigating for its effects on the brain. One use of screening tests is to allow this kind of collaboration with chemists.

Their second use is to find out how drugs act; the pharmacologist wants to classify drugs according to their action. The first thing he wants to know is whether a drug that affects behaviour is acting on the brain, or on the periphery. Adrenaline, for instance, acts partly centrally and partly peripherally, and it is important with all drugs to find out where they act. Once this is established in a series of screening tests, you can classify drugs by their profiles, as I hope Dr. Janssen will tell us. In his experiments pentobarbitone is more or less unspecific; it has equal effects in all the different tests. Chlorpromazine is very much more active in some tests than others, being particularly active as an antagonist of amphetamine, for example. The kind of test in which you prepare the animal by injecting some toxic drug, and then try to antagonize it, seems to me to be the most interesting kind of test to do; you can classify drugs very specifically in that kind of way.

When two drugs antagonize one another, it is important to know whether they are competing for the same receptors (Gaddum, 1961). When the following conditions are fulfilled it is reasonable to conclude that this is so:

1. The antagonism is specific, in the sense that the effect of the agonist is abolished by a dose of the antagonist which does not affect similar effects produced by other drugs.
2. The same two drugs act as antagonists at various different sites.
3. When the dose of agonist is increased ten times its action can still be abolished by increasing the dose of the antagonist.
4. The two drugs have a common pharmacodynamic group, which would make it likely that they would combine with pharmacological receptors in the same way.

There is good evidence that the antagonism between atropine and drugs such as acetylcholine or arecoline is sometimes due to competition at the receptor level. I will not try to review all the evidence for this, but would like to draw attention to some work on behaviour and to some work from my own laboratory. The effects of atropine and allied drugs on conditioned reflexes have been much studied in the

Soviet Union (Anichkov, 1961; Denisenko, 1962). Pfeiffer and Jenney (1956) and Jenney and Healey (1959) studied the antagonism between arecoline and atropine in an avoidance test and found atropine effective even when the dose of arecoline was increased 40 times. This suggests competition at the receptor level. I do not know whether such high dose ratios are commonly seen in experiments on behaviour.

Antagonisms at the receptor level can be conveniently studied by the technique of iontophoresis (Nastuk, 1953; del Castillo and Katz, 1955) and this method has been used in my laboratory by Krnjević, Phillis and others (Gaddum, 1963). The drug is carried into the tissue by a brief electric current through a microelectrode and the response is recorded through another microelectrode not more than about 1 micron from the place where the injection is made. With this type of apparatus acetylcholine has been found to have two types of stimulant action in the central nervous system. In the spinal cord it has a nicotine-action on Renshaw cells, which is antagonized by dihydroerythroidine, but not by atropine. In the cerebral cortex it has a muscarine-action which is antagonized by atropine and allied drugs.

The release of acetylcholine can be detected by techniques in which a small piece of brain is continuously washed with Ringer containing an anticholinesterase; the acetylcholine is released into this fluid and then detected pharmacologically (Mitchell, 1963). In a push-pull cannula the fluid runs into the tissue through a fine needle and is collected in a concentric polythene tube. The rate of release in the cerebral cortex is increased by local stimulation, or by transcallosal stimulation or by stimulation of peripheral sensory nerves, and the optimum rate of stimulation is about 1 per sec.

Mitchell and Ramwell (1963) have used such techniques in my laboratory to detect the release of some other unknown substance, which causes a contraction of rat uterus in the presence of atropine and other antagonists. The evidence is still incomplete, but such experiments might lead to the discovery of new chemical transmitters.

REFERENCES

ANICHKOV, S. V. (1961). *Ann. Rev. Pharmacol.*, **1**, 21.

DEL CASTILLO, J., and KATZ, B. (1955). *J. Physiol. (Lond).*, **128**, 157.

DENISENKO, P. P. (1962). *Proc. First Int. Pharmacol. Meeting*, p. 199. London: Pergamon.

GADDUM, J. H. (1961). *In* Neuro-Psychopharmacology, **2, 92**, ed. Rothlin, E. Amsterdam: Elsevier.

GADDUM, J. H. (1963). *Nature (Lond.)*, **197,** 741.

JENNEY, E. H., and HEALEY, S. T. (1959). *Fed. Proc.*, **18,** 407.

MITCHELL, J. (1963). *J. Physiol. (Lond.)*, **165,** 98.

MITCHELL, J., and RAMWELL, P. W. (1963). *J. Physiol. (Lond.)*, **166,** 14P.

NASTUK, W. L. (1953). *Fed. Proc.*, **12,** 102.

PFEIFFER, C. C., and JENNEY, E. H. (1956). *Ann. N.Y. Acad. Sci.*, **66,** 653.

U.S. Public Health Service (1962). Behavioural research in preclinical pharmacology. *U.S Dept. Health, Education & Welfare Publication No. 968.*

TRANSMITTER SUBSTANCES

Stein: I have recently speculated about depression (Stein, L. [1962]. *Recent Advanc. biol. Psychiat.*, **4**, 288). Essentially, my idea is that the depressed patient suffers from insufficient positive reinforcement or reward. Even normal people become depressed during periods of low "pay-off". The depressive, however, despairs even when the environment supplies a normal amount of reinforcing stimulation. It is possible that the brain centres for reward in the depressive are pathologically hypoactive even under conditions of normal input. One may assume further that this hypoactivity is due either to an intrinsic deficiency in the reward system (withdrawn or passive depression) or that it results from the inhibition of an essentially normal reward system by the excessive activity of an antagonistic anxiety-punishment system (agitated depression). On this view, drugs effective against depression should increase the ability of the brain to respond to positive reinforcement, either by stimulating or sensitizing the reward system, or by selectively inhibiting the punishment system.

These speculations may be extended biochemically (Sigg, E. B. [1959]. *Canad. psychiat. Ass. J.*, **4**, S75) by assuming that the activity of the reward system is regulated by monoamines, perhaps catechol amines. The antidepressive effects of monoamine oxidase inhibitors may be due to their ability to build up levels of monoamines. The antidepressive activity of imipramine, the temporary relief produced by amphetamine, and perhaps the euphoria of cocaine, may be accomplished by an activation or sensitization of adrenergic synapses. Conversely, the calming or depressing action of chlorpromazine or reserpine may be due to the blocking or depletion of catechol amines in the reward system.

Barnes: Can you demonstrate these rewards on animals?

Stein: Yes, by self-stimulation experiments.

Steinberg: Is there much correlation between the distribution of rewarding areas in the cortex and the distribution of these amines in the brain?

Stein: Yes, the distribution of rewarding points conforms closely to the distribution of catechol amines but also of serotonin, unfortunately

(Olds, J. [1962]. *Physiol. Rev.*, **43**, 554; Vogt, M. [1954]. *J. Physiol.* (*Lond.*), **123**, 451).

Bradley: Dr. Gaddum, why do you think that substances which are liberated from the brain, either picked up by a cannula or in the cerebral circulation, are likely to be transmitter substances? I should have thought that one of the requirements for a transmitter is that it should be destroyed very rapidly. In the case of the acetylcholine which you showed, I presume that the animal was eserinized and therefore acetylcholine could be liberated easily.

Gaddum: We have certainly only detected acetylcholine when anticholinesterases were present.

Bradley: Yes. But, since with these unknown substances one does not know what the enzyme for their destruction is, one cannot do this sort of thing. Do you still think that these are likely to be transmitters?

Gaddum: You might be lucky. When one is pumping saline through the cannula all the time, there is the possibility that the transmitter will be washed away before it has a chance to work. Loewi had a lot of luck; he detected the substance liberated by the vagus by putting the pipette into the heart itself. You cannot do that with any other chemical transmitter substance.

Barnes: Can you isolate acetylcholine without the use of eserine in your preparation?

Gaddum: One does not get any evidence of release then.

Feldberg: Perhaps if you were to use a cold-blooded animal you might be as lucky with other transmitters as Loewi was with acetylcholine on the frog heart.

Gaddum: We have tried in the spinal cord of a frog or a toad, and one has to put an anticholinesterase there. It is rather a remarkable fact that stimulation of motor nerves liberates acetylcholine, but that stimulation of the sensory nerves does not (Mitchell, J., and Phillis, J. W. [1962]. *Brit. J. Pharmacol.*, **19**, 534).

Miller: Apparently, tetanus toxin will block inhibitory transmission. As you know, Eccles and others have worked this out beautifully in the spinal cord. Have you tried that?

Gaddum: No, I have not. Botulin is another drug I ought to try, but have not.

SCREENING TESTS

Janssen: The Chairman has asked me to describe my own screening methods. Let us start by trying to define the rules of the game as we like to play it. I agree with Dr. Gaddum that screening tests are primarily interesting because they create a means of working together with chemists. We use the tests primarily to find compounds with properties that we feel might be interesting.

In our laboratory we like to make as many chemical homologues as possible, if we happen to be interested in an organic series. The first goal is to reach some understanding about the relationships between the chemical or physical properties of a series of homologues—hundreds of them, if possible—and their action in certain tests. In order to do this we need a battery of tests, because most tests are not specific in their results; and we also need a method to help us remember what we have seen. If one analyses twenty compounds a day, say, by twenty different tests, one ends up with so many data that some technique of symbolization is needed, even if that symbolization means giving up certain types of information. That is the sole purpose of our drug profiles (see for example, Figs. 1 to 4).

After we have studied a large number of chemicals of a certain type; when we have the impression that we are starting to understand something about the correlation between structure and activity; after we are satisfied that we have made a series of compounds that all have similar properties in a whole battery of tests, so that it becomes probable that all these substances have a similar mode of action—then we try to understand the reason for this common property. We try to tackle this problem by seeking a mathematical correlation between one or the other electrophysiological, or biochemical, or, let us say, "deeper" phenomena that we observe in biochemical or neurophysiological analyses, and the property of the drugs in these tests.

Suppose we ask ourselves the question: does the inhibition of monoamine oxidase have anything to do with the effect of these drugs on behaviour? We would try to answer this by making many of these drugs and by looking for a correlation, for instance, between the behavioural effect and the biochemical effect. If this occurs thousands of times with no exception whatsoever, then I am in a good position to

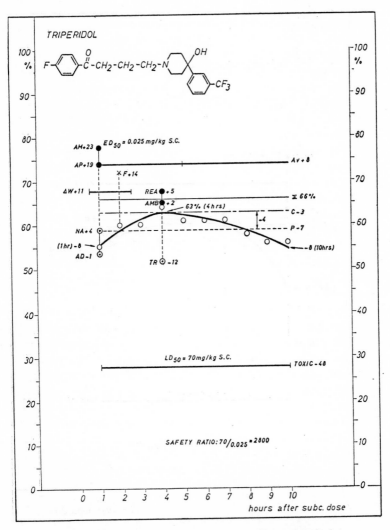

Fig. 1 (Janssen). Profile of triperidol (see text for explanation).

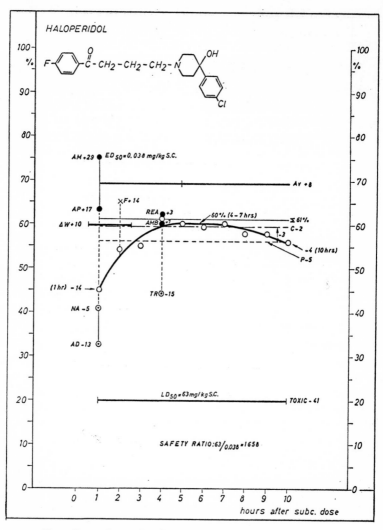

FIG. 2 (Janssen). Profile of haloperidol (see text for explanation).

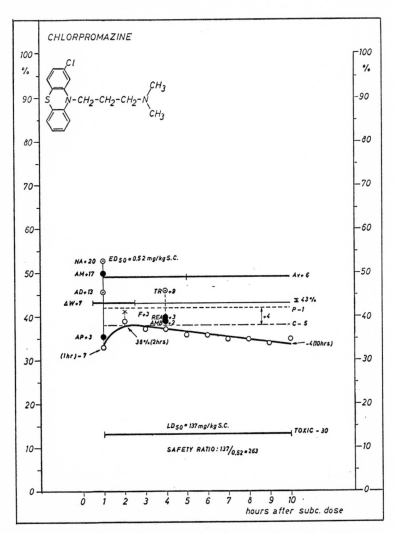

FIG. 3 (Janssen). Profile of chlorpromazine (see text for explanation).

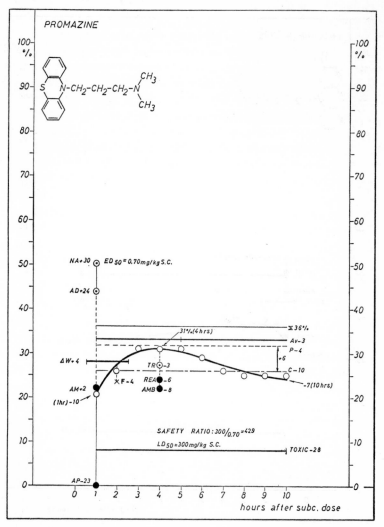

FIG. 4 (Janssen). Profile of promazine (see text for explanation).

consider a general statement. That is the purpose of making all these compounds.

Chemists use many tools similar to these, for instance, infrared spectra. Practically speaking, these spectra are very interesting; they are fingerprints. Although the chemist does not understand how these profiles are related to structure they are useful because they allow for reasoning by analogy. We have tried mainly in three fields, namely, atropine-, morphine-, and chlorpromazine-like substances, to devise such profiles.

All these experiments are done with an inbred strain of animals. We use male Wistar rats, three months old. All the drugs are given by subcutaneous injection. Conditions are kept as constant as possible. These experiments are run on a sequential analytical basis, one animal per day for a certain dose, in order to eliminate day-to-day variations; and they are conducted blind, by technicians working with coded solutions.

All drugs are studied at 20 different dose levels, all fractions or multiples of 10—that is to say, $2 \cdot 5$, 5, 10, 20, 40—in geometric series; going from $1 \cdot 25$ μg./kg., the lowest dose, to 640 mg./kg., the highest dose. In all these tests we study a given number of animals per dose level, for instance 5 or 10 animals per level. In order to produce these spectra we have to adopt the "all-or-none" criterion of effectiveness; it is obviously possible to use other criteria as well, but then one cannot produce such spectra.

However, although in general we study all these drugs at 20 dose levels, this is only partly true in some tests. Actually, we try to have 3 dose levels where the effect is zero and three consecutive dose levels where the effect is 100 per cent. Then we assume that anything above this would be 100 per cent and anything below it zero per cent. This, of course, is not correct, because at toxic dose levels the 100 per cent value must go down to zero; therefore the scale is based on an incorrect assumption.

We have not used ED_{50} values for many of these drugs because the slopes are very different, and one really cannot compare drugs on the basis of ED_{50} values. The method of presenting percentages has the advantage that you assume nothing, but simply add all the positive reactions. In other words, 100 per cent means full activity at the

1·25 μg./kg. dose level; zero per cent means no activity, in these particular tests, at a dose of 640 mg./kg. in rats.

Tests are selected for the simple reason that all the compounds are active in them. Many of the tests are rather specific for chlorpromazine-like drugs, which means that we do not know many substances that, in some of the tests at least, produce activity unless they are what we call "chlorpromazine-like".

What does "chlorpromazine-like" mean? This is the result of a simple observational test. Rats are put into individual small observation cages, and at hourly intervals two independent observers ask themselves the questions, whether the animal has catalepsy during handling and what the animal's tendency is to keep its eyes open or closed. They use a nominal score system for catalepsy, which merely expresses the confidence they have in their own judgement, so that we can check for inter-observer reliability. They evaluate palpebral ptosis in a score system going from 1 to 4.

At the end of the day the results are analysed statistically to find out whether the observations have been made reliably or not. If there is no reason to reject them, we accept the results as being probably true.

In the profiles (Figs. 1 to 4), "Σ so many per cent" is the total number of animals showing abnormal effects—either catalepsy or ptosis at any interval after injection. P and C are the number of animals producing ptosis or catalepsy. The horizontal line Av is the number of animals which have lost their shock-avoidance habits in a jumping-box or hurdle-box situation.

The test labelled ΔW is a measure of the inhibition of eating behaviour with rats on a 22-hour food-deprivation schedule; they are given the drug half-an-hour before the test; then follows the 2-hour feeding period. Eating is depressed by all the chlorpromazine-like drugs in these conditions.

You can also see "rearing" and "ambulation"—REA and AMB—4 hours after injection. This is inhibition of rearing and ambulation behaviour in an open-field experiment, as described by Dr. Broadhurst (p. 228).

One hour after injection we record four tests that have something to do with antagonistic properties of these drugs: NA is antagonism towards noradrenaline intravenously injected at a dose of 1·25 mg./kg., which produces mortality in all control rats. This is a function of the rats that are saved by pre-treatment with the drug 1 hour beforehand. *AD* is the same thing for adrenaline. *AM* and *AP* are the numbers of animals that show the chewing behaviour, typical in rats after intravenous injection of amphetamine and apomorphine, that was described earlier. Both types of compulsive gnawing or chewing are specifically blocked, in our rats at least, by all known chlorpromazine-like drugs.

Four hours after injection there is another test, labelled *TR*. This is a test described by Tedeschi in which tryptamine-induced convulsions are blocked by a neuroleptic drug.

There is also a test, labelled *F*, of the inhibition of what we call "ferocity". This is inhibition in a certain type of rat, of an inborn tendency to kill mice immediately. These drugs never actually inhibit the killing at any dose; a practically toxic dose is needed for this. What they do inhibit is the eating habit—normally they first kill and then eat and the eating is inhibited at certain dose levels.

Toxic effects are not recorded in all rats because some of the substances are too insoluble to be injected at sufficiently high dose levels and for other substances we did not have enough material available. The therapeutic ratio, the "safety ratio" as we call it, is the ratio between the lowest active dose in any of these tests and the LD_{50}. All the phenomena described in these spectra are obtained at dose levels several hundreds of times lower than the toxic dose level.

What does this all mean? Primarily it allows us to reason by analogy. You can compare one spectrum directly with another without looking at the substance and ask yourself if they are similar, how similar, and so on. You can answer questions about duration of action: as you can see, some of these drugs are slower and longer acting, others are rapid and short acting. Some produce ptosis first and then catalepsy; others produce catalepsy first and then ptosis; these differences may be very marked. The antagonism tests are sometimes specific, which means that antagonism is observed in a significant number of animals at dose-levels showing no overt signs of behavioural abnormalities; other drugs are non-specific; they are active in these tests, but only at dose levels producing pronounced ptosis and pronounced catalepsy.

If you take a new drug and construct such a spectrum without any preconceptions, and then compare the spectrum with those of a whole range of clinically known drugs, you can decide whether it compares best with drug *a*, or *b*, or *c*. If you see no essential differences between the new spectrum and that of a known drug, you can then predict relatively safely that in all probability this new drug will do to human beings what the known drug does. We have done this 35 times for neuroleptic drugs and so far as they are concerned the predictability by this method is good.

You can also predict the side effects that occur with these drugs. All drugs that are known clinically to produce a lot of autonomic side effects, such as orthostatic hypotension, are quite specific antagonists of noradrenaline and adrenaline; promazine is an example of this sort. Other drugs, like fluphenazine, that are known not to produce orthostatic hypotension readily, are aspecific as antagonists of adrenaline and noradrenaline.

All drugs that are specific producers of catalepsy in animals and are known in the clinic to produce extrapyramidal symptoms regularly, are specific antagonists of amphetamine and of apomorphine. They all produce cataleptic features first and palpebral ptosis later. In other words, noradrenaline and adrenaline inhibition seems to have something to do with the production of palpebral ptosis, both phenomena being well correlated for a series of 50 substances. If you know how active any substance in this series is as a palpebral ptosis inducing agent, then you can virtually predict in quantitative terms how active it will be as an antagonist of noradrenaline and adrenaline. What this means is another question, but these activities are correlated.

Other correlations are found among practically all these behavioural tests. In my opinion, it is relatively safe to assume that what we measure in most of these tests is basically always the same thing. These compounds produce cataleptic immobility, of course, and at somewhat lower dose levels the fact that they produce cataleptic immobility is detected in a more refined observation test—the avoidance test. The really typical neuroleptic agents produce block of avoidance at dose levels that are several times lower than those which produce visible effects.

This, however, does not give the whole picture. There are other properties of these drugs that do not lend themselves very well to being symbolized in this fashion. I am referring specifically to those tests where at low dose levels these compounds produce excitation and at higher dose levels produce inhibition. Here, all that I have tried to summarize are the inhibitory effects. The excitatory ones are left out.

What does one mean by excitation ? In the ambulation and the open-field experiments, for instance, typical neuroleptic substances devoid of autonomic effects, that are specific blockers of amphetamine and apomorphine, tend at low dose levels to increase ambulation and rearing by 30 to 50 per cent. Less than other compounds, like imipramine and norimipramine, but nevertheless significantly. At higher dose levels these compounds produce inhibition in the same tests. It is, of course, impossible to produce both phenomena in one spectrum, but they are important because all these compounds that tend to produce symptoms of excitation—more ambulation, more rearing, a greater tendency for undisturbed rats to open their eyes—tend also to produce what is known clinically as akathisia at low dose levels, that is, a tendency towards a compulsive drive in patients treated with these drugs to walk around and become sleepless.

Edwards: Dr. Janssen, you said that conditioned avoidance is a sensitive test for catalepsy, and indeed that often is the case, as can be seen in

Table I (Edwards)

A COMPARISON OF MEDIAN EFFECTIVE DOSES FOR SEVERAL DRUGS ON THREE TESTS OF RAT BEHAVIOUR

Drug	Conditioned avoidance	Unconditioned avoidance	Catalepsy
Bulbocapnine HCl, s.c.	$7\cdot2 \pm 2\cdot2$	$19\cdot0\pm6\cdot0$	$38\cdot0\pm10\cdot0$
Chlorpromazine HCl, s.c.	$0\cdot86\pm 0\cdot05$	$4\cdot4\pm0\cdot7$	$2\cdot9\pm 0\cdot5$
Reserpine, s.c.	$0\cdot45\pm 0\cdot12$	$1\cdot2\pm0\cdot3$	$1\cdot6\pm 0\cdot2$
Morphine SO$_4$, s.c.	$2\cdot9 \pm 0\cdot4$	$4\cdot0\pm0\cdot6$	$5\cdot0\pm 0\cdot5$
Hyoscine HBr, s.c.	$0\cdot16\pm 0\cdot06$	inactive	inactive
Chlormezanone, p.o.	$157\cdot0 \pm21\cdot0$	$200\cdot0\pm 32\cdot0$	inactive
Phenobarbitone Na, s.c.	$47\cdot0 \pm 6\cdot0$	inactive	inactive

Table I, but in some classes of compounds, conditioned avoidance and catalepsy are not identical. We usually find that unconditioned avoidance, as measured by the technique developed at the Lilly Research

Laboratories (Rathbun, R. C., Henderson, J. K., Kettau, R. W., and Keller, C. E. [1958]. *J. Pharmacol. exp. Ther.*, **122**, 64A), gives intermediate values. I think of the avoidance reaction as being largely determined by catalepsy and also to some extent by a taming or confusional factor; the animal is not able to respond appropriately to the conditioned stimulus.

Cook: I quite agree with Dr. Janssen's philosophy as to the importance of setting up a pharmacological profile in screening. I have two questions: first, in determining safety margins you mentioned that you used the lethal or toxic effect for one criterion and the criterion at the other end was the minimum dose to produce an effect. Is your rationale here following the assumption that the most sensitive effect produced by a drug has special relevance with regard to its clinical efficacy?

Janssen: The words "safety margin" are probably wrong, but I know of no better expression. We pay hardly any attention to the toxic dose levels because they are so ridiculously high, hundreds of times higher than the dose levels we are actually interested in. It is merely a graphical method of showing that what we are measuring is at dose levels that are safe for the rat at least. We will not kill rats with those dose levels in which we are interested.

Cook: Generally, the specificity of a pharmacological action is determined by a comparison of two effects. Usually it is assumed that one effect is desirable and that another is undesirable.

In a recent review (Cook, L., and Kelleher, R. T. [1963]. *Ann. Rev. Pharmacol.*, **3**, 205) I was interested in comparing the results from various laboratories of studies on fighting induced by foot-shock in pairs of mice. All three laboratories agreed that the relative potency of inhibition of this response was similar; chlorpromazine was most potent, phenobarbitone came next and meprobamate was least potent. Each laboratory used a different pharmacological effect to make a comparison of specificity. These "undesirable" effects used were depression of spontaneous motor activity, muscle relaxation, or ataxia. Each group chose one of these effects. The results were finally tabulated as shown in Table I.

All three laboratories agreed on the relative potency of the three drugs; each laboratory, however, arbitrarily used a different pharmacological effect to determine specificity. My second question, is,

Table I (Cook)

EFFECTS OF THREE DRUGS ON FOOT-SHOCK INDUCED FIGHTING IN MICE

Lab.	"Side Effects"	Chlorpromazine	Phenobarbitone	Meprobamate
A	Muscle relaxation	Non-specific	Specific	Non-specific
B	Ataxia	Specific	Non-specific	Non-specific
C	Decrease of motor activity	Non-specific	Non-specific	Specific

on what grounds do we determine specificity, and on what basis do we regard an effect as desirable or undesirable?

Janssen: We use the word "specificity"—I do not know of any better word—to mean that we are able to measure a certain effect, whatever it is, at dose levels at which we cannot detect any effect by simply observing the animals.

Cook: You are apparently using drug-induced symptoms, on the basis of gross observation, in determining specificity. Does this mean that you prefer screening for the potential therapeutic application of a drug using a specific test or group of tests, and that you would rather not have very obvious effects because you feel that they may have no therapeutic application?

Janssen: Considerations of utility play no rôle in this work; that I must stress. Any effect is as desirable as the next, *a priori.* It is for the clinicians to find out whether it is practically desirable or not.

We like to classify drugs, of course, if we can. We do have certain categories; this is only one example. I could show you similar profiles for morphine-like analgesics; they are also all practically alike with only minor differences. You can classify some drugs as meprobamate-like "muscle relaxants", and others as strychnine-like compounds. The purpose then is to classify these new structures within that framework. Whether you happen to be interested in them later on for practical purposes is an entirely different question.

Another feature of this method of approach is that by using it you can recognize something you have never seen before. Suppose that you make a very powerful drug that somehow does not fit into any category at all. That would be a most interesting finding. In such an instance it is almost impossible to predict the clinical effect with any degree of probability. Such drugs are interesting to try out clinically, in order to see what they mean for human behaviour.

Russell: What you are saying essentially is that predictability from these measures with rats to effects in man is good, once you have established the validity of a particular profile in man. To put it another way: you know from clinical experience with chlorpromazine that it has certain effects; if you then get a drug which has a similar profile, you predict that this drug will be effective in such and such clinical cases.

Janssen: If I have tried it in rats, mice and dogs—several different species—and in these species I cannot distinguish two compounds one of which is, say, chlorpromazine, then I am prepared to say, "This other drug will probably do approximately what chlorpromazine does", irrespective of its chemical structure.

Bein: We have rather a different philosophy behind our testing procedures. Dr. Janssen and the testing procedure he uses are more concerned with discovering pharmacologically active analogues of drugs already known. I think it is much more important, whether in university or in industry, to try to devise new methods with which to test unknown substances. Only in collaboration with a clinician can one see whether such a test has helped to find a new drug.

Janssen: Yes, I agree with that. I think that is the main purpose of the thing. If the new drug is just like an old one, I am not interested. It is unlikely to be of more benefit to mankind than some we already have.

Bein: But what you told us was concerned more with the characterization of a new drug by its similarity to other existing drugs. Do you devote some of your work to finding entirely new drugs in the behaviourally active field? I know that this is extremely difficult, but I feel that we are at a critical point in the pharmacological testing of such drugs, because of the need for new methods.

Dr. Gaddum mentioned antagonistic action, suggesting that one should use, say, a stimulant or a depressant and then test drugs for antagonism of that action. We have been doing this for ten years (*e.g.* Tripod, J., Bein, H. J., and Meier, R. [1954]. *Arch. int. Pharmacodyn.*, **96**, 406; Bein, H. J. [1957]. *In* Psychotropic Drugs, p. 325, ed. Garattini, S., and Ghetti, V. Amsterdam: Elsevier; Bein, H. J., and Tripod, J. [1958]. *Schweiz. med. Wschr.*, **88**, 1160) and have tested hundreds of compounds in this way, but we have not yet found one compound which behaves completely like another. When we consider three well-known central nervous depressants—chlorpromazine, barbiturates and reserpine—we find that they behave quite differently in their tests of antagonism.

Chlorpromazine has a well-marked antagonistic action against mescaline-induced motor excitement, it has an anti-nicotine action, and also acts against other convulsants. The barbiturates, however, have practically no anti-mescaline activity, but enhance the mescaline-induced motor activity. Reserpine, again, has a very marked anti-mescaline activity, but does not antagonize nicotine.

The point which fascinates me is that psychopharmacological drugs which are claimed to be active in the clinic, whether antidepressant like imipramine, or antipsychotic or neuroleptic like reserpine or chlorpromazine, have very marked anti-mescaline activity in the mouse. The anti-LSD activity, for example, is not so marked for some drugs as the anti-mescaline activity.

There is one other point about the elaboration of new tests which I might mention in reference to Dr. Janssen's remarks. I am perhaps a little more cautious in predicting the clinical activity and the side effects of unknown chemical structures.

Janssen: My object here is not to try to make out that our method of approach is the best. I feel strongly that I cannot even compare it with other methods of approach because I am not sufficiently aware of how other people go about their tests.

Before putting a chemical compound into the clinic, of course, we do perform classical pharmacology. Our profiles are just screening; no more than that. It is only when we see that a compound produces catalepsy that we proceed with the rest, and then only when it does so at dose levels which are of interest to us. We start with one screening test and then make up our minds whether we are interested in the drug and want to go further, or not. We can stop at any stage.

Steinberg: Some of your tests, like the test of catalepsy to which you have just referred, have intrinsic characteristics which are perhaps vaguely but nevertheless recognizably related to human effects. But other tests, like the inhibition of chewing produced by amphetamine, are very difficult to translate into human behaviour.

Janssen: What these compounds do is to produce cataleptic immobility in human beings. It is quite obvious in manic patients if you give them a high dose.

Steinberg: The test of inhibition of chewing movements is, so far as I can judge, used on a purely empirical basis, because it discriminates between different compounds in your animal tests. But you have no *direct* reason for thinking that it represents any reaction seen in man. So we are really dealing with two different types of screening tests, that is, tests that have predictive validity only and those which have "face validity" as well (see p. 412).

Miller: Have you any method of selecting your tests? Presumably one could select tests on the basis of ease of observation. One could select them because they are correlated with each other; or because they are uncorrelated with each other, so that they relate to different actions; or one could select them because one has some theoretical or empirical reason to believe that they are more useful.

Janssen: In my paper I enumerate nine criteria of what I consider a good screening test should be (p. 264). By trying to apply these criteria, many possibilities are eliminated. For example, if a test is too complicated, too time-consuming, and impossible to carry out with large numbers of animals, we might use it for special pharmacology but not for screening. We are simply doing what everybody does, I think. We look at the literature for good ideas and apply them, or try to evolve methods ourselves. It is like playing chess; you cannot legislate for the next move.

Dews: Professor McIlwain, at the end of your opening remarks (p. 320) you suggested that the customary ways of preliminary sorting of drugs militated against the discovery of specific agents. Would you elaborate on that a little?

McIlwain: I felt the tests militated against such discovery because an investigator produced a series of compounds related to his first, only if this first compound had some measurable activity. The aim at that stage was enhancing activity. The completely specific agent would have no analogues of lesser activity. Dr. Gaddum said, almost as an aside, that granted you had a compound active to some degree, in collaboration with chemists you could enhance the activity, and I agree, though much chemical ingenuity may be needed at this stage. The present discussion has however centred on this very interesting point of picking an initial active compound.

Dr. Bein mentioned that he had already adopted Dr. Gaddum's suggestion of using drug antagonists to select initial substances. He then enumerated a number of drugs which are quite well known to have distinct actions and said that the antagonistic tests showed that they did have distinctive actions. Surely what we should be interested to know on the question of specificity is whether, when such tests have produced some hundreds of other compounds, do these other compounds also tend to fall into the same clearly defined groups? Is it always a group of caffeine-like substances which antagonize a particular agent? Is there always a group of amphetamine-like agents which respond in a particular way to the tests adopted? In other words, are the divisions natural ones, reflecting cerebral make-up, or are they relatively artificial and conditioned by the tests?

Bein: The majority of compounds are completely inactive, unfortunately. Some few compounds are active in one or more of the tests. Consider, for example, analogues of phenothiazine or chlorpromazine. Of course one could enumerate quite a large number of compounds which are active as anti-mescaline or anti-LSD agents, and so on, but groups of pharmacologically unknown substances with anti-mescaline action are seldom observed.

In our experience every compound has its own profile, with the exception of a very few close analogues. Sometimes one could be quite misled by pharmacological screening where one has similar results in various tests. But if one then adds a new test, sometimes there is a difference. One example in particular comes to mind: the muscle-relaxant properties of chlorpromazine and chlordiazepoxide. Both strongly inhibit the polysynaptic pathways. If the animal is spinalized, chlorpromazine and chlordiazepoxide produce this effect only with much higher doses. That means that both substances must act on some higher centre in order to inhibit the spinal pathway. When we found this, we thought that chlordiazepoxide and chlorpromazine would be quite similar. But studies with the γ-motor neurone system showed that this was not so; chlorpromazine markedly depresses it whereas chlordiazepoxide has practically no effect (Fehr, H. V., and Bein, H. J. [1962]. Unpublished observations). I mention this to illustrate the fact that if you probe deeper into an analysis of drug action, you can be sure to find differences in the mode of action.

Gaddum: Dr. Bein, do you really mean that there are dozens of different classes of drugs?

Bein: I do mean that.

Irwin: I second the motion. There are numerous possible permutations. Incidentally, my philosophy of approach is quite different from Dr. Janssen's in important respects. What he has created is a highly individual operation, unlike anything elsewhere in the world. The result is that he may very well come up with findings that the rest of us are unlikely to make, and *vice versa*.

My own approach is a preferred emphasis on the direct behavioural actions of a drug, rather than on drug antagonism *per se*, although I necessarily carry out tests involving drug antagonism. I start with the assumption that a drug affecting behaviour must have behavioural actions which can be demonstrated without resort to other drugs, although special procedures may be required. Proceeding on this basis, we have been able to demonstrate with every known behaviour drug a behavioural action at doses comparable with those used clinically. If you really look, you can demonstrate the behavioural effects of drugs directly. Nonetheless, I must admit that for the purpose of screening, I prefer to use the reserpine-reversal test initially to detect a monoamine oxidase inhibitor.

By way of an example, in attempting to set up a procedure for detecting antidepressant activity in animals, it was first necessary to develop a conception of what the essential component of depression might be; from this, one could proceed to develop a model or analogue of it. The hypothesis considered was that depression involves a condition of hopelessness in which the "will" to perform or to survive is impaired, particularly under stress conditions. From this framework, studies by Richter (Richter, C. P. [1957]. *Psychosom. Med.,* **19,** 191) with wild Norwegian rats were of particular interest, for he found that, when held gently with a gloved hand so that they could not escape, or placed in water where they were required to swim for survival, many of the animals died within 15 minutes. He further showed that this "sudden death" involved parasympathetic rather than sympatho-adrenal mechanisms, and that the event did not occur if the animals were first familiarized with their surroundings and with handling.

We have been able to develop a somewhat different procedure, also involving swimming, but with docile laboratory animals, in which the "sudden death" described by Richter occurs with great reliability on the first exposure, but not in animals familiarized with the experimental procedure. In this procedure, a wide variety of drugs have been found to be protective, but at doses that were almost homoeopathic, for example 0·001 mg./kg. of imipramine or chlorpheniramine; anticholinergics and phenothiazine tranquillizers were also effective. Because of its lack of specificity in differentiating drugs, and because the dose requirements for protection were far below those employed clinically, this procedure, although of academic interest, was not considered acceptable for drug screening purposes. In general, I am not prone to accept a procedure for use unless the dose requirements are comparable with those used in man. However, by modification of this initial procedure, we have been able to achieve a suitable system and, happily, have found it to be highly selective in discriminating antidepressant drugs of the monoamine oxidase inhibitor or imipramine type. I do not at this point wish to go into the details of the method but, with it, all other classes of drugs we have tested are either without effect or produce impairment rather than protection, for example, amphetamine-like agents, anticholinergics, corticoids, and the major and minor tranquillizers. An interesting point, however, is that morphine is also protective, at doses of 0·3 to 1·0 mg./kg. given subcutaneously, and that tolerance does not develop to this action. This further supports the potential value of the method for measuring antidepressant activity, since morphine and opium have long been used successfully in the treatment of depression, particularly in Germany, and continue to be used for this purpose today. Parenthetically, morphine has still other interesting therapeutic applications for which it is not used because of its addiction liability, as in the treatment of anxiety and phobic behaviour.

In general, I agree with Dr. Bein on the need to develop new tests and new techniques. However, I much prefer one with a rational basis. I would rather spend my time studying behaviour, if that is the important thing, than studying drug antagonism. I think that one will learn more from it; yet I recognize the implicit value in making certain differentiations on the basis of drug antagonism studies.

Ciba Foundation Sessions on the Relevance of Behavioural Effects of Drugs in Animals to their Effects in Man

SESSION 5: EXTRAPOLATION FROM ANIMALS TO MAN

CHAIRMAN: Dr. M. Shepherd*

INTRODUCTION

Russell: In describing some of his results on experimental neuroses Dr. Masserman once quoted a verse sent to him by a friend:

> "Masserman the cat-man
> makes felines neurotic.
> Are cat and human
> really asymptotic?"

This verse expresses the basic problem with which we are concerned when we speak of extrapolation to man of behavioural effects of drugs on animals. Extrapolation of this kind falls within the broad area of issues which arise whenever attempts are made at species generalization within the biological sciences. It is not uniquely our problem by any means. Recently it has been particularly prominent in discussions among those concerned with the very extensive and much more experienced screening programmes for anti-cancer drugs, where the same kinds of issues are being raised (e.g. Gellhorn and Hirschberg, 1955; Lasagna, 1958; Owens, 1962).

The broad issue of generalization of observations within the biological sciences involves two levels of extrapolation: from a finite sample of observations to the general population from which the sample

---

* Dr. Shepherd deputized for Sir Aubrey Lewis, who was prevented by illness from taking the chair in Sessions 5 and 6.

is drawn and from observations on one species to statements about another species. We have statistical techniques for handling generalizations of the first kind. This is possible because, although there is variability among individuals, the variable under observation is *homologous* so far as all individuals in the population are concerned. The key term here is *homologous*. I wish to begin by considering certain theoretical aspects of this extrapolation problem, most of which centre on the distinction between *homologous* and *analogous* (Russell, 1951).

In the older sciences where comparisons across species have been central issues for a long time, the concept of homology has been particularly critical. For example, in the science of comparative anatomy those structures that are alike in origin and fundamental structure are termed *homologous*. A major problem in this science has been to differentiate homologies from analogies. For the comparative anatomist, structures that are alike in function and sometimes superficially alike in form but different in origin are termed *analogous*.

During this symposium we have had frequent reference to behaviour patterns that are analogous in this sense. An example was Dr. Dews' discussion of behaviour under different schedules of reinforcement, where superficially similar patterns may be produced, but where the effect of drugs on these analogous behaviour patterns may be quite different. From a theoretical point of view we would expect the accuracy of prediction or extrapolation from one animal species to another to be affected by the extent to which the behaviour patterns involved are homologous or merely analogous.

Predictions are further complicated by the fact that the intervening biochemical events by which drugs act may also be either homologous or merely analogous in different species. To give one of many possible examples, Axelrod's (1954) early study of the drug amphetamine showed that there are marked differences in the metabolism of dexamphetamine in different species of animals; dogs and rats hydroxylate considerable amounts of the drug; rabbits and guinea pigs, on the other hand, apparently metabolize dexamphetamine by another pathway.

Recently Brodie (1962) has made a strong case for the view that "the greatest difficulty in projecting data from animal to man arises from species differences in biotransformation of the drug".

I do not wish to pursue this point further at a theoretical level, but it is clearly one which is inherent in any situation where interspecies generalizations are involved. It is not, as I said earlier, a private problem of psychopharmacologists, but it is nevertheless one of the major problems when our goals are the identification and development of drugs for their clinical usefulness in man. It is only realistic to recognize that one of the major difficulties involved is in establishing clearly that apparently similar behaviour patterns in different species are truly homologous. How then can we maximize the chances that observations of the effects of drugs on behaviour in infrahuman species can be extrapolated to man? I wish to raise for discussion six major points which I see as central to answering this question.

PREDICTIVE VALIDITY

The first point is that the success of extrapolation from animals to man is judged pragmatically in terms of drug-behaviour interactions in man. The latter interactions are the criteria against which the *predictive validity* of tests on infrahuman animals is evaluated. This places a great responsibility on studies of the clinical effectiveness of drugs, studies which have their own peculiar difficulties. The need for sound information on clinical effectiveness has been satisfied more fully then ever before by the so-called "mass clinical trials" of psychoactive drugs which have been carried out during recent years. Earlier in this symposium Dr. Edwards reported briefly on an attempt to establish some order in the results of such trials, an order which might help us in evaluating the capabilities of our animal tests to differentiate relative degrees of clinical effectiveness.

Predictive validity is the final basis upon which measures of behaviour must be evaluated as screening devices for drugs of potential value for the treatment of behavioural disorders in man. To be efficient a screen should reveal most of the best agents and not suggest as promising many drugs which ultimately prove to be useless: it should give a minimum of false negatives and false positives. Here is an applied situation in which extrapolation of research findings from animals to man is essential if preclinical behavioural studies are to have any rôle whatsoever in the technological process of identifying new psychoactive agents for uses in therapy.

CONCURRENT VALIDITY

My second point concerns what has been called concurrent validity, which is evaluated by showing how well behavioural tests discriminate between experimental groups of animals to whom drugs have been administered over a wide range of dose levels, including placebo controls. Those measures of behaviour that are significantly affected have concurrent validity for the specific drug, or perhaps the general class of drugs under study. Dr. Janssen's drug profiles are an illustration of this kind of validity in operation.

A battery of behavioural measures which reveals no sensitivity to a particular drug within a clinically useful dose-range raises a serious dilemma: it may be that the drug is indeed not psychoactive or it may be that the battery contains no measures with concurrent validity for the drug in question. The latter possibility could lead to the rejection of potentially useful agents. On the other hand, a behavioural measure which responds to any drug that comes along will not provide information of differential value. The practical problem here is the development of behavioural tests for infrahuman animal subjects which will minimize false positives and false negatives when their results are extrapolated to man.

RELIABILITY OF MEASURING INSTRUMENTS

The third point concerns the nature of behavioural tests as measuring instruments. Basically such measuring instruments involve the assignment of numerals to events in accordance with the same sets of rules which apply to measurement in all sciences. Tests situations are designed to generate behaviour patterns, numerals are assigned to dimensions of the behaviour in accordance with the rules of nominal, ordinal, interval or ratio scales. No good research worker in any science would be worth his salt who did not pay particular attention to the internal consistency and stability of his measuring instruments. It is unlikely that extrapolation of behavioural data from animals to man will be successful unless the data themselves are reliable. The same holds true, of course, for the clinical data which constitute the criteria for evaluation of predictive validity. One frequent cause of difficulty in extrapolating results from animals to man lies in the lack of reliability of behavioural measuring instruments, which introduces large experimental errors into observations and thus covers up relationships which may in fact exist.

SELECTION OF BEHAVIOUR PATTERNS TO BE MEASURED

With these issues in mind, my fourth point concerns the problem of selecting behaviour patterns to be measured. On what bases may behaviour patterns be selected for preclinical drug tests?

1. Analysis of criterion behaviour. One possible basis is an approach which I shall call "analysis of criterion behaviour". This approach involves the following steps: (*a*) analysing an aberrant human behaviour pattern, for example, schizophrenia, for its basic characteristics; (*b*) selecting animal behaviour patterns which are as similar as possible to these characteristics; (*c*) searching for chemical agents which affect these behaviour patterns; (*d*) testing the effects of the drugs on the human aberrant behaviour pattern originally analysed.

There are major difficulties in this approach, even though it sounds very attractive superficially. The difficulties centre on the fact that the aetiology of human aberrant behaviour is as yet unknown; we are searching for drugs which will affect behaviour, the origin of which is not well-defined. In such circumstances it is impossible to select for preclinical tests behaviour patterns in animal subjects which are likely to be truly homologous to the aberrant behaviour in man. Long ago, while working on other problems, psychologists learned that the *face validity* of behavioural tests did not guarantee predictive validity. One cannot be confident of valid extrapolation from one form of behaviour to another just because the two appear to be similar.

2. Analysis of criterion drugs. Another possible approach in selecting behaviour patterns to be measured is by what I shall call "analysis of criterion drugs", an approach to which we gave some attention earlier in discussing screening tests (pp. 264–392). Drugs whose effects on human behaviour are already known may be used as criteria for establishing identifiable profiles of effects on measures in a battery of behavioural tests for infrahuman animals. Such profiles then serve as bases for classifying the behavioural effectiveness of new drugs. Dr. Janssen has told us that, in his experience, extrapolation from animal data to human effects on the basis of such profiles has been accurate; in other words, predictive validity has been high. Professor McIlwain spoke of the usefulness of data from the analysis of criterion drugs in the development of more potent homologues of a drug.

3. Construct analysis. A third approach to selecting behaviour patterns to be measured is based upon predictions from some theoretical model of behaviour. Explanatory constructs of the model suggest that drugs with certain mechanisms of action should have specified effects upon behaviour. Following the construct-analysis approach the investigator asks: from this theoretical model, what prediction would I make regarding behaviour patterns which should be affected by various psychoactive drugs? Secondly, he selects or constructs specific techniques to measure these behaviour patterns and proceeds to test for variations in them resulting from the administration of drugs with different modes of action. Professor Miller's paper (p.1) illustrates this approach, and there are other examples of its application, for example, Eysenck (1957), Russell and Steinberg (1955).

4. A priori selection. A fourth approach begins with an *a priori* classification of behaviour, and then selects behaviour patterns which are representative of some or all of the classes. Specific techniques for measuring these representative behaviour patterns are combined to form a standard test battery. The classification is always based upon rational considerations; sometimes the considerations arise from the results of empirical analyses, based for example, upon factorial analyses of a wide variety of behavioural measures.

5. Selection by empirical interest. It is probably true that behaviour patterns are often selected for measurement purely on the basis of the empirical interests of the investigator. He asks himself: "I wonder what would happen to behaviour X if I gave my animals drug Y?" Sometimes, looking at the literature, I think this is the most frequent basis for selecting behaviour patterns! In reading the past literature the feeling sometimes arises that anyone with a dusty old multiple T-maze in his cupboard can bring it out, clean it, borrow some drugs from the local pharmacy, and think that he is in business as a psychopharmacologist. This approach leads to individual and fragmented studies, with serious problems of comparability from study to study. It may be useful for some purposes, but it is not geared to extrapolation of the kind we are now discussing.

IDENTIFICATION OF DRUGS WITH NEW BEHAVIOURAL MODES OF ACTION

It is clear that each of these methods of selecting behavioural measures has weaknesses. Because of its particular importance, I wish to make one of these weaknesses my fifth point for discussion. This is the matter of provision for identifying drugs which may have *new* behavioural modes of action and therefore some potentially useful application in directions not covered by established classes of psychoactive agents. Test batteries which have been standardized for identifying behavioural profiles of established criterion agents may produce false negatives because they do not include adequate measures of behaviour patterns sensitive to drugs with as yet unidentified behavioural modes of action. This would argue against complete dependence upon test batteries standardized for particular purposes, and in favour of provisions for the broadest possible coverage of different aspects of behaviour.

It will be interesting to learn of the procedures you use to ensure, systematically, that new classes of psychoactive drugs are not over-looked.

EVALUATION OF SUCCESS IN PREDICTING

As a final point I wish to consider a useful exercise in which we have not engaged to any great extent in the past, at least so far as reports in the literature are concerned. This is the issue of evaluating the degree of success actually achieved in predicting from studies of drug effects on animal behaviour to their effect on human behaviour. I know that this kind of evaluation is, in some form or other, a routine procedure for many workers in our field, and that is why I emphasize that, so far as the literature is concerned, one finds very few reports of studies attempting to evaluate the success of extrapolation from animals to man.

An example of recent attempts is a report by Dr. J. T. Litchfield (1961) under the title: "Forecasting Drug Effects in Man from Studies in Laboratory Animals." Litchfield's general procedure was to analyse laboratory data available on retrospective studies of six different drugs and to try to predict from these what would happen subsequently in man, already having information about what in fact does happen to man. His analysis was conducted in terms of simple, non-parametric statistics. It employed only symptoms which could potentially occur in all the various species of animals studied, thereby eliminating symptoms characteristic of one species alone. Litchfield classified the selected symptoms in a simple two-category system of occurring or not occurring and analysed the significances of differences in occurrence by means of the chi-squared test. Included in the final list of symptoms were: impaired reflexes, hypertension, ataxia, decreased activity, weight loss, tremors, ptosis, urinary incontinence, catatonia, lacrimation, and diarrhoea. These did not include measures of behaviour found in current batteries of tests designed for detailed behavioural screening in psychopharmacology. The results of Litchfield's study indicate that predictability was more accurate for certain of the symptoms than for others and that certain species of animal subjects were more useful in predicting than were others.

Several other reports (e.g. Barnes and Denz, 1954; Brodie, 1962; Litchfield, 1962; Paget, 1962; Owens, 1962; Schiele, 1962) have raised the general question: What is the empirical evidence that present tests on animals provide information which can be extrapolated successfully to man? They have suggested variables which affect such prediction. On the whole they have been rather pessimistic in tone. The fact that reports of this kind have been appearing more frequently during recent years suggests that the question of extrapolation from animal data to man is becoming a matter of increasing concern. Statements made earlier in these sessions have indicated that information can be made available which in fact establishes the validity of such extrapolation, at least under certain conditions of generalization. It seems to me that the issue is of sufficient importance to warrant a concentrated effort to present the evidence systematically, to describe the methods by which it may be obtained, and to specify the conditions under which it may properly apply.

In opening this session on "Extrapolation from Animals to Man" I have tried to point out that, theoretically, success in interspecies generalization depends primarily upon the presence of homologous behaviour patterns and of homologous processes in the biological transformation of the drug under study. From a practical point of view these conditions are seldom, if ever, obtained. The question then arises as to how success in extrapolating may be maximized. In suggesting an answer to this question I was led to consider the concepts of concurrent and predictive validity, since the ultimate criterion of success in extrapolating is drug-behaviour interactions in man. This pragmatic approach to evaluating predictability places great importance upon the selection of behaviour patterns from which extrapolations are to be made; I have discussed the bases for selection. Finally, I have given special attention to the problem of identifying drugs which may have quite new behavioural modes of action and to the importance of presenting publicly empirical evidence of success in forecasting from preclinical results to clinical effects. I hope that this approach to organizing the general topic will lead to a full discussion of issues which pervade both basic and applied research in psychopharmacology today.

REFERENCES

AXELROD, J. (1954). *J. Pharmacol. exp. Ther.*, **110**, 315.

BARNES, J. M., and DENZ, F. A. (1954). *Pharmacol. Rev.*, **6**, 191.

BRODIE, B. B. (1962). *Clin. Pharmacol. Ther.*, **3**, 374.

EYSENCK, H. J. (1957). The Dynamics of Anxiety and Hysteria. New York: Praeger.

GELLHORN, A., and HIRSCHBERG, E. (1955). *Cancer. Rep.*, Suppl. No. 3.

LASAGNA, L. (1958). *Ann. N.Y. Acad. Sci.*, **76**, 939.

LITCHFIELD, J. T. (1961). *J. Amer. med. Ass.*, **177**, 34.

LITCHFIELD, J. T. (1962). *Clin. Pharmacol. Ther.*, **3**, 665.

OWENS, A. H. (1962). *Cancer Chemother. Rep.*, **16**, 57.

PAGET, G. E. (1962). *Clin. Pharmacol. Ther.*, **3**, 381.

RUSSELL, R. W. (1951). The Comparative Study of Behaviour. London: H. K. Lewis.

RUSSELL, R. W., and STEINBERG, H. (1955). *Quart. J. exp. Psychol.*, **7**, 67.

SCHIELE, B. C. (1962). *J. Amer. med. Ass.*, **181**, 126.

SELECTION OF BEHAVIOURAL TESTS

Steinberg: Litchfield did not actually name the individual drugs he studied, he just gave classes.

Barnes: Litchfield was mainly concerned with toxic side effects of drugs, and with how far one could predict toxic effects in man from observations made on animals, rather than the effects of drugs on behaviour.

Russell: That is true. As I mentioned, only a few of his final list of symptoms were behavioural in nature, for example, impaired reflexes, ataxia, decreased activity. I searched the literature for attempts to evaluate the predictability of human effects from animal studies in the field of interactions between drugs and behaviour and could find very few, most of which were incidental to predicting toxic effects. I therefore used the Litchfield paper as an example of one approach that might be taken because, after all, it did involve *some* aspects on behaviour.

Dews: Could I make a minor comment before we get into deep water? Professor Russell referred to *extrapolation* from animals to man. In other areas of pharmacology and physiology man is not always at one extreme of the continuum among the species. In many attributes he falls *between* dogs and rats, or *between* monkeys and pigeons rather than off beyond the monkeys, so that I think in many cases of behaviour affected by drugs one could usefully think of *interpolation* of the effects seen in man.

Russell: I referred to extrapolation from animals to man only because this was the title of the topic assigned to me. Your point is very well taken.

Herxheimer: It seems to me that a very simple way of classifying behaviour in order to test drugs is simply to select a text-book of psychology and take, say, two representative headings from each chapter. Has anybody used this kind of approach? In that way one could be fairly sure that no major class of known behaviour is left out.

Russell: I believe that the response of many psychologists would be that the chapter headings in most general psychology texts have not changed significantly for 50 years! The organization of text-book material has not kept up with the times, and to use it as a basis for classifying behaviour, would, I think, be inadequate. If one wished to cover the whole gamut of behaviour patterns as fully as possible, one would be more likely to succeed by turning, for example, to some of the broader attempts to analyse factorially a great variety of empirical measures of behaviour into categories that are discrete or at least clearly differentiated. Such a rational categorization would enable one to look at the various measures of behaviour that contribute to each factor and to select the one specific measure weighted most heavily for it. This is an approach which Anderson (Anderson, E. E. [1938]. *Comp. Psychol. Monog.*, **14**, No. 6, 119), Thorndike (Thorndike, R. L. [1935]. *Genetic Psychol. Monog.*, **17**, 1) and others began to use some 25 years ago. We have not taken it up to any extent in psychopharmacology.

Summerfield: Some of the contributions on behavioural analysis of drug action earlier in this symposium, by Dr. Jarvik for example, illustrate lines of attack which may approximate to the sort of analysis Dr. Herxheimer has in mind. Perhaps you would classify them under your category of using some sort of theoretical approach, Professor Russell. People have started from an idea about the organization of psychological processes in man. They have then tried to look for selective effects on different psychological processes, for example registration, retention and retrieval in the study of memory.

Chance: The field of behaviour is really 80 per cent unexplored, and there is an urgent need to draw up a programme at some stage for the expansion of behavioural studies. But this is quite beside the present point because there are certain regions of behaviour where we have reasonably well-documented information and a number of tools exist in the form of drugs. My major difficulty in discussions with clinicians is that we are not talking about the same things; schizophrenia, they say, is a mixed bag, and when you try to identify the game birds that the bag contains, clinicians become a little distressed, as if you were poaching! This is quite natural because they are taking decisions from day to day on the lives of people and their treatment and one cannot expect doctors who are doing that to stop to inspect the basis on which they make their decisions. At some point, however, some doctors have got to come out of their clinics to talk to us in the field where we don't have to make immediate decisions.

Cook: In extrapolation of behaviour from animals to man one object is to identify similar behavioural processes occurring in both animals and man. It has been shown that when man is placed in the same experimental conditions as an animal, the same behaviour is frequently seen. We and many other people have reported this, in experiments which measure timing behaviour or conditioned avoidance behaviour. When the experimental contingencies are specified the behaviour is often the same. When drugs are used as independent variables the effects produced are also frequently the same. This is well established.

My second point is that besides showing a correlation of drug effects in different species under the same experimental conditions, it is necessary to ask, what is the relationship to a clinical syndrome?

Jarvik: I wonder whether Professor Russell isn't a little over-optimistic about the value of factor analysis, which has been rather disappointing in what it has produced so far. Even the most enthusiastic proponents would agree that you cannot get more out of factor analysis than you put into it. It is a way of pulling yourself up by your own boot straps; given the proper data of course, it is a perfectly legitimate procedure, but obviously factor analysis is not going to tell you whether anything important has been left out of a test battery in the first place.

Russell: I referred to factor analysis only when talking about the *a priori* selection of behavioural measures in making the point that one method of selecting behavioural measures is to try to cover the whole gamut of behaviour. This requires classification of behaviour in some way and, in an aside, I suggested that one such method might be through the use of factor analysis. This is an empirical method. I also mentioned that there are other *a priori* rational methods of classification, which would no doubt include the "chapter heading from the psychology text-book" approach, as Professor Summerfield has just elaborated it.

EXPERIMENTS ON ANIMALS AND MAN WITH DRUG MIXTURES

Steinberg: We seem to range between two opposite points of view: that one cannot predict from animals to man and that prediction is relatively easy. My colleagues and I have tried to carry out somewhat related laboratory experiments in animals and man, and we have obtained results which do seem to fit together, if rather roughly. They were carried out with amphetamine-barbiturate mixtures which, as I have said, are often used by relatively normal people, and perhaps therefore this sort of comparison is easier. The animal data are shown in the form of dose-response curves in Figs. 1 and 2 (Rushton, R., and

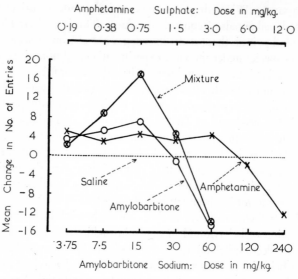

EXPLORATORY ACTIVITY IN 5 MINUTES

FIG. 1 (Steinberg). Activity of rats influenced by amphetamine sulphate and amylobarbitone sodium, given separately and in combination, over a range of doses. The figure shows the number of entries into the arms of a Y-shaped runway during 5 min. expressed as mean differences from the activity of the saline control group, the mean number of entries of which was 14·7, S.D. 5·8. Each point represents the mean results for a different group of ten rats. The ratio between the two drugs was kept constant at 1:20. Reproduced from Rushton and Steinberg (1963) by permission of the Editor of *Nature*.

Steinberg, H. [1963]. *Nature [Lond.]*, **197**, 4871, 1017). The test method was similar to that described on p. 208. The mixture in Fig. 1 contains about five times as much barbiturate as one which is much used clinically as Drinamyl (Smith, Kline & French). With this mixture, there was a very big peak of activity at one particular dose combination which was much bigger than the effects of any dose of the separate drugs. Fig. 2 shows similar data using a Drinamyl ratio; the curves were very similar, though the peak mixture effect occurred with half the amount of barbiturate, as compared with Fig. 1. We also studied

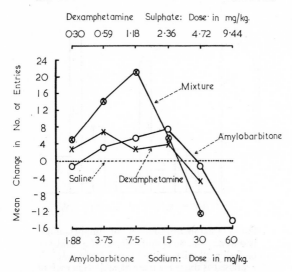

FIG. 2 (Steinberg). Results of second series of experiments. Conditions were similar to those described for Fig. 1, except that dexamphetamine sulphate and amylobarbitone sodium were used, in the ratio of 1:6·5 (Drinamyl ratio). There were eight rats per group. Reproduced from Rushton and Steinberg (1963) by permission of the Editor of *Nature*.

ataxia by measuring the variability of the spacing of the rats' footprints (Rushton, R., Steinberg, H., and Tinson, C. [1963]. *Brit. J. Pharmacol.*, **20,** 99). The smallest dose of mixture at which significant ataxia was detected in Fig. 1 was the dose which produced maximum effects on activity; but in Fig. 2 ataxia was only detected at double the peak activity dose.

Recently we have compared the effects of two mixtures of amphetamine sulphate and cyclobarbitone in man (Dickins, D., Lader, M., and

Steinberg, H. To be published). A dose ratio similar to that in Fig. 1 produced more reports of feeling "sociable" than the separate constituents, but it also produced more reports of feeling "unsteady". A mixture similar in ratio to Drinamyl was similar in that it produced

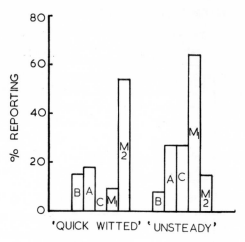

Fig. 3 (Steinberg). Effects of amphetamine-barbiturate mixtures on feelings. The incidence of feeling "quick witted" and "unsteady" is expressed as the percentage of subjects in each of five groups of students who reported the feeling. The groups had received respectively: a control tablet (B), amphetamine sulphate, 15 mg. (A), cyclobarbitone, 300 mg. (C), A and C combined in a single tablet (M_1), and A combined with cyclobarbitone, 75 mg. (M_2). The ratio of the two drugs in M_1 is similar to the ratio in Fig. 1 and that in M_2 to that in Fig. 2.

many reports of "sociable" but it also yielded more reports of feeling "alert" and "quick witted" and fewer reports of being "unsteady" than the first mixture. Thus it seems that mixtures containing proportionately more barbiturate produced their "desirable" effects in both rats and man at the price of also producing motor unsteadiness, while mixtures with the Drinamyl ratio did it without unsteadiness (Fig. 3).

Edwards: I am very interested in this type of analysis. From time to time in the drug industry, of course, mixtures are considered and the question often comes up as to whether they have any merit whatsoever. For the first time your research group has set out to determine just what are the effects of various stimulant-barbiturate mixtures.

Irwin: We tried to duplicate Dr. Steinberg's results and were unable to do so. Ours was the Charles River rat, and I am reminded of some of the studies on aggregate toxicity that Dr. Chance reported. There seem to be strain differences in aggregate toxicity, some strains being completely insensitive to the effects of aggregation (Weaver, L. C., and Kerley, T. L. [1962]. *J. Pharmacol. exp. Ther.*, **135**, 240), just as drug protection against audiogenic seizures has been shown to vary on a strain basis to a remarkable degree. It may well be that the differences between our results and Dr. Steinberg's are due to strain differences, or perhaps other factors are involved. I am sure we did not handle our animals in quite as neat a manner as Dr. Steinberg, although we used an identical Y-maze.

Janssen: There are strain differences; with our rats, for instance, amphetamine in the open-field test that Dr. Broadhurst describes, instead of increasing ambulation primarily increases rearing.

Steinberg: Yes, we also recorded rearing, but we have reported the results only in terms of walking about. With rearing we usually got marked effects with amphetamine.

Janssen: You have seen that too? We are agreed then!

Steinberg: Yes, but for showing up the effects of mixtures the explorations were more striking. Dr. D. R. Maxwell in this country has confirmed the increased "ambulation" with mixtures of dexamphetamine and amylobarbitone as compared with the separate drugs in an open-field test similar to that described by Dr. Broadhurst (p. 228). His rats were Wistar albino males, and they had been reared under ordinary animal house conditions.

McIlwain: I wonder if this synergism between two drugs that might have been expected to be antagonistic shows itself in properties other than these rather sophisticated behavioural characteristics. This question was asked by Sir Aubrey Lewis on an earlier occasion, when he queried how a drug firm arrived at this particular ratio of 6·5:1. One might doubt that this happened on the basis of behavioural tests, but it could have been arrived at on the basis of, say, measurements of body temperature or of sleeping time.

Steinberg: As far as we have been able to find out, the ratio was arrived at on the basis of clinical experience only.

Bradley: The barbiturates in small quantities are known to produce excitatory effects in animals; and the quantity of barbiturate in your combination was not one that normally produces sedation. So a synergism at this dose level is perhaps not surprising.

Steinberg: No; but you will have seen that the peak of the mixture curve in Fig. 2 was not over the barbiturate peak, but at half that dose. We have since tried different combinations, and the effect does depend on the balance between the *two* drugs.

Cook: Dr. Steinberg, were these two drugs administered simultaneously?

Steinberg: Yes, in a single injection. There are all sorts of problems about this, of course, because amphetamine is longer-acting than the barbiturate, and one might in theory give the two drugs separately at different times. But our technique was a compromise, and clinically the two drugs are given in a single tablet.

Cook: The dose relationships in animals and man are not always the same for all drugs. A certain dose relationship for the barbiturate might be different from that for amphetamine. In many drug-combination studies the relative proportions of the mixture used in the clinic are usually difficult to evaluate in animals, because they are disproportionately sensitive to different drugs.

STRAIN AND SEX DIFFERENCES

Hamilton: The question of variability between strains is of fundamental importance in clinical applications. The human species is extremely varied, comprising innumerable strains; in a sense, the human species is a "wild" species, of tremendous variability. It might even be that our population of patients is to some degree a selected strain. This is more than an idle speculation; it may have a practical significance, because the attempt is constantly being made to investigate general laws of behaviour, to discover the characteristic effects on behaviour of certain drugs, but always in a general sense. The fact that different strains produce different results is regarded as a complication, an added difficulty in evaluating the general laws of the effects of drugs on behaviour. But it may well be that we should turn the problem upside down, and look at it the other way round. Perhaps we should interest ourselves not in the general laws, but in the specific differences, the differences between strains and what determines them, and in this respect, the points about different interactions with drugs can be of fundamental importance.

Bein: Sex differences are known with the action of many drugs, but I wonder whether such observations are common in experimental psychopharmacology?

Hamilton: Sex differences are not infrequent in behavioural studies, particularly with phenothiazines. I hope to tell you later of some work we did in the United States (see p. 448) in which we carried out an analysis of variance for men and women separately, and one of the remarkable things was that the women had a variance three times as great as the men, although they were rated in exactly the same way, so that something else was clearly involved which justified one in drawing separate conclusions about them.

Irwin: In locomotor activity studies with rats we have found females to be very much more sensitive to stimulant or depressant drugs than males. This we found to be correlated with their very much higher baseline levels of activity (Irwin, S., Slabok, M., and Thomas, G. [1958]. *J. Pharmacol.*, **125,** 206). On the other hand, the conditioned avoidance procedure gives the opposite result; here the important factor in drug sensitivity seems to be the speed with which the rats learn the avoidance response. In this situation females learn the avoidance response more quickly, with fewer errors in a given number of trials than males, and are thereby more resistant to drugs suppressing the behaviour than males (Irwin, S. [1960]. *In* The Dynamics of Psychiatric Drug Therapy, p. 5, ed. Sarwer-Foner, G. J. Springfield: Thomas).

Jarvik: Referring to the increase in the activity observed by Dr. Steinberg with the barbiturates, how general is this phenomenon; how often does one find that small doses of centrally acting drugs produce an increase in general activity or similar behaviour, while larger doses produce a depression? Does anybody know of a drug that will produce the reverse effect, with small doses producing a decreasing activity and large doses an increase?

Irwin: This seems to be of frequent occurrence. Indeed, such a reversal is in line with Professor Paton's theory of drug action (Paton, W. D. M. [1961]. *Proc. roy. Soc. B*, **154**, 21). With small doses of amphetamine, for example, one observes an initial *depression* of wakefulness. As one increases the dose, one overrides this effect. In studies with amphetamine, as the drug wears off one again observes the depression, both in wakefulness and in locomotor activity. We frequently observe this phenomenon with depressant drugs as well.

Miller: This is what you might expect from the action of these two drugs and the behaviour of these animals. The animals are in a conflict between moving around to explore their new environment, and crouching because they are frightened by their strange surroundings. I think that the barbiturate tends to get rid of the fear and loosen them up a little. Exploring habituates very quickly, which is perhaps analogous to experimental extinction (although we may be taking too much of a leap here) and amphetamine seems to make animals particularly resistant to extinction, so at least retrospectively one can make sense of the results Dr. Steinberg obtained with this combination of drugs, in terms of these two competing factors.

Stein: There is one thing I would add. I think amphetamine has a larger facilitating effect on the tendency to explore before, rather than after, habituation. Perhaps that is why amphetamine exceeded saline in unhabituated ("inexperienced") rats but not in habituated ("experienced") rats, and why the mixture had a much greater absolute effect in "inexperienced" than in "experienced" rats, and in part why the mixture had no more effect than saline in "experienced" rats.

Miller: I think amphetamine *prevents* habituation in this situation.

Dews: The interaction of amphetamine with other drugs is not confined to the barbiturates; interesting relations with reserpine have been reported (Smith, C. B. [1962]. *Fed. Proc.*, **21**, 418; abstract). Measuring the activity of animals with a simple photo-cell arrangement, Smith found that the activity 24 hours after administering reserpine was essentially zero. The dose-response curve for amphetamine alone shows the familiar pattern. In mice treated with reserpine, starting from a baseline of zero, the dose-response curve for amphetamine rises before the normal amphetamine curve and actually goes to a higher peak, so that even though one starts from a zero baseline, one can get a potentiation of amphetamine activity following reserpine.

Irwin: Referring again to Dr. Steinberg's report, one of the characteristics in the behaviour of the amphetamine-treated animal is "rearing" against the walls of its enclosure. On combination with a barbiturate, the amount of time devoted to rearing activity is reduced; simply eliminating that facet of their behaviour means that they have an opportunity of spending more time on locomotion. It is all motor activity but, when both drugs are given, it is expressed in one dimension, rather than in two.

Steinberg: We have actually looked at some of the sums of rearings and explorations in order to get an overall measure of motor activity. In the peak activity dose in Fig. 2, for example, the effect on this overall measure was about three times as much as with either of the separate constituents. Moreover all three substances produced about the same number of rearings. Dr. Irwin's interpretation is therefore not borne out. With some of the combinations we have used, however, the animals are so ataxic that they are apt to fall over when they try to rear, and some hardly rear at all.

CATATONIA

Feldberg: There is one problem concerning extrapolation which has not yet been mentioned, namely, that physiologists finding behavioural similarities between animals and man can sometimes interpret them in terms of central neuronal mechanisms. I made an attempt of this sort with one form of behaviour which can be obtained both in animals and man: catatonia (Feldberg, W. [1963]. A Pharmacological Approach to the Brain from its Inner and Outer Surface. London: Edward Arnold). Dr. Sherwood and I (Feldberg, W., and Sherwood, S. [1954]. *J. Physiol.* [*Lond.*], **125**, 488) had found this condition in cats 2 hr. after an intraventricular injection of di*iso*propylfluorophosphonate (DFP). The cat could be put into abnormal positions and would retain them without struggling, but when pushed it could jump without impairment of movement. This is very similar to catatonia in man. Since DFP is an anticholinesterase, the question arises: is the effect due to accumulation of undestroyed acetylcholine, and if so, how does the acetylcholine act?

Before discussing the problem of how acetylcholine, in my opinion, acts, I want to point out that there is another symptom of schizophrenia which can be produced by anticholinesterases. D. Grob, J. L. Lilienthal, Jr., A. M. Harvey and B. F. Jones ([1947]. *Johns Hopkins Hosp. Bull.*, **81,** 217) used DFP in the treatment of myasthenia gravis. They gave daily intramuscular injections but had to discontinue the treatment because the patients complained of nightmares, became confused and—another characteristic symptom of schizophrenia—they had hallucinations.

In our cats we also observed behavioural changes which suggested that the cats had hallucinations. All these actions of DFP are most likely an effect of undestroyed acetylcholine, but I don't think the acetylcholine in these instances acted by exciting nerve cells, but by paralysing them. We know that prolonged action of acetylcholine blocks synaptic transmission in autonomic ganglia and neuromuscular transmission at the motor end-plate. For instance, in the presence of an anticholinesterase the main effect of stimulating a motor nerve, after an initial augmentation of the contraction, is neuromuscular block. Acetylcholine when undestroyed may have a similar paralysing action on synaptic transmission from central cholinergic neurones. The second reason why the actions of DFP may be due to a paralysing action of undestroyed acetylcholine is based on the fact that we cannot reproduce catatonia in animal experiments by electrical stimulation of any part of the brain, but it is a typical effect of certain lesions. If acetylcholine acts by blocking central synaptic transmission, which can be regarded as a kind of pharmacological lesion, the similarity between the results of lesions and of persistence of acetylcholine becomes clear. The third reason why I think the acetylcholine works in this way is that it would explain why at least one effect, hallucinations, can also be produced by an antagonist of acetylcholine. A characteristic feature of atropine and hyoscine poisoning is hallucinations. If excess of acetylcholine acts by blocking central synaptic transmission then it should have the same effect as the central synaptic block produced by an antagonist. I might point out that B. W. Rowntree, S. Nevin and A. Wilson ([1950]. *J. Neurol. Psychiat.*, **13,** 47) found in schizophrenics that injections of DFP resulted in an activation of the psychosis. In my opinion, the hallucinations and the catatonia seen after DFP are due to an effect of undestroyed acetylcholine. But when these symptoms occur in schizophrenic patients without treatment with DFP we are not allowed to conclude that they result from excess of acetylcholine. The most we can say is that they are due to impairment of function of nerve cells normally impinged upon by cholinergic neurones. This kind of interpretation is an attempt not just to demonstrate similarities, but to obtain information about the neuronal mechanism involved.

Stein: How do schizophrenics respond to atropine treatment?

Janssen: I think the best atropine-like substance normally used in cases of schizophrenia is benactyzine and that apparently does not do very much even at high dose levels. All the anti-Parkinsonian drugs that are being used in this connexion do not seem to modify the picture very much.

Feldberg: One might expect in fact an activation of the psychosis by atropine-like drugs, because any impairment of function of nerve cells impinged upon by cholinergic neurones should be further aggravated by a blocking agent.

Stein: We can then eliminate the alternative, on the basis of these negative trials with anticholinergic drugs, that there is too much acetylcholine activity in the schizophrenic brain. If there is an impairment it must be on some other basis.

Irwin: There could be too little, couldn't there?

Feldberg: Yes, the most we can say is that nerve cells, which are impinged upon by a cholinergic neurone, are not functioning. That this is the result of excess acetylcholine, I doubt. The impairment may be due to some unknown pathological changes.

Bein: Dr. Feldberg and Dr. Cook have now come together; both have mentioned a most important point, namely, the elucidation of a patho-physiological mechanism. Dr. Cook drew our attention to the clinical syndrome and Dr. Feldberg stressed that we have to elucidate its mechanism. We do not know enough about the underlying physiological mechanisms and a better understanding of these would make it easier to provide better and more significant tests in the laboratory.

Russell: I agree. In my opening remarks I tried to emphasize that the criteria against which we evaluate our behavioural measures must eventually be in these terms. In the Psychopharmacology Service

Center of the U.S. National Institutes of Health we have started holding regular joint meetings of preclinical and early-clinical test research people and I think this is beginning to be advantageous for both. Clinical people are beginning to explore the application of some preclinical concepts to clinical observations and *vice versa*.

Dews: There has been a clinical trial of atropine in schizophrenia, just for the record (Forrer, G. R. [1951]. *Amer. J. Psychiat.*, **108**, 107). Repeated doses of 32 mg. were given with benefit claimed for many of the patients, although one died.

Janssen: There is a lot of interest these days in anticholinergic drugs with central action. Lakeside has produced many piperidine derivatives, esters of benzilic acid and so on, that have LSD-like actions. There seems to be no parallelism between the central and the peripheral effects.

Cook: Those drugs with high atropine-like activity, such as Dr. Janssen's imipramine-type of drug, seem to be more efficacious as antidepressants than in the schizophrenic area.

Stein: Imipramine was originally discovered by aggravating agitations and manias.

Jarvik: Dr. Allen Rothballer and I have injected physostigmine into catheters chronically inserted into one carotid or vertebral artery of cats (Rothballer, A. B., Jarvik, M. E., and Jacobs, G. G. [1961]. *In* The Regional Chemistry, Physiology and Pharmacology of the Nervous System, p. 442, ed. Kety, S. S. London: Pergamon Press) and we have never seen anything like catatonia, but we have observed some remarkable unilateral effects. First of all, animals with carotid catheters would circle quite vigorously away from the side of injection, whereas those injected intravertebrally would show ipsiversive circling. Intravertebral physostigmine produced scratching of the ipsilateral side of the body. With carotid injections we were able to elicit convulsions starting on the side of the body opposite to the injection but we were always able to stop these manifestations abruptly with hyoscine.

Feldberg: It may be that the effects you observed were brought about by the excitatory action of undestroyed acetylcholine.

Jarvik: We have seen something that looks like a catatonia by injecting chlorpromazine into one carotid artery (Jacobs, G. B., Rothballer, A. B., Coppola, F. C., and Jarvik, M. E. [1962]. *Int. J. Neuropharmacol.*,

I, 323). This is a peculiar flaccid paralysis on the opposite side of the body. The animals allow their limbs to be moulded into any position but only on one side of the body.

Barnes: Professor Feldberg, did you get catatonia with physostigmine administered intraventricularly?

Feldberg: Yes, and also with large doses of acetylcholine, but the best way to get it is to use DFP. It is a late effect; we happened to notice it for the first time after we had finished our observation of the acute effects, and by chance looked again to see whether the cat had recovered and then found the cataleptic condition. With physostigmine, the condition is reached earlier, and passes off more quickly.

Gaddum: Do you get it with antagonists of acetylcholine?

Feldberg: We have not tried. We did not get it with atropine. Bulbocapnine produces it on intraventricular injection of extremely small doses, about two-hundredths of the dose effective on intramuscular injection.

It is not surprising that other drugs, such as bulbocapnine, produce catatonia. Anything that impairs certain cells impinged upon by cholinergic neurones should produce catatonia, but the interesting point is that excess of acetylcholine seems to have this effect.

Chance: Perhaps your catatonia is what we call catalepsy. There seem to be two components here. The fixing of a posture by an animal in the course of its normal behaviour is a very characteristic thing seen in crouching animals such as a hare before it runs suddenly. Certain drugs such as G.K. 26, on the other hand, produce very rigid postures and an alternation of behaviour between fixed posture and rapid movement. One element here is the fixity of a posture, and this is no more than the extension in time of part of what behaviour normally consists of, that is to say, a series of postures with rapid movements between them. On the one hand, the elements of plasticity can be present with a tonic strength in the muscles, as I presume you have demonstrated in the cat, and this is what I would call catatonia. On the other hand my rat lying on its back (p. 68) was cataleptic in the sense that it was flaccid; it was plastic so that one could put it into any shape one liked and it would stay there in a relatively relaxed state. It would gradually unfold if one curled it up so that it had no support. If one put it in such a position that it had virtually no muscle requirement—energy requirement—

it would stay there. This is what happens in very intense flight situations lasting for, say, a minute. Rats, of course, go into that state without any drugs and this is characteristic also of what is called "feigning death" in a variety of animals.

Irwin: I agree, there is a distinction between catalepsy and catatonia. What we see in animals is most likely to be catalepsy; what we usually see in man is catatonia, although one can produce a cataleptic state in man with drugs. My impression of catatonia is that it is a volitional state; catatonics exhibit the behaviour because they want to do it, and will adjust their posture accordingly. Catalepsy, on the other hand, seems something imposed on an individual by the nature of the drug action, involving a cessation of movement, or perhaps of the desire to move.

Hamilton: The term catatonia is used to describe a number of symptoms of patients, which are characterized by disturbances of behaviour and mobility. But what has been described here in animals is, in fact, a very uncommon manifestation of the catatonic state, which we call "waxy flexibility". "Waxy flexibility" is not volitional in the sense that Dr. Irwin mentioned. It isn't common; generally speaking, mental hospitals have only one or two among 2,000 or 3,000 cases. Usually the patient seems to be completely apathetic: he just stands, or sits, he is not interested in what is going on, and if you lift up an arm, it just stays. The impression given is that the patient is preoccupied with other matters; but I remember very vividly one patient who seemed to be under tremendous emotional tension, and stood rigidly, with a very intense, dramatic stare, the mouth gripped very tightly, and in this case there seemed to be some sort of intense concentration involved. "Waxy flexibility" is what everybody has been describing here, but the "normal" catatonic is simply an individual who just spends most of his time immobile, literally motionless, for hours on end.

Feldberg: Like our cats; they just sit still.

Hamilton: The catatonic will sit—sometimes in extraordinarily odd and uncomfortable positions—for hours. That is the immobile type. There is another type of catatonic, the person who is excited, restless, moves about, and may even hit out at other patients, and there is no doubt that the change from one to the other can occur, even quite suddenly.

Janssen: Dr. Edwards, do you call the state produced in rats by morphine, catalepsy? We refer to this as lead-pipe rigidity but not catalepsy. If we inject 5 mg./kg. of morphine into our rats, they display what we call lead-pipe rigidity; they are rigid and do not move, but you cannot induce a very abnormal posture because they will fall over; they have lost their equilibrium altogether.

Edwards: If you want the waxy or plastic state, you must use much higher doses of morphine, say, 20 or 30 mg./kg. This test as we conduct it does not require that degree of catalepsy, but that it is a matter of degree rather than a qualitative difference.

Janssen: That must be a strain difference then, because with our rats it is altogether different, even at, say, 30 mg./kg. They are not cataleptic at all; they either have no behavioural characteristics that resemble catalepsy, or they have what we call lead-pipe rigidity. One can pick them up and they are as rigid as a lead-pipe. It is entirely different with chlorpromazine with which they are flaccid and will fold up.

Edwards: Well, I think it is a dose-contingent matter. I am reasonably certain that I have seen the type of catalepsy you describe with chlorpromazine, induced by morphine in rats. When I was beginning this work a pharmacologist remarked that a fellow student in pharmacology once medicated a rat with morphine and then posed him in a standing position holding a cigarette for the benefit of the professor, who walked in to find the rat standing on his desk. I imagine this is the type of catalepsy you have in mind. It can be done, with the right dose.

Irwin: My experience is that although there may be strain differences in responses, one certainly does obtain catalepsy in the rat with morphine-like compounds, with far greater degrees of rigidity than with chlorpromazine-like compounds—but there may be differences in the manifestations of the catalepsy.

Janssen: Do you get what you call catalepsy *without* rigidity?

Irwin: With morphine, no. But the point is that it is catalepsy nonetheless, no matter how you wish to define it.

Janssen: I agree. It simply means that we have not defined our terms.

Edwards: I prefer to reserve the term catalepsy for states in which there is some degree of muscular tension. I regard this as essential to the definition because even in the instance of the plastic animal there must be sufficient muscular tension to hold the position. Nevertheless, the degree of muscular tension must surely vary from one compound to another.

Irwin: I wonder if what one gets with morphine is not closer to catatonia, than with chlorpromazine-like compounds; the term "catatonia" implies to me the presence of a considerable degree of rigidity.

Edwards: An added complication is that the term catatonia implies a form of psychosis, specifically a sub-category of schizophrenia, and I would rather not imply that these animals are schizophrenic. There are some semantic problems here, certainly.

Hamilton: What is meant by catalepsy in *animals*?

Janssen: What you call "waxy flexibility".

Edwards: Can we agree that tonic immobility is the meaning of catalepsy, that is, not paralysis but an immobility with increased muscular tension?

Miller: To revert to catatonia, I like your hypothesis very much, Professor Feldberg, because even though it may be wrong, it does suggest things to investigate! Perhaps one could use the iontophoretic technique used by Dr. Gaddum to find a cell that reacts to acetylcholine. You could then give one of these drugs, that on your hypothesis should impair the function of this cell although it does not have the anticholinesterase action, and see if indeed the response of that cell to electrical stimulation is impaired. This would confirm the mechanism you suggest.

Feldberg: The disadvantage of applying drugs by the intraventricular route is that they irrigate relatively wide areas of the inner surface of the brain. The action could be on the hypothalamus, on mesencephalic structures or on the amygdala.

Cook: Would it not be helpful if you would amplify the cautions and possible limitations that may exist in adapting your theory to the mode of action of these agents, as opposed to the physiological conditions one would ordinarily assume?

Feldberg: This is difficult. One method would be the one suggested by Professor Miller. Other methods would be the use of the push-pull cannula or of the four-barrelled micropipette. Our method of limiting the site of action of drugs to certain regions of the ventricular spaces is confined to components of behaviour which can be investigated in anaesthesia. Because in this condition we can limit the drug perfusion to given compartments of the ventricular space, either to the anterior or posterior horn of a lateral ventricle, or to the third ventricle, or to parts of the third ventricle, the part lying dorsal or ventral to the massa intermedia. The wall of the third ventricle lying ventral to the massa is the hypothalamus. The principle of the method we developed consists of perfusing the ventricular system with three to four separate slow injectors from such various places as the anterior horn, the middle of the lateral ventricle, the posterior horn, the third ventricle. By adding the drug to one injector only and perfusing cerebrospinal fluid from the other injectors the drug is prevented from entering those parts perfused with cerebrospinal fluid.

Stein: This technique shows specific effects with specific substances?

Feldberg: Yes, but more important, we can say this or that effect must be due, or cannot be due to an action on the hypothalamus, the caudate nucleus, septum, hippocampus or amygdala. This may sound little, but we are pleased to be able to establish as much! Unfortunately this approach is only possible in anaesthetized animals.

Janssen: I know of at least five different ways of producing this same syndrome that we are talking about in cats, and I cannot see any correlation between them. First there is the method Professor Feldberg described; secondly, injection of very small amounts of neuroleptic agents in cats (so far as we know this has nothing to do with acetylcholine, except perhaps at high dose levels); thirdly, injection of several derivatives of phenethylamine related to mescaline. Bulbocapnine is a fourth example. Finally, if you inject 50 ml. of distilled water rapidly by the intraventricular route in a rat it will be catatonic for several hours.

I see no reason to believe that the mechanisms of action of all these methods have something in common. Clinicians have described how these neuroleptic agents that actually produce catalepsy can also apparently cause this catalepsy, or waxy flexibility, to disappear. Dr. Buchwald of Los Angeles (Buchwald, N. A. [1961]. *Exp. Neurol.*, **4,** 23) trained rats to discriminate between two objects. By stimulating the head of the caudate nucleus he induced a brief period of catalepsy or immobility before the discrimination response was made. The response then occurred normally. Dr. Feldberg, do these findings have a bearing on your theory?

Feldberg: I did not know of the experiments of Buchwald, but the fact that other drugs produce catatonia does not oppose my interpretation. If we take a smooth muscle which is supplied by cholinergic fibres, it will contract to acetylcholine. The fact that it also contracts to histamine does not affect the existence of a cholinergic nerve supply. That a nerve cell responds to bulbocapnine and the other drugs you mentioned, does not detract from the theory that it may be impinged upon by cholinergic neurones. However, the fact that we obtain the effect with DFP suggests that the cell is impinged upon by cholinergic neurones.

Bradley: A word of caution may be appropriate here; in using the iontophoretic method of injection, we can look at individual cells, but we are unable to identify those cells, in general, with function. These techniques will tell us something about synaptic transmission in the brain, and may tell us about the pharmacological properties of different cells or of cell populations. But it would be dangerous to go straight on with a technique like this at this stage. First of all we must know if the drug is getting into the brain, and secondly, if it is getting in, where it is getting to. For this the appropriate techniques exist; the biochemical techniques for looking at the acetylcholine levels in different parts of the brain. Ultimately we should use the microelectrode techniques, but I think it would be a mistake to start with them.

Feldberg: I agree with you; before we use micro-methods, we should use the technique which you used with Dr. Roberts, because we want to study behaviour and not the activity of a few cells.

You asked, Dr. Bradley, whether DFP gets into the brain. Evidence that a drug penetrates from the inside is the fact that it produces central effects when applied by the intraventricular route. We have not done experiments with DFP but with histamine and the dye bromophenol blue, and L. J. Roth, J. C. Schoolar and C. F. Barlow ([1959]. *J. Pharmacol.*, **125**, 128) have done experiments with the inhibitor of carbonic anhydrase, Diamox. They injected labelled Diamox intravenously into cats and found that it is secreted into the cerebral ventricles and then penetrates the brain from its inner surface. All three substances were shown to penetrate the ventricular wall and the pattern of penetration was the same for all three.

Irwin: Dr. Feldberg has suggested a certain model which he considers may be applicable to the catatonia seen in man. The difficulty, however, is that drugs which are most effective on that particular model are of no value whatsoever in relieving catatonia in man. Whenever we set up a model, we are faced with the problem of testing its generality. We know very well that atropine, for example, will block DFP-induced catalepsy, and that anticholinergic drugs in general will antagonize the catalepsy produced by phenothiazine tranquillizers. My point is that if we stick to catalepsy, which we can directly measure, I think that anticholinergic drugs will overcome this effect and will reverse this same effect produced by DFP.

Janssen: Certain types of catalepsy are antagonized by atropine-like substances, and others are not. For instance I left out reserpine, which is another example of a drug producing typical catalepsy (waxy flexibility) in animals, and this is not blocked by atropine-like substances, whereas catalepsy produced by chlorpromazine-like neuroleptics is blocked by atropine-like substances. Catalepsy apparently has many underlying mechanisms.

EXTRAPOLATION FROM NORMAL TO ABNORMAL

Shepherd: We have been interested in the human pharmacology of antidepressants of the imipramine type. Abnormal subjects raise many difficulties for the purposes of experiment and in clinical doses these drugs appear to exercise very little effect on the normal people. We have therefore concentrated on trying to convert normal subjects into "abnormal" subjects, as it were, by giving them some other substance, or substances, which in animals are said to be antagonized by the antidepressant drug. This might be another way of setting up a model for the action of drugs on human beings, one which might be more directly relevant to abnormal states (Dick, P., and Shepherd, M., to be published).

Irwin: The implicit danger in this, of course, is that you may be employing a model which, although used by pharmacologists, may have no actual relevance to the antidepressant action of the drug. The validity of the test remains to be established. Thus, one may be accepting or rejecting a compound on the basis of a totally unreliable procedure. It would be of interest to test this model in man, but we should not rely on it until its predictive validity has been established.

Bein: It is quite well known that if you give a large dose of reserpine to a normal person, say 1–5 mg., you find more or less unpleasant reactions and I understand that that is confirmed by your own experience, Dr. Shepherd, with high doses in normal volunteers. But in the psychiatric patients, you tell me that if you give such large doses you see no prominent side effects, which are encountered only in normal patients. I know from clinical experience that drugs which are active in the psychopharmacological sense can sometimes be tolerated by psychotic patients to a much larger extent than by normal subjects— not because patients cannot react, say, intrinsically, but because such side effects do not occur in them.

Steinberg: It is always difficult to know how far reactions observed in normal volunteers will apply to clinical patients. But there are drugs which are used quite a lot by so-called "normal" people, and for such drugs conclusions based on laboratory experiments with volunteers are probably more valid. The amphetamine–barbiturate mixtures that I talked about (p. 421) are probably of this kind.

McIlwain: I would like to turn to two questions arising from Professor Russell's introduction, and not as yet developed. First, the extent to which biochemical characteristics in animals and man can be regarded as homologous or analogous. I feel there is very little that one could call identical in origin and structure. Immunological observations indicate that chemically different proteins can carry out corresponding reactions in different species or sub-species even when the reactions are identical.

Secondly, Professor Russell tended to refer to patterns of behaviour and the action of drugs mainly in adult animals, but we should also take into account the development of behaviour. In fact this offers many analogies with mental disease; one thinks, for example, of a condition such as schizophrenia which tends to develop at a particular time of life and yet is to some extent genetically conditioned. Something must have been happening, ready to be triggered at a given time.

A relevant animal test for drug selection might try to express this, on the one hand in the animal's life as on the other hand in man's. This must make considerable demands on conditions of test, and present analogies between man and animals which are of a very different character from those that have been discussed so far.

Cook: Can one consider a linear relationship between normal and abnormal patterns of behaviour? Many people use normal behaviour as a substrate for drug studies; yet how can these be related to abnormal behaviour? Some time ago we used a mescaline effect as the substrate, in mice, to evaluate drugs. We found that certain drugs antagonized the effect and others enhanced its action. This was very similar to Dr. Bein's findings: phenothiazines antagonized and meprobamate and barbiturates enhanced mescaline effects. We then found that if we used normal patterns of conditioned behaviour we found similar effects. As I reported in my paper (p. 27), chlorpromazine decreased fixed interval responding, and meprobamate and barbiturates enhanced such responding. As a pharmacologist, the question that is always in my mind is whether or not it is relevant to use normal patterns of behaviour in testing; with the possibility that there may be a linear relationship, in some way, to abnormal patterns.

Irwin: This is certainly the approach we all use, to one degree or another, when dealing with compounds already known to be of interest and to have activity. With chemical structures, as with genetics, there are certain properties, in this case physiological responses, that tend to be associated together. For example, with a narcotic analgesic, no matter what type of structural entity you investigate, there are certain basic qualitative features that tend to be present and associated, despite quantitative differences, such as analgesia, Straub tail, rigidity, circling behaviour, and so on. One could use any of these for the purpose of detecting a narcotic analgesic; by using several of the measures, one could quite reliably identify a new drug as a narcotic-type analgesic. This type of approach can be applied to almost any established series of compounds.

The real problem arises when you want to develop a totally new type of drug—where one must establish totally novel criteria for measurement. When dealing with a disease entity for which no drug is available, what are the tactics to be? In such a case, one attempts to develop a new approach or model, recognizing all its limitations but, as Dr. Bein pointed out, at least one is measuring something new! In finding an active drug with a new model, a form of serendipity may be involved, leading instead to the discovery of a totally different type of action from that intended. Nonetheless, this approach can be successful. I do not know how else the problem of the normal versus abnormal condition can be avoided; one way or another it has got to be circumvented, however unsatisfactorily. Until, as Dr. Cook pointed out, we have more definitive information on the aetiology of the disease states in man and the factors that contribute to them, we are unable to function otherwise.

Hamilton: To begin with Dr. Cook's point, I think both types of phenomena can be found. We know from clinical practice that the effect of amphetamine on normal individuals is to increase their alertness and to raise the level of their consciousness and responsiveness to their environments; it also produces a heightening of mood, a slight euphoria which is clearly recognized in normal individuals. When amphetamines are used for the treatment of depression we are using these properties to counteract the apparent changes of state in the depressed patient, who has a lowered mood, who is less responsive to his environment and less active. We know it is not very effective and it is what I would call, as a clinician, a "masking" effect; the drug masks the effects of the illness by hiding its manifestations.

This is the point Dr. Cook was making, for here is a clear linearity; but this is quite different from the effects of imipramine. When imipramine works (and it does not always do so) it produces quite an obvious clear-cut, radical change in the patient's condition. But it has no such effect on normal individuals; it does not make them more alert or more interested in their activities, although so far as I know those normal individuals who have taken imipramine rarely complain of its side effects. So here is an example where there is no linearity. We are apparently dealing with completely different phenomena.

Chance: So far as we have examined the action of drugs on the behaviour of rats they have one effect which is quite clear, namely, they bias the behaviour and make it more restricted. This is something one can teach students quite easily. You give them a normal rat and one treated with any drug having a central action, and they quickly realize that the normal rat does more different things in a period of time than does a drugged rat; indeed on that single criterion they can decide which is the drugged rat and which isn't. This brings us back to Dr. Gaddum's point, that if you have a drug which does bias behaviour in a way in which you can argue analogically is producing a condition which is apparent in man, then you have a reasonable model for attempting to counteract the abnormal behaviour in man.

With regard to the *development* of behaviour mentioned by Professor McIlwain, I doubt if there are enough data on this yet. Of course, there are a number of genetic strains which show behavioural abnormalities, but these appear to be abnormalities in a different sense from most of the behaviour referred to here, which I would not consider to be at all abnormal in the appropriate context. It is simply one of the series of responses of which animals are capable in situations encountered in the laboratory. The laboratory is a very restricted environment and nature provides situations which are not within our compass of imagination; we should perhaps go out into the field and find out what these situations are. They have only to occur once in a lifetime, if only for a week or a day, for the animal to have within its repertoire the most extraordinary ways of behaving. The genetic differences look very gross, and they may be gross in the sense that they are also ataxic, that is to say, there is a heavy element of ataxia in them.

It is interesting that some mice, when mothered on a species of voles, do not develop certain social responses and then as adult animals do not possess them; thus it is possible without the appropriate stimulus to reach an adult state which is behaviourally defective.

Miller: We should use any clues we can find of any kind, and I should like to suggest two different approaches which might be valuable. In some physical illnesses there are marked changes in mood; for example, people are usually in a depression after infectious hepatitis and several other illnesses seem to do this too. In some cases the female menstrual period has associated changes of mood. It might be worth studying these phenomena and the mechanisms involved in them. The study of these reversible phenomena in more or less normal people might lead us to some understanding of depression.

Working along these lines, Holmes and I (Holmes, J. E., and Miller, N.E. [1963]. *J. exp. Med.*, **118**, 649) tried to produce abnormal animals by injecting a bacterial toxin. I became interested in this because the toxin stops them drinking and also eating. With a saline injection the normal rat keeps bar-pressing for food or water. However, when bacterial toxin from *E. coli* is given, the rats stop bar-pressing for water between 30 and 45 minutes afterwards. If the rat is bar-pressing for a central reward, an Olds-type electrical stimulation of the brain, and he is given the toxin, you find big pauses in the record. The animal stops the bar-pressing for the central reward. If you stimulate the rat in a place that has both a rewarding and an aversive effect so that he has to press the bar to turn it on, or press the bar to turn it off, you greatly reduce pressing the bar to turn it on but do not very much affect pressing the bar to turn it off.

We have a few more data on animals in an activity wheel driven by an electric motor. By pressing a bar once, the rat can stop the motor from driving it and thus making him walk. We work the rat up to the point where he has to press the bar five times to stop the wheel; the toxin certainly does not stop *that* behaviour: very probably it makes him press the bar *more* to stop the wheel rotating; just as in certain kinds of illness I tend to say: "turn off that confounded radio". Incidentally I have observed that one of my own children, who normally has an angelic disposition, occasionally becomes a little demon. We have gradually learned to expect that a day or two later that child will come down with an illness. Th s work suggests two approaches to personality change: either by studying how psychological effects vary with various illnesses, and with the associated biochemical effects of those illnesses in people, or by producing and studying similar effects in animals by using bacterial toxins.

FACTORS WHICH MODIFY THE EFFECTS OF DRUGS ON BEHAVIOUR

Dews: In studying behavioural effects in animals, from a given dose of a drug one can get more or less what one chooses by selecting the right situations in which to study it. One can have amphetamine increasing activity, one can have amphetamine having no effect, and one can have amphetamine reducing activity. In comparing the effects of imipramine in depressed patients and in normal subjects, as Dr. Hamilton did, it is gratuitous to assume that any difference seen is specifically related to the illness until one has shown that a normal subject, under the same sort of behavioural control as the depressed patient, does not show the effects of imipramine. With imipramine in animals, for example, one can get changes in behaviour or one can get no changes; one can get increases or decreases in activity by arranging the conditions appropriately. It may be the same in man. The idea that a drug has a single behavioural effect in man that can be described in a sentence and that this is the only effect of the drug is simply not true. Effects of drugs on behaviour are largely a function of the situation in which they are studied and they can be profoundly modified, both qualitatively and quantitatively, by the circumstances of the test.

Cook: I want to emphasize my strong agreement with Dr. Dews. It is important to point out that by using various types of normal patterns of behaviour, however they may be elicited and controlled, one can classify drugs, identify drugs and separate them into various pharmacological entities. The utility of normal patterns of behaviour is no less relevant than those test situations which we call abnormal in animals and use to anthropomorphize towards some clinical syndrome. There is as much assumption in the relevance of the altered "abnormal" behaviour in animals, however applied, as there is in normal patterns of behaviour. Both have been shown to be able to identify and classify drugs. I think that utilizing normal patterns of behaviour, in the way that Dr. Dews emphasized, by careful evaluation of the parameters involved, offers at least as good an approach in identification, measurement, and classification of drugs as using the "abnormal" pattern of behaviour. I have yet to see proof that any of the behavioural patterns induced by various drugs has any more relevance with regard to picking up a pharmacological application, than normal behaviour.

Bein: I agree.

Bergel: The only drug I know well is not included in the present-day psychopharmacopoeia, namely the active principle of cannabis indica, the tetrahydrocannabinols. It is accepted that oriental man goes into a kind of euphoric-catatonic state by taking the drug, whereas the occidental apparently does not. There is therefore not only a difference between normal and abnormal man, but also a sub-specific difference between normal and normal, the origin of which might be cultural or traditional or it might be racial. We ought to pay careful attention to this because, after all, science is global.

Cook: One further point. In testing mescaline, which has been reported to have bizarre effects in man, it is interesting that Dr. Bein used motor activity as a criterion of drug activity whereas we used a mescaline-induced scratch phenomenon in mice. As pharmacologists we all know, however, that the interaction or antagonism between drugs is not complete; it is usually limited to certain actions. In other words the entire pharmacological action of drug A is not completely antagonized by drug B, and the nature and degree of their apparent antagonism may depend on the criteria we happen to measure. If by chance you use motor activity as a measure of mescaline activity you may get a completely different type of effect with antagonists from that you would find if you use the scratch phenomenon. When you give a drug to animals that has hallucinogenic effects in man, the criterion of drug activity you use in the animals is most important, and not necessarily relevant to hallucinations.

Bein: I would like to emphasize this point with another example which has nothing to do with psychopharmacology. If you use an antagonist to protect animals from death due to strychnine convulsions you get measurements different from those obtained, for example, from a test involving the antagonism of synaptic facilitation.

Chance: I want to emphasize what Dr. Dews and Professor Bergel have said about the labile effects of a drug. When I was discussing the effect of amphetamine on motivation in these rats with Professor Trethowan before I left, he provided me with a paper on about 12 cases in which amphetamine had been used in the treatment of patients with abnormal sexual behaviour (Bell, D. S., and Trethowan, W. H. [1961]. *J. nerv. ment. Dis.*, **133**, 489). The literature contains a lot of contradictory reports on the effect of amphetamine on sexual behaviour. We said that this kind of behaviour was truncated, which means to say that certain elements are increased and others are decreased, so that in effect behaviour is not restored to normal by this drug. Trethowan pointed out that the *libido* is universally increased in patients, but if they have special deviations these are also increased, although the male patients are almost all impotent in the final analysis.

Steinberg: There is also clinical evidence that in agitated children amphetamine can often produce sedation (Bradley, C. [1950]. *Pediatrics*, **5**, 24).

Stein: Dr. Dews' point is perfectly clear, namely, that drugs may produce different effects on behaviour depending on the behavioural baseline. Can we also agree that these differences arise, not because the behaviour changes the action of the drug on the brain, but, rather, because different behavioural processes are mediated by different brain processes which may vary in their chemistry. The drug itself has a more or less constant effect on the brain. Of course, there may be some interaction between behaviour and brain processes. But the primary cause of striking differences in the action of a drug on different baselines is surely the dependence of those baselines on different brain processes.

Dews: I have no disagreement with Dr. Stein about his hypothesis that drugs have constant effects on brain processes, but would like to add the hypothesis that drugs also have constant effects on behavioural processes. When I said that one can get more or less what one wants with a drug, I did not intend to imply any capriciousness. Given constant conditions these things are extremely reproducible even though one can systematically change the conditions and get different effects. Dr. Stein can hardly object to my additional hypothesis, otherwise he would be maintaining that "brain processes" have nothing much to do with "behavioural processes", which is hardly a position a physiological psychologist would take. Our disagreement concerns not at all ultimate aims, but merely immediate strategy—he, trained as a psychologist is turning his attention to brain processes and I, trained as a physiologist, am inclined to think that the identification of behavioural processes is more urgently necessary.

Miller: We all agree that one gets a situational–drug interaction, but what we must do now is to try to understand it. Amphetamine, for example, has two actions at least, one of which is an anti-appetite action; this means that if you are using hunger-motivated behaviour you will get a reduction in activity. The other action is a negative effect on experimental extinction which means that it will disinhibit, or tend to revive, kinds of behaviour that are subject to experimental extinction. At least some of the behavioural effects of amphetamine can be explained by the relative amounts contributed to the test result by hunger-drive and by experimental extinction respectively.

Cook: In order to support Dr. Dews' point, may I refer to my paper again? We studied two different food-motivated behavioural patterns at the same time. Chlordiazepoxide enhanced responding in one component (fixed-interval), and decreased responding in the other (fixed-ratio). These were different qualitative effects. Both patterns of behaviour were maintained on the basis of food motivation and the only difference between the two was the experimental schedule contingencies. So your point is not only supported, but it can be extended even further than just different motivations as factors which are determinants of drug effects.

Feldberg: Are there any controlled behavioural studies on patients during the withdrawal symptoms of morphine or alcohol?

Dews: The experiments of Hill and his co-workers (Hill, H. E., Belleville, R. E., and Wikler, A. [1957]. *Arch. Neurol. Psychiat.* [*Chic.*], **77,** 28) showed that they could change the response of people to pentobarbitone by changing the schedule on which they gave them morphine as a reinforcement for going through the task set.

Steinberg: I also think this an interesting and relevant experiment. The authors showed that if subjects who were morphine addicts were given a small incentive, pentobarbitone had its normal depressant effects on reaction times; but if the subjects were offered a high incentive, namely injections of morphine the amount of which was greater the shorter their reaction times, they actually gave shorter reaction times under the influence of pentobarbitone than with a control substance. In other words, when there was a high incentive pentobarbitone behaved like a stimulant.

Hamilton: May I mention another type of interaction which has not come up yet at this symposium. In an investigation I conducted at St. Elizabeth's Hospital, in Washington, D.C. (Hamilton, M., Hordern, A., Waldrop, F. N., and Lofft, J. [1963]. *Brit. J. Psychiat.*, **109,** 510), we tested the effects of trifluoperazine on chronic schizophrenics. One group of patients was given the drug, another group was given placebo, and we had two other groups of patients: one given the drug, plus a very intensive social rehabilitation programme, and the other given the intensive rehabilitation without any drugs, so we had all the possible combinations. The effects we found were roughly these (Fig. 1); in *men,* those on placebo and routine care showed a very slight improvement compared with their starting point, but trivial and perhaps due to increased tension or slight optimism on the part of the assessors. Those men who were given trifluoperazine, however, improved considerably.

So did those who were given intensive rehabilitation but no drug. But the point I want to emphasize is that the combination of drug and social therapy was quite clearly inferior to one or the other. I have been brought to task for my suggestion that phenothiazines have an essentially toxic effect. It has been described by others as a psychic straitjacket, and I suggest that the interaction I have just described does suggest something along these lines. When you are considering the clinical application of drugs, the circumstances in which they are used

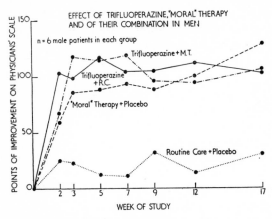

FIG. I (Hamilton).

are of fundamental importance. This is nothing new to psychopharmacology; we all know the difference between solitary drinking and social drinking, we are all aware of the different effects obtained by alcohol under different circumstances. Although we know about these things, however, not sufficient attention is paid to them when we are trying to evaluate the clinical use of psychopharmacological agents.

Russell: Was there any phase of the experiment in which you removed both the social and drug treatment?

Hamilton: No.

Bein: Did you also vary the dose of the drug in the double-blind studies?

Hamilton: In this investigation the dose was varied according to individual requirements. In all cases the patients received capsules, and the dose was increased rapidly until the physician in charge obtained what he thought was some sort of optimum result. If the patient showed side effects, Parkinsonism or akathisia, the dose was reduced, and if necessary covered with an anti-Parkinsonian drug, but the physicians who assessed the patient were never those who prescribed the drug. The dose given to the patients was as much as the patients could tolerate without side effects, and the range of dose was quite extraordinary. It ranged from one to nine capsules.

Bein: Isn't it dangerous to infer from your results that phenothiazines have a toxic effect, because besides the social rehabilitation you obtained quite a good therapeutic effect?

Hamilton: Yes, indeed. The symptoms of the patient, the overt symptoms, did diminish to some extent and the patient showed an improvement. These symptoms could also be diminished under intensive rehabilitation, but when the patient is given the drug, he is apparently unable to respond to the social or environmental influences as well as if he had not had the drug. Unless you prefer to put it the other way round, that the social rehabilitation was toxic and prevented him from responding to the drug!

Bein: I am very interested in your results but I do not see that you can infer from them that the drug is toxic.

Hamilton: Perhaps the word "toxic" may seem somewhat pejorative to you, so let us call it a "psychic strait-jacket". In a sense, the patient is somehow prevented from being able to respond to favourable environmental influences.

Steinberg: Analogous, perhaps, to Dr. Chance's idea of a drug induced narrowing of responsiveness in animals?

Chance: All the psychotropic drugs I have observed in rats undoubtedly restrict their repertoire. With amphetamine, for example, the animal explores its cage all the time. Presumably it is just going through the motions of exploration, but it certainly does not wash itself, it does not eat, it does not curl itself up in the corner and go to sleep; all these things are eliminated. And in various ways you see the same sort of thing with all other drugs.

I would like to ask how selective this group was, Dr. Hamilton. If all drugs bias behaviour, and you are working with patients whose behaviour is biased in the opposite direction, the drug is likely to restore variability in behaviour by pushing the bias back again, but only, of course, if you have carefully selected patients who are *biased in the same way*, and I am not convinced that this can be done clinically.

Bradley: What happened to the patients receiving both the drug and the rehabilitation treatment? Did they receive one or other of the treatments subsequently and reach a similar level to the others?

Hamilton: Concerning the selection of patients, these were originally taken from the continued-treatment wards of St. Elizabeth's Hospital. They were chronic patients with an average stay in hospital of something like 12–15 years. We originally said that nobody was to be included who had not been in for at least two years, but I do not think any were as low as that and some had been in hospital more than 20 years. They were picked for being grossly deteriorated and degraded in behaviour.

Gaddum: Does the result depend in any way on the assessment? What criteria did you use?

Hamilton: The criteria of assessment were based upon interviewing the patients and attempting to elicit their symptoms. This was done by two physicians, at the same interview, scoring the results independently on a rating scale and then taking the sum of their figures. The assessment was of quite specific symptoms, some of which changed, while some did not. This varied from patient to patient.

Miller: Did all or most of the symptoms show the pattern you described, or were *some* of the symptoms improved by the combination of the drug and social rehabilitation, whereas *others* were unaffected or showed deterioration under the combined treatment?

Hamilton: We did not analyse that because there is already a fair amount of unreliability in the assessment of schizophrenic patients and to do it on individual symptoms seemed impossible. This was in fact a total, overall pattern.

To satisfy you concerning the subsequent fate of these patients, let me add that there were a large number of patients involved in this trial, all taken from continued-treatment wards where their chances of improvement or discharge from hospital could be regarded as negligible. Had we not taken them on the trial there is little doubt that they would have stayed in these wards for a long time. At the end of the trial a few of the patients were discharged and I have since heard that many others have been shifted to other wards, and are now engaged in working in the hospital and other activities.

Bein: Is this true for the groups which have been treated only with trifluoperazine, or only by social rehabilitation?

Hamilton: This investigation was complicated because we not only investigated trifluoperazine but we also at the same time examined prochlorperazine. We did this not only in men, but also in women, and we got different results with different drugs. Prochlorperazine in *women*

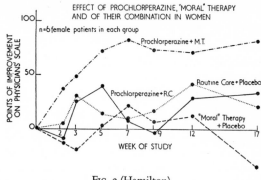

FIG. 2 (Hamilton).

showed the opposite effect (Fig. 2). Women who received neither the social treatment nor the drug showed very little change, those who received prochlorperazine showed some improvement, those who received social rehabilitation showed a similar improvement but those who received both drug and treatment in combination showed a more marked improvement than either alone. I did not want to introduce this particular point, because with the women there was tremendous irregularity over the period of time, and for this reason it would be very unwise to draw specific conclusions. But in the case of men the results were much more regular, and the picture was quite clear cut.

Cook: If you have an antagonism in this combination of two therapies, either alone having been shown to be efficacious, perhaps the milieu has been changed by the drug so that another social psychotherapy would be more appropriate.

Hamilton: This is obviously a matter of investigation. What I want to bring out is the development of the theme suggested by Dr. Steinberg, concerning interactions. They are both very complex and of great practical importance.

Chance: Can we clarify this question of interaction. Was the therapy quite continuous, and how often were the patients under the drug? Could each treatment be introducing a waviness into the system?

Hamilton: The social rehabilitation was a continuous programme of activity of various kinds done very intensively with a nurse for each small group of patients. The drug was given three times a day.

Bradley: In the group that received both treatments, did any patients subsequently receive one or the other treatment and then show further improvement?

Hamilton: I do not know the fate of individuals.

Irwin: In a recent analysis by Dr. Philip May of California, in which he reviewed a considerable quantity of hospital records, so that it was not a nicely planned and designed study, drugs came out significantly ahead of social therapy. However, he did not see any detriment on combination of rehabilitation with drugs.

Janssen: Dr. Hamilton, is the ordinate in your graph a ratio scale or a nominal scale?

Hamilton: It is a nominal scale. It is above a base line of symptoms, and it represents an improvement in the score.

Janssen: So it is a nominal scale bearing the figures 1, 2, 3, 4, 5, or perhaps the ranks A, B, C, D, E. How then did you manage to transform nominal scales to ratio scales, because I assume that the score system is essentially based on nominal scales? How can you add or subtract figures representing rank orders?

Hamilton: This is a technical point. I understand that differential weighting of a series of items in a rating scale produces very little differences in the overall result. It is surprising how little advantage is gained by giving different weights or using some very elaborate method of standardizing or normalizing the various points in the scale.

Irwin: Only if one can establish linearity in a rating scale by some device can one be wholly justified in doing this.

Janssen: This is an interesting matter of principle with wide application.

Miller: All our scales are probably at best crude rank-order scales, whether they are bar-pressing or any other index expressing a relationship of a drug to whatever phenomenon we are interested in. None of them is a cardinal scale; they are at best ordinal scales. This limitation applies to the experimental psychologist's work as well as to the clinician's work (Miller, N. E. [1959]. *In* Psychology: A Study of a Science. Study 1, Vol. 2, p. 280, ed. Koch, S. New York: McGraw-Hill).

SESSION 6: CLINICAL IMPLICATIONS

CHAIRMAN: Dr. M. Shepherd

INTRODUCTION

Edwards: Dr. Stein has referred to the monoamine oxidase inhibition hypothesis for anti-depression. Fig. 1 of my paper represents a series of drugs ranked by Dr. Jonathan Cole in the current order of efficacy, and there is no correlation with monoamine oxidase inhibition. I

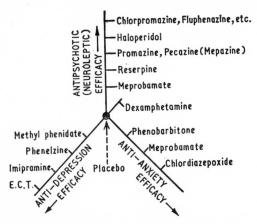

FIG. 1 (Cole and Edwards). Relative efficacy of some psychotropic drugs ordered along three clinical dimensions. [See also pp. 289, 297.]

would like your comments on the ranking of antipsychotic compounds. At present we may have tests for side effects but there is no general agreement upon any test or tests for the antipsychotic action of a drug *per se*.

Stein: There are certainly many ways of relieving depression apart from monoamine oxidase inhibition.

Janssen: Where does mania come into your scheme?

455

Edwards: I do not believe we have a place for that.

Stein: Yes, you have; erase the word "antipsychotic" and replace it by "anti-mania".

Edwards: No, that is not our intention. The simple dichotomy of stimulation/depression has been overworked in both pharmacology and medicine.

Stein: I quite agree, except that those drugs do not seem to have a very specific antipsychotic or anti-schizophrenic action. Phenothiazines are most selectively active against agitated or manic states.

Edwards: I agree that a large dose will calm down anyone, rat or man. There is some reason to believe, however, that we are getting at an antipsychotic pattern with these compounds. Not nearly as successfully as we would like, of course, and we do not mean to imply, for instance, that imipramine is the answer to depression, or that chlordiazepoxide is the answer to anxiety. The diagram (Fig. 1) is merely an indication of a current, rank-ordering of drugs as to their effectiveness against those conditions.

Cook: Dr. Edwards, is depression a psychosis?

Edwards: Dr. Heinz Lehmann favours the view that depression is a syndrome which cuts across all three categories of normal, neurotic and psychotic. One can have a normal depression, a neurotic depression or a psychotic depression. There is no evidence that neurotic depressives react differently from psychotic depressives in response to drug therapy, thus favouring the hypothesis of a common causal factor for depression.

Dews: It is rather interesting that you should emphasize that Fig. 1 represents the current ranking, because with the single exception of chlorpromazine, the drugs arranged along the axes are also arranged chronologically, with the newest drug in each case as the most active and the oldest drug nearest to the placebo. Apart from chlorpromazine, all your drugs are moving in the direction of the placebo as they grow older (or more familiar?). However, I do not wish to extrapolate!

Edwards: Chlorpromazine certainly was on the scene as early as reserpine: ECT of course preceded the drugs on the anti-depression axis. I feel personally fairly confident about the anti-anxiety axis. When I worked in an industrial laboratory and Librium first came on the market I was able to get a sample of the material and to test it on several procedures. We decided that if it had come through as our own experimental compound instead of as a competitor's product, we certainly would have recommended it in preference to the compounds that we then had available.

Janssen: Dr. Edwards, would you explain how you go about setting up these ranking orders?

Edwards: The method is that which has served psychiatry and medicine for many years, namely, intuition. This is Dr. Cole's evaluation on the basis of reports that he has received, his own clinical experience, and the result of our various clinical collaborative findings. A great many cases have been seen in the Veterans Administration and Psychopharmacology Service Center collaborative studies. The results show that chlorpromazine is as efficacious as a number of the other phenothiazine drugs and that reserpine and phenobarbitone are definitely less active. The ranking of the drugs in Fig. 1 is not developed from a rating scale or other "quantitative" approach, but rather on the basis of Dr. Cole's present knowledge of the field. This is a good deal better than nothing, we feel. There have been very few psychiatrists willing to take a firm stand as to what dimensions are involved, and how present drugs compare with one another. This approach, in fact, grew out of continual pressure on Dr. Cole by members of our pre-clinical psychopharmacology committee, who felt that they needed some target to aim at in the evaluation of the various animal-test procedures available, and who were not able to find in the psychiatric literature any definite statement of how one compound compared with another.

Cook: I think the situation to which we drew attention was the need for a description of the interaction of these drugs with relevant symptomatic and behavioural criteria seen in the clinic. This diagram is an arbitrary general classification of drugs according to three empirical dimensions, and I wonder if it adequately serves as a model of the manner in which these drugs interact with behaviour. We have already discussed the fact that the concept of a linear relationship of chlorpromazine, reserpine and meprobamate contradicts the experimental findings we have shown. This diagram presumes linearity of qualitative effects between meprobamate and, say, chlorpromazine.

Edwards: Perhaps it would be better to leave out the lines representing the axes. If we restrict ourselves to just three points—placebo, meprobamate and chlorpromazine—what is implied is that meprobamate is better than placebo but certainly chlorpromazine is better than either meprobamate or placebo.

Cook: In the same type of patient?

Miller: Yes. But these are not pharmacological axes, they are psychiatric axes.

Russell: What the committee asked for, at one stage, was a ranking of various drugs in terms of the most objective information available from mass clinical trials. The idea at that time was that if these drugs could be ranked in order of clinical effectiveness, we might then go back to see whether preclinical tests with animals would also rank them in the same way.

Miller: Yes, I do not think there is much disagreement on this; we all agree with Dr. Cook. First, let me say that a ranking of these drugs in terms of what they will do on schizophrenic patients is better than having nothing at all. But we would prefer to have the ranking broken down to behavioural units, showing what these drugs will do to specific symptoms of this alleged entity called schizophrenia.

Irwin: I believe that Dr. Cole's formulation (Fig. 1) is guilty of both omission and commission and that it serves no very good purpose. Its whole basis is highly controversial.

Dews: It seems to me that as clinicians, Dr. Cole and Dr. Edwards have a right to demand of the pharmacologists specific descriptions of the effects of these drugs in the behavioural sphere. We cannot give them such descriptions yet, and so they tentatively come up with something that is helpful to clinicians in the interim. To snipe at the details seems to me to be quite unfair.

Edwards: There is certainly a real problem in communication between the laboratory scientist and the clinician. We have started on a collaborative venture between the preclinical committee and the early drug evaluation group at the U.S. Psychopharmacology Service Center by holding periodic meetings, and from this, in time, at least one small group of clinicians and one small group of laboratory investigators will perhaps reach the point where they can converse profitably with each other. This is going to take a great deal of effort on the part of scientists and clinicians, for it is not merely a translational problem. It is not simply a matter of having someone like Dr. Jarvik, for instance, who has both medical and behavioural training, act as an intermediary between those who do not have both kinds of training. Rather, hypotheses will have to be formulated as to just what drug data from, for instance, a multiple FI/FR schedule mean in trying to treat an outpatient, and likewise, how comparable clinical observations can be translated into testable laboratory hypotheses. Then the necessary experiments will have to be carried out to test these hypotheses. If Fig. 1 does no more than to point to some of these problems—and this was its real purpose—by trying to give at least one psychiatrist's viewpoint, for the benefit of those in the laboratory who wish to have some hierarchy or ranking of drugs, it will have been useful. There appears to be no comparable reference that one could turn to, previously, in spite of a decade of quite active clinical work in psychopharmacology. That this may be a model-T formulation we do not hesitate to admit, but we hope that with constructive criticism it will be improved as succeeding models appear!

PRECLINICAL INVESTIGATIONS

Edwards: I want to turn now to a number of other items. Dr. Hamilton has observed, I believe, that it takes two to three weeks for an antidepressant such as imipramine to act. We know that it takes a rather similar period of time for the chlorpromazine-like agents to work, and yet most of our laboratory experiments are done on acute preparations. What are the implications of this fact? What does it mean to compare data obtained on a rat within four hours following medication with clinical efficacy determined over two months of chronic administration?

Can we hope to determine efficacy, as opposed to side effects, of antipsychotic drugs by testing them in *normal* animals and men? This is a matter that has come up for discussion from time to time and does present some real problems. There is certainly good reason to believe from the literature that normal men seem to be more like normal rats than either are like psychotic people, in respect of the effects of neuroleptic drugs.

Another idea, suggested in private conversation by Dr. Janssen, is that perhaps some such organization as the Psychopharmacology Service Center should attempt to determine the extent to which laboratory techniques are comparable from one laboratory to another. (Dr. Janssen, collaborating with Dr. Nathan Eddy of the National Institutes of Health, has made such a study in regard to the Eddy hotplate technique.) For example, an undertaking might be co-ordinated by an organization such as the Psychopharmacology Service Center for the purpose of encouraging investigators in various parts of the world to agree to use one test-procedure on, say, two or three compounds and to send their results for evaluation by the central group so that we could find out to what extent their results agree, and in what ways they differ.

Shepherd: Professor Russell, would you care to comment on the predictive value of animal studies as they are currently used in clinical work?

Russell: During the past several months there has been much concern expressed about this matter of predictability. For example, at a recent meeting the view was expressed that there was no reasonable accuracy in predictability from preclinical behaviour studies to clinical effects in man. Therefore, it was held, testing should start with man. There was some disagreement with this view, but it was at least stated openly and supported rather vigorously. To me, this emphasized the importance of our trying to evaluate the predictability of our methods.

One of the important points in making such evaluations is arriving at some criteria against which to evaluate the procedures we use. It was in this context that Dr. Cook, Dr. Miller, Dr. Jarvik and several others pressed the clinical members of the Psychopharmacology Service Center to give us more clearcut criteria, stated in terms that we could translate into preclinical, animal tests. Dr. Edwards' ranking of drugs on the basis of clinical effectiveness, which has caused so much controversy here, was one step in that direction. But we would like it to go much further. We do not yet have adequate validity criteria and I cannot really answer your question in greater detail except to say that we consider it a very important one.

Summerfield: Would you go further, Professor Russell, and say that, so far, there have been *no* systematic studies of the validity of the relation between preclinical trials of drugs in animals and their effects on man?

Russell: I think there are none that are very prominent in the literature. I know, in fact, that there are some studies involving the procedures that I mentioned in my opening remarks, such as criterion drug analysis used to establish profiles in behavioural measures, but there are virtually no published studies.

Cook: There is an enormous need for correlative studies. However, I believe we should at least be aware that some correlations and relationships do exist between laboratory animal studies and clinical findings. For example, if we compare the relative potency of various phenothiazines in blocking conditioned avoidance responses in rats with their relative potency in severe mental and emotional disorders in the clinic, we find that the rank orders of potency of these drugs are correlated. This may suggest that inhibition of conditioned avoidance responses has a primary relevance to such therapeutic application of these drugs; however, it is important to emphasize that this relationship does not hold true if drugs other than phenothiazines are included.

I have frequently seen people decide as to the importance of a laboratory test on the basis of whether it measured an action of a drug before the drug became established clinically. But the fact that certain drugs were in use in the clinic before the preclinical scientists started to examine them does not undermine the value of a subsequent laboratory finding. Although the actions of many of these drugs have been determined in the clinic, there still seem to be certain preclinical and clinical relationships. In the behavioural pharmacology studies there exists some parallelism between the effects of meprobamate, phenobarbitone and chlordiazepoxide. Most clinicians would also agree that there seems to be a parallelism of the qualitative effects of these drugs in their patients; particularly as opposed to the clinical effects of a phenothiazine. In the laboratory we have by now established behavioural pharmacological profiles which enable us to identify meprobamate or a meprobamate-like drug. The fact that this was established after its clinical use in no way detracts from the significance of these findings (Cook, L., and Kelleher, R. T. [1962]. *Ann. N.Y. Acad. Sci.*, **96**, 315).

Dews: I think we are being pedantic. In support of Dr. Cook, the fact is that there are many useful new drugs coming out of the laboratories which have not been obtained by screening thousands of compounds in man. They have been selected for use in the clinic on the basis of preclinical tests. Many of them have turned out to be useful and, therefore, there is successful prediction.

Summerfield: I deliberately referred to "systematic" studies of predictability in my question.

Stein: One of the reasons why you cannot point in the literature to many examples of the relationship between animal tests and clinical efficacy is that these correlations are largely being done in drug firms, at least in the United States, on a routine basis, and for various reasons are not always published.

Janssen: In addition, the negative findings are very often not published, for example, if a drug is tried clinically and has apparently no value.

Irwin: Could I try to put this into perspective? Paul de Haen ([1960]. *F-D-C-Reports, The Pink Sheet: Drugs and Cosmetics,* **22,** 16) has accumulated statistical data on this point. In 1958, out of an enormous number of new compounds tested, roughly one per cent was selected for human trial. Of this number, which was something like 1,900 compounds, only 2.3 per cent survived to be marketed; we do not know the criteria for rejection, but we find that, roughly, only 1 out of 45 compounds makes the grade. As was pointed out by Dr. Joyce, this is practically within the framework of statistical chance-probability, so one wonders how well we are doing.

I think that our average really is not as bad as it may seem; nevertheless, a great many compounds which are clinically tested do not succeed. A certain amount of attrition comes from the fact that one may test a number of related structures simultaneously, to determine which one proves to be the best; also, the human response may be qualitatively different in important respects from the animal response. Alternatively, a new drug may be given an early clinical trial for the purpose of sending information back to the laboratory, or to assess the predictive value of a new experimental procedure. By and large, I have rejected most new compounds on the basis either of a poor separation of the actions of interest from the occurrence of side effects or because I did not consider the agents to offer distinct advantages over existing compounds. Let me add that there is *no* problem in classifying compounds of a more traditional nature. Even in protozoa, one can distinguish phenothiazines and rank them in order of potency as in man!

However, the pharmaceutical industry does send a large number of compounds for clinical trial, and one wonders if we could not sharpen our techniques for discriminating useful from non-useful compounds, so as to eliminate more compounds from clinical trial on the basis of animal studies. One must realize, however, that humans may respond differently from animals; this has often happened. A compound may very well survive all animal tests, only to fail because of a qualitatively different response in man, or because of differences in therapeutic ratio between animals and man. Conversely, because of such differences, drugs less than ideal in animals may fare much better in man—but this possibility or hope cannot serve as a basis for taking a drug *to* man.

I feel that the degree of separation of the effective dose (however you wish to define it in behavioural terms) and the dose producing side effects is particularly important in eliminating compounds. Many compounds tested in man might have been eliminated by closer attention to this factor. For example, Sernyl (phencyclidine) was screened and evaluated by me before I was aware that it was a known compound. It was identified as unusual and interesting, but was considered of academic interest only because the *lowest* effective dose produced bizarre, hallucinatory-like behaviour. Only later did I learn that it was a known compound, that it had been tested clinically, and that hallucinations were reported in man. The original investigators, using the same species, failed to make this observation. I think that, in many cases, only the eye can pick up such details. We may require instrumental recording for certain of our measures, but the use of systematic, careful, direct observation is essential in making predictions from animals to man. All prediction is necessarily validated on the basis of what the clinical investigator sees and records; as a consequence, we must adjust our behaviour to emphasize those measures in animals that the clinician is likely to see in man. When we do so, we find that the correlation really is quite good, as, for example, in predicting the nature of the drug action, the effective dose, the nature of the side effects and the ratio between the effective and side effect dose. In general, I think there is a great deal that we can do on the basis of animal studies; I object strongly to those who suggest that we test everything in man. From a practical standpoint, we cannot do this.

Dews: The implication of our discussion seems to be that we hold a very narrow view of the contribution of pharmacology and think that pharmacology has only to get a drug into the hands of the clinicians, with certain guesses as to what they are going to report about it. This attitude implies that the clinician is by definition right and that what he sees and thinks about the drug is the right answer. I submit that when a drug has been shown to be safe and appears to have some clinical usefulness, the problem of the pharmacologist is, in fact, only just beginning. The clinician is working under more difficult circumstances than the experimentalist in the laboratory and it is very difficult for him to learn how to use the drug. For example, Dr. Hamilton says that if you give phenothiazines to patients you are poisoning them, while other clinicians regard them as extremely useful drugs. No matter how carefully you design your double-blind clinical trials, until you have a good understanding of the basic pharmacology and what the relevant variables are, it is very difficult to get any further. Pure pharmacology has much more to contribute to the best clinical use of a drug than merely discovering it and sending it to the clinician, and clinicians have a right to demand much more information about what the drug will do.

Chance: The question of clinical implications seems to me to be wrong in itself. It is wrong for several reasons, because it has so many different purposes. Clinical tests are basically evaluated on the criterion of usefulness—we are trying to get drugs for particular purposes and this is not a systematic approach to the subject. The question of predictability from animals to man is a scientific problem and we should really be arguing first about a framework of reference. But we have to get rid of the criterion of usefulness if we are going to do that. This means taking human behaviour, as much as any other form of behaviour, out of its clinical context.

It is also not simply a question of pharmacologists coming together with clinicians to agree on some statement which is not of any further value in prediction but stops argument. We really want to encourage argument! We need to discard a lot of our concepts because if we cannot yet predict, the framework of reference must be wrong; that is always true of science.

Shepherd: The issue seems to be that some people feel that you can predict in the clinical situation and others do not. If we refer to the clinical situation as "abnormal" human behaviour, as distinct from "normal" human behaviour, your distinction between usefulness and non-usefulness will disappear.

Chance: No, because I do not think we know what "abnormal" means. The biologist certainly does not use the term in the same way.

Consider epilepsy as an example: I feel fairly convinced that a form of discharge underlies adaptive behaviour in animals which is indistinguishable from certain types of epileptic discharge. The discharge itself is not the pathology; the pathology is the way the discharge fails to be integrated into the behaviour. These are fundamental facts which will reorganize our whole way of thinking about these things.

Janssen: I suggest that we all in fact agree that we can predict certain things which I will enumerate to show that prediction has been successful in the past.

We can predict that a compound that produces chlorpromazine-like activity in animals (by chlorpromazine-like I am referring to the kind of results that I presented in Session 4) will do approximately the same thing in man. We can do this for barbiturates too. This has been done many times and as far as I know there is no barbiturate-like compound in animals that is not barbiturate-like in man. We can certainly predict in this way for morphine-like drugs and for amphetamine-like drugs. I have not heard of one drug that is amphetamine-like in animals and that is not amphetamine-like in man. Strychnine-like drugs are the same, and we can enumerate many more classes of drugs like this.

Hamilton: Benactyzine is then an exception to this rule?

Janssen: I did not mention benactyzine, because the picture here, in my view, so far as clinical tests are concerned, is not so clearcut. I am not clear in my own mind about the situation so far as the effect of atropine-like substances on the central nervous system is concerned, and benactyzine is just one example of this rather confused field. I did enumerate a few classes of pharmacological compounds and I would be interested if anybody knows of a substance being amphetamine-, chlorpromazine-, morphine- or barbiturate-like in animals that does not have similar activity in man.

Bradley: You mentioned morphine-like substances, but surely morphine itself is an example of an exception to this rule because it can produce completely different effects in animals from those in man; it depends upon which species you examine.

Janssen: I was simply saying that if we classify drugs on experiments in animals, then morphine-like drugs are those drugs that will produce excitation in mice and cats; produce mydriasis in these two species; make the animals less responsive to noxious stimuli; be antagonized by nalorphine, and so on. There is a complete morphine-like picture and if any of us sees a compound with all these properties, he would immediately say that it was a morphine-like substance. I am talking about this kind of classification now. We can similarly enumerate a number of properties that are very typical for what we call chlorpromazine-like drugs and for amphetamine-like drugs.

I was simply referring to the possibility of reasoning by analogy; if we investigate a new compound and find it very similar to what we have previously seen with, say, amphetamine-like drugs in general, we feel sure that we are on safe ground in predicting the major clinical effects. I feel strongly that this degree of predictability is possible.

Irwin: I agree. I do not see that the problem of drug classification, in that sense, raises any problem in prediction. The real problem comes in distinguishing the more subtle differences between drugs of the same class, in determining whether the differences noted are sufficient to justify the clinical trial of a new agent. There is always a framework within which reasonable predictions can be made, even with a totally new drug; but we cannot always predict the finer aspects of the human response to drugs.

Janssen: If we do not recognize that a new substance is similar to what we have seen before, the difficulties of predicting certainly become greater.

Bradley: May I put my question to Dr. Janssen in a different way: if you did not know the effects of morphine in man and you looked at its effects in different species of animals, which animal would you predict from?

Janssen: In that hypothetical set of circumstances, if I were to detect the first morphine-like compound known, I would *not* feel sure in predicting anything, except for certain side effects. If I saw that morphine produced respiratory depression in all species, I would guess that this would also happen in man. However, morphine produces primarily excitation in certain species and primarily depression in others. I would certainly be puzzled by that and would ask whether man was more like a cat or a dog in this respect.

Hamilton: May I try to clarify this point? It seems to me that there are two quite distinct problems being discussed. The point that Dr. Janssen is making, with which Dr. Irwin agrees, is that if you already know the experimental profiles of certain drugs and take a completely unknown substance and demonstrate that it has a certain similar profile, you can predict that its action in man will be very similar to the drugs which produced the known, standard profile. In this sense, as Dr. Janssen says, the prediction is reasonably good.

The other point is something quite different. Supposing we have a substance which produces a completely different profile and there is now no known analogy in animals; the question is whether one can now, on the basis of the results in animals, say what it will look like when given to man. It seems to me that here we must agree that there is very little guide as to what it will do precisely.

Irwin: Only in terms of what one cannot measure and cannot anticipate. That which is measurable, particularly information more directly referential to man, one can predict from.

Chance: It follows that the more new techniques are introduced into pharmacology which demonstrate faculties of the brain, the more likely you are to discover new substances. One must regard the brain as an organ of high potentiality in this respect; there is hardly a single process in the body which is not influenced by nervous processes.

Janssen: If we found morphine today and analysed it in different species, we should find that this compound makes the respiratory centre of every species less sensitive to carbon dioxide. We know also that man has a respiratory centre closely resembling the respiratory centre of the other species. I should thus be prepared to predict that morphine would have similar effects on the respiratory centre in man. This goes for a lot of other side effects too.

Miller: But you would be missing the most significant psychological effects of morphine.

Janssen: Yes, that is more difficult.

Cook: In answer to Dr. Bradley: is it not a matter of criteria? Even if morphine came through as an unknown compound today, if our criterion of selection happened to be pain-threshold elevation, would it matter what species you tested it in?

Bradley: Yes, I think it would.

Irwin: It would not, because that response is uniformly observed in all species.

Cook: The main clinical application of morphine is its pain-threshold elevation properties, and these would be detected regardless of the species in which one tested morphine.

Bradley: But, if associated with this were the behavioural effects that one sees, say, in the cat, you would probably reject the drug for the same reasons that Dr. Irwin wanted to reject phencyclidine, which is also an analgesic.

Irwin: No, I do not think this is really true or fair. We would identify the drug as unusual and interesting, and would test it rather extensively in a variety of animal species to determine its varied effects; this information would make it even more interesting. We would find, for example, that it had the same effect on the gut in all the species tested, which might suggest antidiarrhoeal activity; also, its analgesic activity, and a host of other actions. With respect to behaviour, one would observe a lot of variability: it could be a stimulant or a depressant in man, on a variety of functions. Similar considerations would affect the prediction of the proper human dose. Where the dose-level requirement varies very greatly among different species, one has to take account of such variability and admit a wider range of possible dosage in predicting to man than might otherwise be the case.

Bradley: Did you give yourself such a wide range when you made this suggestion about phencyclidine?

Irwin: In this case I asked the chemist to make more compounds, to see if we could more selectively develop some of the unique attributes of the activity of phencyclidine. What impressed me so very much with this drug was that, whereas with LSD-25 and mescaline one observes stimulant effects at doses well below those that produce hallucinations, with Sernyl one observes hallucinatory-like behaviour, ataxia and mydriasis at the lowest effective dose and profound analgesia in higher dosage. I wanted further chemical synthesis, because certain of these features looked promising to me, but I could not see this particular drug as being acceptable for use in man.

INTRODUCTION AND EVALUATION OF NEW DRUGS

McIlwain: In the period after an investigator has initially spotted an active drug, a prototype, he is in a position either of trying to improve its activity as a drug, or of trying to diminish its toxic effects. What we have heard indicates that this is only a relatively small part of the making of a drug. Much more important is the process of producing the initially-active substance, which is very much an art, although it can be greatly aided by systematic testing. I think it was Dr. Irwin who said— "When I have got my first active compound I'll tell you what the test is." This is understandable because if the human population as a whole has the wide variability characteristics of a wild population as Dr. Hamilton suggested, it is evident that those concerned with drug testing will tend to cast their nets very widely. In fact, different investigators appear to have different and complementary attitudes towards their procedures for devising both drugs and tests, and one arrives at a comforting conclusion that this is a good thing, and an excellent reason for there being so many centres where such work is in progress.

Janssen: I should like to ask Dr. Hamilton what psychiatrists think about the value of neuroleptics! In the patients Dr. Hamilton described, the value of these drugs was very limited, but they were chronic cases. Could you describe the type of patient that you think may eventually benefit from the administration of these drugs, if such patients exist?

Hamilton: You mean with phenothiazines and similar substances? I don't think I can say anything that isn't already well known. The neuroleptics are extremely valuable in the acute stages of schizophrenia and in the manias; their value in the chronic states of schizophrenia is not so clear. There have been some complaints that psychiatrists always say that the schizophrenias or depressions consist of many disorders but if you ask them how many or in what way, they are unwilling to commit themselves. This is because the manifestations of these disorders are so very varied, although there are obvious similarities which enable us to classify them.

These drugs obviously have symptomatic effects, rather than anything else, and therefore in individual cases they can be useful. One of the things that is important about schizophrenia is its extreme variability; the same patient may at one period be very disturbed and excited and at another period not, and there is no doubt that under such circumstances, neuroleptics can be very useful indeed both to the patient and to everybody else concerned. I think that now we have got over the initial stage of enthusiasm, we are beginning to find, as is so common in medicine, that the effect of these drugs is not quite as good as we thought and that we have perhaps not achieved as much as we had hoped.

In dealing with the problems of the neuroleptic psychopharmacological agents, it is important to remember that they are extremely complex in their action, and that we know very little about what they do or how they do it. We are at a very empirical stage, much more than we would like to concede or admit, even in clinical practice. Again and again it has been found that the introduction of new drugs into a ward of a hospital, by and large, produces tremendous improvements. But it has also been found that you can then abandon the drugs and not lose those improvements. The improvements that were obtained were quite possibly due to the drugs—it is not purely a question of suggestion or anything like that; they have been what one might call the "therapeutic levers" that started the process, and once improvements in social adjustment have occurred, these can then be maintained without their help. I am sure Dr. Shepherd will agree that we are only just beginning to grasp how complicated these clinical problems are, and that we need a lot more co-operation and help from psychopharmacologists, not so much in providing the drugs, but in learning to deal with clinical problems in a scientific way.

Irwin: I wonder if Dr. Shepherd and Dr. Hamilton would care to comment on the working habits of the clinical investigator in evaluating new drugs and what the state of the art is, particularly with respect to unusual observations that the pharmacologist may make in his laboratory with a new test when he doesn't really know what it means clinically. How does the clinician go about this, and what are the prospects of missing an activity of potential value in man?

Hamilton: The answer is one word—serendipity. The fact is, there is no systematic way of dealing with this question; it is even more empirical than the work of the psychopharmacologist. One starts off with small amounts of drugs and increases them; one tries them on a wide variety of patients, preferably those one knows, and hopes that something will turn up. One must keep one's ears and eyes open, and talk to nurses. I have done very little of this initial phase and what little I have has unfortunately been done with drugs which turned out to be quite inactive, so I am not in a position to say very much. I am sure Dr. Shepherd has more experience than I.

Shepherd: Only in some aspects of the problem. I think the answer, briefly, is that for Britain there are two main avenues for the future. One is the development of properly organized clinical trials through a body like the Medical Research Council which, as you probably know, is in process of conducting such a trial at the present time; this work involves specialized techniques with personnel trained for this particular task. Secondly, we are just beginning to develop the sort of clinician whose absence Dr. Dews deplored earlier; the man who would correspond perhaps to the clinical pharmacologist, a person with a double training in both laboratory techniques and clinical studies, and so able both to acquire some familiarity with the preclinical testing stages and to make the clinical observations himself. This is a slow process because it means persuading clinicians to take time off to obtain this extra experience, but eventually a combination of these two approaches will have to be developed in this country.

Hamilton: I should like to echo your sentiments, with one proviso. I would be very sorry to see established, whether in Britain or in the United States or elsewhere, any official body whose task it was to evaluate drugs, and which would be regarded as the only body capable of making a decision. We have heard of the variety of approaches that psychopharmacologists have to screening drugs and to evaluating them, and this is most important from the clinical point of view. We cannot have *ex cathedra* statements; no group of clinicians can lay down the law about the way to evaluate a particular drug and on that basis decide whether it is good or bad. It is most important that every encouragement should be given to many different bodies using as wide a variety of techniques, methods and principles as possible. I am wholly in favour of the Medical Research Council organizing these things but I should be very sorry indeed to see any suggestion that it should develop a monopoly along these lines. Something like that may begin to appear soon in the United States, partly because of the problems of the Food and Drug Administration and partly because of the remarkably good organization of the Veterans Administration, which is apt to put others off.

Edwards: I don't believe that such action is contemplated at the present time by any U.S. Government agency. Actually, there is a strong desire to avoid taking the responsibility that would be implied in making such decisions. Because of the new laws and regulations concerning the Food and Drug Administration, closer scrutiny of what the clinical pharmacologist is doing will occur, and this may or may not have an undesirable effect on originality and the total amount of research effort; but I don't believe it is the intention of anyone to tell the medical fraternity as a whole what drugs should be used or how to evaluate them. It is rather more of a monitoring system than a system for making decisions about drugs.

INDEX OF AUTHORS

Numbers in bold type indicate a contribution in the form of a paper or the introduction to a discussion; numbers in plain type refer to contributions to the discussions.

SUBJECT INDEX

Abnormal behaviour, 285, 414, 439–446, 464–465

Acetylcholine, action in CNS, 388
and effect of morphine, 351, 352
antagonism with atropine, 387–388
causing sleep, 359
effect on brain stem, 348
effect on eating and drinking, 355–356, 359
effect of di*iso*propylfluorophosphonate (DFP) on, 429, 430
effect of serotonin on, 150
in hypothalamus, 359
muscarinic and nicotinic actions of, 357, 388
peripheral action of, 357, 388
producing catatonia, 433
relation of anatomical site and behaviour, 153–155, 359
release of, 351, 352, 388, 391

Acetylcholine system, and behaviour, 144–162

3-Acetyl pyridine, 172

Actinomycin D, 60, 336

Activity in animals, effects of drugs on, 78, 81–82, 116, 208–216, 219, 243–246, 398, 427, 444
in groups, effects of drugs on, 238–248
see also under Exploratory activity

Adenylic acid, effect on memory, 36

Adrenaline, CNS depressant effects of, 175, 371–373
effects on brain electrical activity, 175–190
effects on eating and drinking, 355–356
effects on hippocampus, 189
effect on neocortex, 189

Adrenaline,
intraventricular injection of, 175, 371–373
sites of action of, 175–190, 387

Adrenergic neurones, 348–349

Age, effect on action of sympathomimetic amines, 176–187

Aggregate toxicity, 117, 227, 228, 240, 242, 425

Aggression, and isolation, 241
as component in behaviour, 65, 67, 69, 70, 223
endocrinological aspects, 324
effect of drugs, 72–78

Alcohol, effect on brain, 167
effect on delayed response, 48–50
effect on escape response, strain differences, 229–230
effect on memory, 48–50, 62
synergism with barbiturates, 63
tilting plane test, sex differences in, 226
withdrawal symptoms, 448

Alvodine, effect on behaviour, 352

Amine oxidase inhibitors, 258, 323, 455

Amphetamine, and aggregate toxicity, 117, 227, 228, 240, 242, 425
and brain stem reticular formation, 120, 122
and electrical activity, 120, 175–188
and neural reward mechanisms, 91–118
and self stimulation of brain, 94–112
anorexic action of, 95–98, 250–255, 447
chemical basis for action of, 111–112
clinical effects of, 289, 442, 455

Printed by Spottiswoode, Ballantyne & Co. Ltd., London and Colchester

NOTES

NOTES

NOTES

NOTES